# Sanibel
## & Captiva
### A Guide to the Islands

Julie and Mike Neal

coconut
press

COCONUT PRESS
Sanibel Florida

# Sanibel & Captiva: A Guide to the Islands
Second Edition

ISBN 0-9709596-3-X
ISSN 1536-8947
Library of Congress Control Number:
2001119648

Second Printing, April 2004

*Published by*
COCONUT PRESS INC.
5429 Shearwater Drive
Sanibel, FL 33957-2327

Although the Publisher and Authors have made every effort to ensure the information in this publication was correct at the time of going to press, they do not assume and hereby disclaim any liability to any party for any loss or damage caused by errors, omissions, misleading information, or any potential travel disruption due to labor or financial difficulty, whether such errors or omissions result from negligence, accident or any other cause. Readers may call our attention to errors or omissions by writing us at the address above.

Find us online at www.coconutpress.com

Printed in Canada.

*Photographs and illustrations*
Unless otherwise indicated all photos by Mike Neal, © 2003, 2004 Coconut Press Inc. Fish illustrations by Diane Rome Peebles, provided by the Florida Fish and Wildlife Conservation Commission, Division of Marine Fisheries. Maps © 2003, 2004 Coconut Press Inc.

*Other acknowledgments*
We thank the following people for their help in supplying materials and content: Jean Bair, Emily Compton, Sean Middleton, Joseph Pacheco, Brad Sitton and Bird Westall; Dr. José Leal and Libby Grimm at the Bailey-Matthews Shell Museum; Bill Strange and Gary Greenplate at Sanibel Seashell Industries; Dick Walsh and Tom and Mary Ann Gilhooley of McSpoil; Patricia Allen and the staff of the Sanibel Public Library; Dr. William H. Marquardt and the Florida Museum of Natural History; and Sharon Arnold, Bev Ball, Peggy Ford-Elsea, Kevin Godsea, Monica Hardy, Rob Kramer, David Meardon, Milbrey Rushworth and Leslie Sheffield for their hard work gathering photographs and illustrations.

We also thank all the islanders who agreed to be interviewed for this book, including Steve Alexander, Steve Alvarez, Kristie Anders, Diane Badalich, Francis Bailey, Sam Bailey, John Barden, J.D. Bolden, Gates Castle, Luc Century, Melissa Congress, Jorge Coppen, Keith Cruickshank, Terri Cummins, Dave Defonzo, Rob and Cathy DeGennaro, Daniel and Monica Dix, Jim Dowling, Richard Finkel, Liz Fowler, Jim Hall, Layne Hamilton, Charlotte Harlow, Malcolm and Susan Harpham, Marty Harrity, Frank Kik, Erick Lindblad, Dr. Rob Loflin, Greg Martinez, Brianne "Bubbles" Meyer, Albert Muench, Dick Muench, Jerry Muench, Ron Orr, Maurice Oshry, Susan Peck, Helene Phillips, Cindy Pierce, Anita Pinder, Bev Postmus, Toni Primeaux, Bob Radigan, Dawn and Joe Ramsey, Andrew Reding, Bruce Rogers, Joan Simonds, Hollie Smith, Robbie Smith, Charlie Sobczak, Jim Sprankle, Sandra Stilwell, Nola Theiss, Larry and Kathy Thompson, Keith Trowbridge, T.C. Tyus, Marcel Ventura, Steven and Susan Wener, Rudy and Sandy Zahorchak, as well as all those who participate in our surveys and e-mail us their opinions.

*For Micaela, our island girl*

**Page 1:** Looking for shells on Christmas morning, the authors' daughter walks along Bowman's Beach. **Previous pages:** A snowy egret reacts to the surf behind Gulfside City Park. **Facing page:** Visitors prepare to depart Fort Myers for Sanibel, 1908. Signs promote the Matthews (today's Island Inn) and the Casa Ybel resort. **Page 7:** A mermaid takes a drink in front of The Bean restaurant, Sanibel. **Page 11:** Listening to her 3-year-old son, Andrew, New Jersey's Suzanne Ozazewski enjoys an afternoon on Captiva. **Page 12:** Visiting from North Carolina, sisters Olivia and Rebekah Horning, ages 4 and 7, escape Captiva's breaking surf.

ING
AND SHELLING.
ISINE.
CASA YB
SANIBEL FL
NOW OPEN FOR SE
ASK KINZIE

# About This Book

*"Guidebooks are usually so impersonal. You get them for all the great info they have — landmarks, hiking trails, accommodations — but don't really expect creativity. This __is__ a great guidebook, in that it contains all the usual info you'd want and expect. But it goes so much further, and gives you such a feel for the islands, in such a creative way. They poll the locals on the best restaurants. They poll local kids on topics so you know what your kids will want to do. They have essays and poems from locals to impart real native flavor. Not only has this book given me all I could want on Sanibel and Captiva, it's the best written and most interesting guidebook I've ever seen!"* — A reader from Virginia

*"I've been going to the islands for years and thought I knew a lot. But after reading this book I can't wait to go back again for all the great things I've been missing. The most amazing thing about this book is the pictures and identifiers for all the wildlife and shells you can find on the islands. This is the only book you'll ever need to enjoy Sanibel and Captiva to the fullest.* — A reader from New Hampshire

We live on Sanibel, and love it here. But we've noticed that many visitors don't really know what to do. They go to the beach, but don't know how to take advantage of it. They want to see wildlife, but don't know where to look. They drive right past the best restaurants; the places every islander loves. If they only knew what they were missing! That's why we wrote this book; so you don't miss out. So your days here are as fun and rewarding as ours.

This book gives you dozens of ideas on how to have fun at the beach. You'll learn how to find the best shells and where to go to see rare and endangered wildlife. We clue you in on island hiking and biking, boating and fishing, museums and theaters. Other chapters cover planning your trip, the history of the islands and what it's like to live here.

**Author Julie Neal** surveys island residents

Throughout the book you'll also find contributions from many other island residents, including vacation tips, restaurant choices, even poems.

For this second edition, we made a list of what readers said they liked about the first book — the detail, tips, trivia, feature stories and photos — and added more of the same. The restaurant reviews have more meat to them. And we updated the information on attractions and accommodations, and added listings and reviews of the islands' new shops and restaurants.

In short, SANIBEL & CAPTIVA: A GUIDE TO THE ISLANDS is designed to help you have the time of your life.

— JULIE AND MIKE NEAL

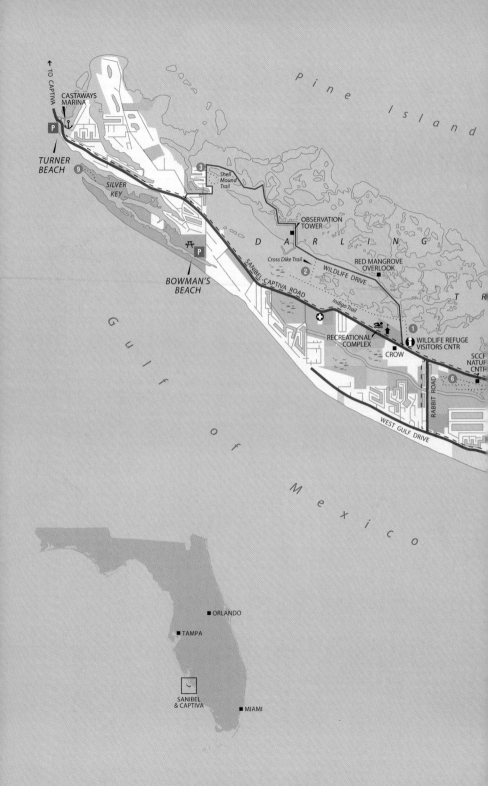

TO CAPTIVA

CASTAWAYS
MARINA

P

TURNER
BEACH

9

SILVER
KEY

P

BOWMAN'S
BEACH

SANIBEL-CAPTIVA ROAD

WEST GULF DRIVE

RABBIT ROAD

3

Shell
Mound
Trail

OBSERVATION
TOWER

Cross Dike Trail

2

WILDLIFE DRIVE

RED MANGROVE
OVERLOOK

Indigo Trail

D A R L I N G

RECREATIONAL
COMPLEX

CROW

1

WILDLIFE REFUGE
VISITORS CNTR

SCCF
NATURE
CNTR

6

*P i n e    I s l a n d*

*G u l f*

*o f*

*M e x i c o*

ORLANDO

TAMPA

SANIBEL
& CAPTIVA

MIAMI

Sound

San Carlos Bay

A C T
Tarpon
Bay

Water
trail

TARPON BAY
EXPLORERS

SHELL
MUSEUM

HISTORICAL
VILLAGE

BIG ARTS

SCA
THEATRE

SCHOOL
HOUSE
THEATER

BEACHVIEW
GOLF
COURSE

CASA YBEL ROAD

GULFSIDE
PARK
PRESERVE

BAILEY
TRACT

TARPON BAY RD

5

4

7

8

PERRY TRACT

GULFSIDE CITY PARK

MIDDLE GULF DRIVE

PERIWINKLE WAY

DIXIE BEACH ROAD

DUNES
GOLF
COURSE

CHAMBER OF
COMMERCE

BOAT
RAMP

SANIBEL
MARINA

TO MAINLAND

DONAX ST

LINDGREN BLVD

EAST GULF DRIVE

FISHING
PIER

SANIBEL
LIGHTHOUSE

P

LIGHTHOUSE
BEACH

N

TARPON BAY
ROAD BEACH

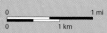

0            1 mi
0            1 km

## SANIBEL ISLAND

J.N. "Ding" Darling
National Wildlife Refuge

SCCF Preserve

City/County Property

State Conservation Area

Commercial Area

Major Road

Wildlife Drive

Secondary Road

Bike Path

Hiking Trail

Wetland

■  Point of Interest

P  Beach Parking

⬤  Tourist Information

⊠  Post Office

🚗  Car Rental

🚲  Bike Rental

⚲  Kayak Rental

⊼  Picnic Tables

⚓  Marina

⛳  Golf Course

☰  Public Pool

▲  Campground

📖  Library

✚  Medical Clinic

🚹  School

ⓘ  Hiking Trail (information
   on pages 188–190)

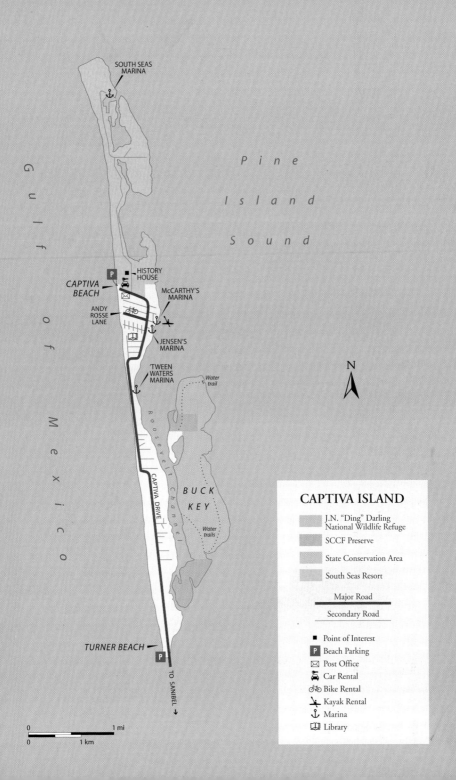

SOUTH SEAS
MARINA

_P i n e_

_I s l a n d_

_S o u n d_

_G u l f_

_o f_

_M e x i c o_

HISTORY
HOUSE

*CAPTIVA
BEACH*

McCARTHY'S
MARINA

ANDY
ROSSE
LANE

JENSEN'S
MARINA

'TWEEN
WATERS
MARINA

Water
trail

*Roosevelt Channel*

*CAPTIVA DRIVE*

B U C K
K E Y

Water
trails

N

*TURNER BEACH*

TO SANIBEL

## CAPTIVA ISLAND

J.N. "Ding" Darling
National Wildlife Refuge

SCCF Preserve

State Conservation Area

South Seas Resort

Major Road

Secondary Road

■  Point of Interest

P  Beach Parking

✉  Post Office

🚗  Car Rental

🚲  Bike Rental

🛶  Kayak Rental

⚓  Marina

📖  Library

0                    1 mi

0          1 km

# Contents

About this book 6
Sanibel map 8
Captiva map 10

**Overview** .................. 14
*Inside Tips* ................... 25

**Planning Your Trip** ... 26
What to pack .............. 27
Money ........................ 28
Business hours ............ 29
When to go ................. 30
Suggested itinerary ...... 31

**Getting Here** ............ 34
By air .......................... 35
By car ......................... 37
By sea ......................... 40

**History** ...................... 42
Early history ............... 43
The Civil War ............. 45
*What's in a Name?* ........ 46
Settlers arrive .............. 47
Paradise on earth ........ 51
Farming ...................... 60
An isolated world ........ 62
Developers move in ..... 68
*Island Originals* ............ 70
Sanibel takes control ... 71
*Big Mac Attack* ............. 72
Historical sites ............ 74
*Hurricanes* ................... 76

**Beaches** ...................... 78
Gulf beaches ............... 79
*Nude No More* ............. 82
Bay beaches ................. 83
*Beach Reads* .................. 84
Beach sunsets .............. 87
Tips for beach fun ....... 89
*Beach Science* ............... 93
Stay legal, stay safe ........ 96
*Dawn at
    Bowman's Beach* ......... 97

**Shelling** .................. 100
Tips for good shelling .. 101
More shelling fun ........ 104
Shelling charters ........ 104
*Shell Science* ............... 106
What you'll find ........ 107
Other beach finds ...... 128

**Wildlife** .................. 132
Birds ........................ 133
*Fine Feathered Fiend* ... 139
Insects ...................... 152
Land animals ............ 154
Sea life ...................... 162
*A Fishy Femme Fatale* .. 168
Where to see wildlife .. 176
*Would 'Flipper' Bite
    a Human?* ............... 180

**Conservation Land** . 182
J.N. 'Ding' Darling
    National Wildlife
    Refuge ................... 183
*The Inside Story* .......... 189
SCCF ....................... 190
Gulfside City Park ..... 190

**Trees and Plants** .... 192
Palms ...................... 193
*Mangroves* ................... 194
Other trees and plants .. 195
*Alien Invaders* ............ 200

**Biking** ...................... 202
Where to go biking ... 203
Bike path map .......... 205
Rental shops ............. 207

**Boating** .................... 208
Charters ................... 209
Kayaks and canoes ..... 209
Power boats .............. 212
Sailboats ................... 213
Tour boats ................ 213
Watersports .............. 216
*Adventures at Sea* ....... 218
*The Out Islands* .......... 219

**Fishing** .................... 222
Fishing charters ......... 223
Catch and release tips .. 226
*Guide to local fish* ....... 228
*Fishy lawyer, fowl play* ... 230
*Sneaky snook* ............... 231
*Tarpon tips* ................... 232
*Morning on the Flats* ..... 233

**Diversions** ............... 234
Museums .................. 235
Live theater .............. 238
BIG Arts ................... 238
Golf and tennis .......... 241
Libraries ................... 241
Fitness centers ........... 242
Day trips .................. 243
*Starry Starry Nights* .... 244

**Island Living** .......... 246
Who lives here .......... 248
*Island Recipes* ............. 252
*Thoughts While Waiting
    To Make a Left Turn
    onto Periwinkle Way
    at Height of Season* .. 254
Education and
    government ........... 255
Real estate ................. 257

**Restaurants** ............. 258
Reviews ..................... 259
Where islanders eat ... 263
Best Bets ................... 265

**Shopping** ................. 270
*Island Artists* .............. 272

**Accommodations** . 284
Sanibel ...................... 285
Captiva ..................... 290
Off the islands .......... 291
Rental agencies ......... 291

**Resources** ................ 292
**Index** ...................... 296

# Overview

Sanibel and Captiva offer an unbeatable combination: A tropical island wilderness with the convenience of modern life. Only here can you wander a near-deserted beach, have a gourmet lunch, track down an alligator and see an award-winning play — all in the same day.

The islands lie off the coast of western Florida, near Ft. Myers. Tampa is 125 miles north; Key West 140 miles south. With more than 16 miles of beaches, a laid-back attitude and plenty of natural beauty, they are a 21st-century paradise.

The weather, of course, is great. Winters are exceptional, with average highs in the mid-70s. Summers are tropical — wet and hot — but balmy Gulf breezes keep things bearable. Regardless of the season, the sun shines nearly every day.

Sanibel is about the same size as Manhattan — 12 miles long and up to three miles wide. Captiva is five miles long, never more than a half-mile wide. The islands are connected to the mainland by the three-mile Sanibel Causeway.

As barrier islands, Sanibel and Captiva have long beaches and open water on one side; a meandering, tree-lined shore on the other.

## Beaches and seashells

If your ideal vacation includes friendly beaches and warm waters, Sanibel and Captiva are just what you're looking for. The gently sloping sea floor keeps the water shallow and the waves calm, making the island shore ideal for relaxing walks and family fun. Gulf temperatures here average 78 degrees.

Shelling has been the islands' claim to fame ever since Ponce de Leon dubbed the area "la costa de Caracoles," the seashell coast. The beaches are covered with new shells after every tide, and the shallow, sandy sea bottom rolls up most treasures intact. Any visitor can find a bagful of treasures in just a few minutes.

## Wild encounters

The J.N. "Ding" Darling National Wildlife Refuge preserves 6,000 acres of mangrove estuaries and freshwater wetlands. It's home to dozens of endangered or threatened species. Tropical and migratory birds roost in the trees, manatees graze in the bays, raccoons amble along the shore, alligators patrol the ponds — all within easy view of people. You can explore by car, foot, bicycle, kayak or guided tram. There's a four-mile paved road, five miles of hiking paths, and a kayak trail.

**Facing page:** Tranquil waters on Bowman's Beach, Sanibel

Other Sanibel trails wander through freshwater habitats. Buck Key, adjacent to Captiva, has more water trails.

## More island fun

Sanibel is a bicyclist's dream. Twenty-five miles of paved bike paths run alongside every major road, and sometimes veer off through wilderness areas.

Two unique Sanibel museums are worth a stop. The Sanibel Historical Village and Museum has an assortment of buildings from the early 20th century, each restored and furnished. The Bailey-Matthews Shell Museum has well organized displays of shells from around the globe, including rare exotic specimens.

No visit to the islands is complete without getting on the water. Various outfitters rent power boats and kayaks; Waverunners and parasailing are available on Captiva. Tour boats offer group trips, including dolphin cruises and sunset voyages. Don't overlook fishing — the islands have dozens of charter captains, experts in finding tarpon, snook and other rewarding catches.

## Charming communities

Life moves at a slower pace on Sanibel. The fastest speed limit is 35; shops open late and close early. Night life is usually defined as gathering at the beach to watch the sunset, then going out for a beer.

Respect for nature outweighs commercial concerns. In fact, Sanibel's character comes in part from what it doesn't

**Tropical colors** at Sanibel's Old Schoolhouse Theater

**The islands have three** main roads:
- Periwinkle Way runs down the middle of eastern Sanibel, from the lighthouse to mid-island.
- Sanibel-Captiva Road travels western Sanibel, alongside the refuge. When it crosses Blind Pass it becomes Captiva Drive.
- Gulf Drive (officially called East Gulf, Middle Gulf and West Gulf) runs along the beach shore.

**Overleaf:** A mangrove cove at the 'Ding' Darling National Wildlife Refuge

**Facing page:** The majestic wings of a roseate spoonbill

have: stop lights, street lights, four-lane highways, bill-boards, neon signs, fast-food joints. Many roads are paved with shells, not asphalt. There are no true high-rise build-ings; only a handful are above two stories.

On Captiva a development boom is bulldozing small cottages for large trophy retreats, but a unique character stubbornly remains. You'll find it in the shops and restau-rants and on the docks at Jensen's Marina. Captiva has no mailboxes; residents get their mail at the tiny post office.

Neither island has a focused downtown. Sanibel's spiri-tual center is Bailey's General Store. At the western tip of Sanibel is the village of Santiva *(SANibel and capTIVA, get it?)*; it looks like a 1960s postcard. Captiva's heart is the picturesque Chapel by the Sea, and it too has a sepa-rate village: the South Seas Resort.

Restaurants include everything from weathered shacks to arty cafes. The specialty is fresh seafood, especially grouper, crab and shrimp. Locally-owned shops and gal-leries offer their own brand of charm, with imaginative collections of clothing, art and souvenirs.

The media has had a love affair with the islands since 1981, when Christie Brinkley posed on Captiva for the cover of the Sports Illustrated swimsuit issue. Recently the Travel Channel named Sanibel's Bowman's Beach as one of the top 10 beaches in Florida (2002), Conde Nast Traveler magazine selected Sanibel as one of the world's Top 20 Islands (2001), and Money magazine chose Sanibel and Captiva together as one of the world's eight best places for a winter vacation (2002).

**The Travel Channel** films a segment of "Florida's Top 10 Beaches" on Bowman's Beach

**Facing page:** The 1884 Sanibel lighthouse still operates today.

**At 26 degrees north latitude,** the islands are subtropical. Caribbean weather brings tropical influences to vegetation (i.e., coconut palms) and wildlife (spoonbills).

**Island elevation**
Average .................. 4 feet
Maximum ............. 13 feet

**Island rainfall**
Yearly ............... 53 inches
Season ........... June–Nov.

**Overleaf:** The sun rises over Roosevelt Channel

# Inside Tips for a Terrific Vacation
## The best of the islands

Nearly everyone has a good time when they come to Sanibel and Captiva. But some people have a *great* time. Want to remember your trip forever? Here's our best advice:

Which beach is the best? Our choice is **Bowman's Beach,** near the western end of Sanibel. There are miles of soft sand, lots of wildlife, and after a storm the shells can be piled 2 feet high. The shady park is a great picnic spot. And kids love the hidden fitness trail (to find it, veer right after you cross the northern bayou bridge). Bowman's is also the least crowded beach (Lighthouse Beach usually has the most people).

Regardless of the beach you choose, **go at low tide.** There's more to do — the beach is wider, and you can wade far offshore — more shells and more wildlife. If you have the willpower to get up early, go to the beach **30 minutes before dawn** (when it's just barely light). You can't get closer to nature. And **don't miss a beach sunset** — the perfect way to end an island day. The best sunset beaches are those that face west: Turner and Captiva.

What's the **best way to see wildlife?** It depends on your age. In our oh-so-scientific survey of visitors — i.e., Julie walking along the beach with a note pad — kids under 6 said they loved seeing stingrays and the bigger wading birds. If you've got kids this age, a hike up Bowman's Beach or a walk down Indigo Trail (at the J.N. 'Ding' Darling National Wildlife Refuge) might fit the bill. Elementary kids and teens were partial to alligators, dolphins and manatees — maybe plan a refuge hike one day, then a morning nature cruise on the Lady Chadwick *(Captiva Cruises, 472-5300),* where dolphins often jump in the wake (before you board, look to the right of the Captiva Cruises dock for manatees). Adults 18–54 loved seeing dolphins and osprey — that's a day on the water in a rented power boat. Seniors were bird freaks, so maybe a long day at the refuge.

When you go to the refuge, spend most of your time **outside your car.** Go to the refuge **at low tide** to see the most wildlife. **Hike Indigo Trail** in the morning. Look for alligator tracks in the sand (the bicycle-tire-size tail mark stretches across the sand, with claw marks on either side). A gang of ibis hangs out where Indigo Trail meets the Cross Dike Trail, back in the marsh on the south side. If you're in the refuge late in the day, **watch the spoonbills** come in to roost across from the observation tower.

Your memories will double if you **get out on the water.** We love to go to Cayo Costa and Cabbage Key, where you *have* to get a cheeseburger (the key lime pie's good too). Second place: the Waverunner Safari at Holiday Water Sports *(472-2938 or 472-5111, ext. 3433).* Skimming and splashing through the open sea is a guaranteed thrill. We also like taking a kayak tour through Tarpon Bay *(at Tarpon Bay Explorers, 472-8900).*

Bringing kids? **Take the tram tour** *(at Tarpon Bay Explorers, 472-8900)* through the refuge for a breezy and fun 90 minutes. **Rent a surrey** and cruise Periwinkle. You'll learn a lot on a **guided hike** at the Sanibel-Captiva Conservation Foundation *(472-2329).*

For food, there's nothing better than the slab of blackened grouper at the Periwinkle Way **Lazy Flamingo** (get the platter). We stop in for coffee and a couple of Mr. Bean bagels at **The Bean** (ask for the *bueno* salsa) a few times a week; for bigger breakfasts we go to the **Sunset Grill** (try the pancakes). For a high-class dinner, try the relaxed, sophisticated **Greenhouse Grill.** Finally, nothing takes you further away from the workday world than the leisurely pickings of the guitarist during dinner at the **Island Cow.**

---

**Facing page:** Sitting on the front porch of the Island Cow, Brent Moyer plays for diners

# Planning Your Trip

*T*o get the most out of an island vacation, you must have a plan. You should know what you want to do before you get here. Otherwise, the islands' laid-back quality makes it easy to waste your time. You'll spend hours reading pamphlets and making phone calls, time you could be relaxing and having fun.

But first, figure out what you want to do. Look through this book and make a list of the things you and your family will enjoy the most. Then decide how long you want to stay and how much you want to spend.

## What to pack

Island dress is casual. The easygoing outdoor lifestyle here means **shorts and sandals, T-shirts** and **baseball caps.** Dressing for dinner usually means just changing into clean T-shirts and shorts, even at the most expensive restaurants. In the winter add a pair of **lightweight pants** and a **sweater** or light wrap; temperatures can drop into the 50s at night.

Plan on two changes of clothes per day per person; you're bound to get sandy and sweaty. Bring clothes made of 100-percent cotton, which keeps you cooler than 50-50 blends. Also pack **swimsuits** and **sunglasses.** (Sound like too much? Buy some of it here.)

You need $3 **cash** to pay the toll to cross the Sanibel Causeway (the toll booth doesn't take checks or credit cards). Cash is also the only way to pay your admission to Wildlife Drive at the J.N. "Ding" Darling National Wildlife Refuge. **Binoculars** will come in handy to spot wildlife and view the stars. Don't forget your **camera...** or the film, tapes, storage devices, batteries and battery charger to go with it. Other items to consider: **vitamins** and **medications** (including a prescription for more if you think you'll run out), and an extra pair of **contact lenses** or **glasses** in case you lose them.

What you don't need to bring: A suit. A tie. High heels. Makeup. Perfume. Most recreation equipment (golf clubs, tennis rackets, in-line skates, rods and reels) can be rented.

### Sunscreen

Sunscreen is a must here: the islands are about as close to the sun as you can get in the continental United States. Look for a lotion with an SPF ("sun protection factor") rating of at least 30 and quality ingredients: Parsol 1789 (or avobenzone), titanium dioxide or zinc oxide (or Z-Cote). These help block UVA rays, which damage the inner layers of your skin, and UVB rays, which cause sunburn. Put it on about 30 minutes before you'll be in the sun so it can penetrate your skin. Bring it with you, too. Reapply it often, even if it claims to be waterproof. If you get burned, use an aloe-based after-sun product to ease the pain and help repair your skin.

---

**Facing page:** A royal tern rests on a channel marker in Pine Island Sound

'**Where can we eat by the water?'** is the No. 1 question visitors ask. The answers: The bayside Green Flash (above), or the Gulf-front restaurants at the Sundial and Casa Ybel (especially the pool bar).

**Avg. Gulf temperatures**

| | |
|---|---|
| Spring / Summer | 84.1 |
| Fall / Winter | 70.8 |
| Yearly | 77.5 |

**Avg. rainfall** (inches)

| | |
|---|---|
| January | 1.84 |
| February | 2.23 |
| March | 3.07 |
| April | 1.06 |
| May | 3.87 |
| June | 9.52 |
| July | 8.26 |
| August | 9.66 |
| September | 7.82 |
| October | 2.94 |
| November | 1.57 |
| December | 1.53 |
| Yearly | 53.37 |

## Bug repellent

Mosquitoes and "no-see-ums" (teeny sand flies) are a nuisance, especially in the summer. For a repellent we use *Off! Unscented.* This affordable, easy-to-apply spray is sold everywhere. The most effective repellent is *Off! Deep Woods for Sportsmen.* But it's expensive, and has 100 percent deet (technically, N,N-Diethyl-meta-toluamide) which used undiluted can destroy nylon and is harmful to kids less than 2 months old. When our daughter was a baby we used *Avon's Skin-So-Soft,* which contains no deet.

# Money

## What things cost

| Item | U.S.$ |
|---|---|
| Shuttle for 4 from SW Florida Intl. Airport | $50.00 |
| Double room at Sanibel Inn, expensive | |
| Winter/peak | $319 to $539 |
| Summer/value | $169 to $255 |
| Double room at Brennen's Tarpon Tale Inn, moderate | |
| Winter/peak | $169 to $309 |
| Summer/value | $99 to $189 |
| Double room at Anchor Inn, inexpensive | |
| Winter/peak | $149 to $219 |
| Summer/value | $79 to $159 |
| Dinner entree | |
| At Lazy Flamingo | $7 to $15 |
| At Trader's | $19 to $30 |

Restaurant beverages

Bottle of beer ................................. $1.25 to $4.25

Soft drink ....................................... $1.25 to $2.50

Coffee ............................................. $0.95 to $2.50

Admission fees

Wildlife Drive (1 car) ..................................... $5.00

Old Schoolhouse Theater ........................... $25.00

Shell Museum (adult) ..................................... $5.00

Shell Museum (child) ..................................... $3.00

Roll of Kodak film, 36 exposures,

at Eckerd ....................................................... $7.99

Local telephone call (pay phone) ........................ $0.35

## Other expenses

Florida has a 6 percent **sales tax** that is added to most items, although not groceries or medical services. Plan to **tip** at restaurants. The standard restaurant tip is 15 percent, but always check the bill first. Some restaurants discretely add a tip to your bill automatically, then still provide a line on the ticket for you to tip again! Also tip on successful fishing or shelling charters. If you're **renting a car**, ask about sales tax, airport surcharges and other fees while booking your reservation. At the counter, be leery of optional add-ons. You probably don't need the optional insurance (rental cars are probably covered in your auto policy you already have; check ahead of time). Beware the gasoline schemes, too. It's almost always the best choice to simply bring the car back with a full tank of gas.

## Getting cash

You'll find ATM machines at nearly all island banks and most shopping areas and food stores. Check your daily withdrawal limit and credit limits before leaving home. Note: There are no banks on Captiva.

Travelex *(2nd floor of the Southwest Florida International Airport; open Mon.–Sat., 9 a.m.–5 p.m.; Sun., noon–5 p.m.; 561-2204)* is a **currency exchange** agency. It exchanges 120 currencies, with a $5 fee for any amount. Most area banks offer the service, too, but you usually have to order foreign currency in advance. On Sanibel try SunTrust Bank *(2408 Periwinkle Way; 800-786-8787)* or Colonial Bank *(520 Tarpon Bay Rd.; allow 10 days, 472-1314).*

# Business hours

Most banks are open 9 a.m. to 4 p.m. Monday through Friday and sometimes Saturday morning. Business offices are usually open 9 a.m. to 5 p.m. weekdays. Stores

**To report lost or stolen credit cards:**

- American Express
  800-528-4800
- Discover Card
  800-347-2683
- Master Card
  800-307-7309
- VISA
  800-847-2911

**To report lost or stolen traveler's checks:**

- American Express
  800-221-7282
- Thomas Cook
  800-223-7373
- VISA
  800-227-6811

**These Sanibel banks offer cash advances** on Mastercard and VISA:

- Colonial Bank
  520 Tarpon Bay Rd.
- Bank of the Islands
  1699 Periwinkle Way
- Bank of America
  1037 Periwinkle Way
  2450 Periwinkle Way
- Sanibel-Captiva
  Community Bank
  2495 Palm Ridge Rd.
- SunTrust Bank
  2408 Periwinkle Way.
- Wachovia
  2407 Palm Ridge Rd.

**Don't wear perfume** or cologne outdoors on the islands. The sweet scents attract no-see-ums.

**The area code** on the islands is 239.

**You must be at least 21** years old to drink alcohol. You can buy it seven days a week. Florida's drunk-driving laws are some of the toughest in the U.S.

**Avg. temperatures** (°F)

| MONTH | HIGH | LOW |
| --- | --- | --- |
| January | 74.4 | 53.2 |
| February | 75.5 | 54.1 |
| March | 80.0 | 58.7 |
| April | 84.6 | 62.0 |
| May | 88.8 | 67.6 |
| June | 90.6 | 72.9 |
| July | 91.4 | 74.6 |
| August | 91.4 | 74.8 |
| September | 90.0 | 74.2 |
| October | 86.0 | 68.5 |
| November | 80.7 | 60.9 |
| December | 76.0 | 55.0 |
| Yearly | 84.1 | 64.7 |

**Wearing beach shoes** to protect his feet, a young boy collects a bag full of shells on Easter weekend

and restaurants sometimes simply stay open until the crowd leaves. More than once we've called a restaurant and have been asked, "How soon can you get here?"

# When to go

## Spring

Our favorite time. The weather is beautiful, the flowers are blooming, most of the birds are still here. Early spring is peak tourist season, and summer heat starts in April. But most seasonal residents leave at the end of March. Hotel rates often drop after Easter.

## Summer

The islands display their true laid-back nature in June, July and August. Crowds are light. Hotel rates are reasonable. It rains nearly every afternoon for an hour or so, then clears back up. Days are hot (by 9 a.m.) and nights are warm, but temperatures are milder than most of south Florida. The surrounding waters cool the island air.

## Fall

In September the islands are quiet. There are no lines, no traffic, hardly any people. Some restaurants close. Hotel rates are low. Things pick up some in October, but even early December's peaceful. Crowds don't arrive until right after Christmas.

## Winter

January can get chilly, but it's not crowded. Afternoon traffic between Valentine's Day and Easter can be miserable — it can take an hour to drive 3 miles on Periwinkle Way. Restaurant lines are long, hotel rates are high. But this is the weather Northerners daydream about when they shovel snow. Highs are in the 70s and 80s, it's nearly always sunny and there's little rain. Birding and shelling are at their peaks. And there are more festivals, shows, nature tours and other activities.

## Suggested itinerary

If you can, allow at least four days on the islands. To stay fresh, work in a combination of active and passive activities every day. Plan a morning bike ride followed by an afternoon

at the beach. Or hike the refuge and then spend the afternoon at your hotel pool. You can work in the man-made attractions here and there, whenever you need a break.

Before you make your plan, get a tide chart and see when low tide falls. Adjust your itinerary so you go to the beach and refuge at low tide. This makes all the difference; you'll see far more shells and wildlife.

Want to experience a true island-style getaway? Here is a suggested three- to seven-day itinerary that does just that, with a sampling of the best the islands have to offer:

### The first three days

**Day 1: Hit the beach, ride a bike.** Get to the beach at dawn. Watch for dolphins. Build a sand castle. For lunch go to Trader's on Sanibel; order a special. In the afternoon hop on a bike and explore the shops along Periwinkle Way, then pedal out to the Gulfside Park Preserve off Casa Ybel Road. After a dinner of blackened grouper and cold beer at the Periwinkle Lazy Flamingo, go to the Old Schoolhouse Theater for a fun night of music and comedy.

**Day 2: Explore the refuge.** Get out early while the crowds are thin and the weather is gorgeous. Stop at the Center for Education (open at 9 a.m.) and ask the volunteers for information and a map. Watch the 15-minute video to orient yourself, then cruise down Wildlife Drive, stopping often to get out and explore. Have a late lunch at the nearby Island House on Rabbit Road, then visit the Bailey-Matthews Shell Museum, a mile to the east

**Eighty-eight year-old Phyllis Mason** decorates caps at the Sanibel Shell Fair. A seasonal resident of the islands for 30 years, Phyllis answers to many names. Some folks call her the Shell Doctor, for her skills at repairing broken shell critters and jewelry. Some call her the Shell Lady. Martha Stewart called her an artist.

**Sunrise times** (a.m.)

| MONTH | 1ST DAY | LAST DAY |
|---|---|---|
| January | 7:16 | 7:13 |
| February | 7:13 | 6:53 |
| March | 6:52 | 6:21 |
| April | 6:20 | 6:52 |
| May | 6:51 | 6:35 |
| June | 6:35 | 6:38 |
| July | 6:38 | 6:52 |
| August | 6:53 | 7:07 |
| Sept. | 7:07 | 7:20 |
| October | 7:20 | 6:37 |
| Nov. | 6:37 | 6:58 |
| Dec. | 6:59 | 7:16 |

on Sanibel-Captiva Road. Later, have an elegant dinner at Sunset Grill in Santiva, and stroll along the adjacent Turner Beach in the moonlight.

**Day 3: Become Jimmy Buffett.** Rent a boat at the 'Tween Waters boat dock and head off into the bay. Make your first stop Cayo Costa. Tie up at the state-park dock and walk over to the Gulf. For lunch cruise back to nearby Cabbage Key for cheeseburgers. Write a note on a dollar bill and attach it to the ceiling. Explore the island; climb the water tower. Leave and admire Useppa Island from afar, then roam the bay waters. Back on Captiva, have dinner at R.C. Otter's (or, for fatter wallets, Keylime Bistro), and relax as you listen to island musicians.

## Additional days

**Add-on Day 4. Do nothing.** Go to Bowman's Beach. Wander around aimlessly. Listen to the waves. Fall asleep. Later, float on a raft. Waste the whole day.

**Add-on Day 5: Kayaking and island history.** Start with bagels and coffee at The Bean. Rent a kayak at Tarpon Bay Explorers and paddle the Commodore Creek Canoe Trail. Munch a hot dog at Schnapper's Hots, then see island history at the Sanibel Historical Village and Museum. Wash up, then have dinner at the Greenhouse Grill.

**Add-on Day 6: Offshore thrills.** Start off early with Eggs Benedict at the Lighthouse Cafe on Periwinkle Way (ask for a booth). Then get out on the water. Choose (a) a charter fishing trip, (b) parasailing at YOLO Watersports or (c) a Waverunner tour at South Seas. Stop by Turner Beach for the sunset, then head back into Sanibel for a fun dinner and a big dessert at the Island Cow.

**Add-on Day 7. Wind down.** Get the Eggs Santiva at the Sunset Grill for breakfast. Then drive out to SCCF for a guided nature tour. Have a burger and a vanilla malt at Cheeburger Cheeburger on Periwinkle Way, then take a surrey to Lighthouse Beach. Check out the nature trails, meander over to the fishing pier, look for tiny wentletraps in the sand. Head back to your hotel for a shower, then have some of the *perfecto* pasta or pizza at La Vigna.

## For the latest updates…

You can learn what events are planned for the days you're here by stopping at the Sanibel-Captiva Chamber of Commerce *(1159 Causeway Rd., Sanibel; 472-1080)*. Each week it publishes a flyer showing all current island activities. Don't be shy; over 200,000 visitors stop here each year.

**Tropical storms and hurricanes** are most likely here between July and September. Consider postponing your trip if forecasters are predicting a strike. Visitors are not allowed on the islands during a hurricane warning. Most airlines will let you delay your flight with no penalty.

If you are here when a storm approaches, follow National Weather Service advisories, television directives and common sense to act responsibly.

**The island speed limit** is 30 mph unless posted; Periwinkle and Sanibel-Captiva Road are 35 mph (police write many tickets, particularly on San-Cap). It's tough to pass: all roads are two lanes and there are few passing zones.

**Facing page:** Tides fall dramatically during a full moon, exposing more sand and creating more shallow-water areas

# Getting Here

*I*'m finally getting to Florida!" says the visitor. "I'm finally getting *out* of Florida!" says the islander. They're describing the same thing — the wonderful feeling they get when they cross the three-mile causeway and drive onto Sanibel.

You feel you're going someplace special, that it's time to relax. "Crossing the causeway is like shedding your skin," one islander says. "You feel brand new."

## By air

If you're flying to the islands, the view out your window can get you into an island mood even before you land. Flights from Atlanta and other points north often fly directly over the west coast of Florida, including Sanibel and Captiva. Passengers on the right side of the plane have a terrific view. You'll first see a hodgepodge of small islands, including Gasparilla, Cayo Costa and North Captiva. The water varies from dark blue out at sea to aquamarine in the bays. Sometimes you can see the sandy bottom underneath.

First Captiva, then Sanibel come into view. You can identify Captiva by the cleared north tip, where the South Seas Resort's Land's End Village sits. Sanibel is fat and curved like a shrimp. At first glance many passengers don't realize they're looking at Sanibel, forgetting for a moment that most of the island is conservation land. There are few landmarks, except the causeway and the lighthouse, both at the eastern end.

**Southwest Florida International Airport** (RSW) *(16000 Chamberlain Parkway, Ft. Myers; 768-1000)* is the area's commercial airport. It's 19 miles east of Sanibel, one mile east of Interstate 75 at Exit 131 (Daniels Parkway). An average of 200 flights take off and land here a day, carrying 5.2 million passengers a year.

February, March and April are the peak months, as Northerners pour into the region to escape the sleet and snow. Many airlines increase their number of flights for the winter season, starting each December. International and domestic charter flights also fly a regular winter schedule. The airport's two busiest weeks are Christmas and Easter.

In the terminal you'll find an ATM machine, mail box, duty-free shop and currency exchange. There are many fast-food walk-ups and a Chili's Too table-service restaurant.

### Airlines

Twenty-two airlines serve Southwest Florida International. Delta has the most daily flights, including 13 from Atlanta and four from Orlando. Delta also offers service through its commuter airline, Delta Express (including new-for-2002 service to Newark), and has a working relationship with Comair and Sabena. American and its commuter airline, American Eagle, offer five daily flights from Miami. Continental and the Conti-

---

**Facing page:** A child's footprints on Bowman's Beach

- Air Canada
  888-247-2262
- AirTran
  800-825-8538
- Air Transat
  800-470-1011
- America West
  800-235-9292
- American/Am. Eagle
  800-433-7300
- American Trans Air
  800-435-9282
- Cape Air
  800-352-0714
- Comair (Delta)
  800-221-1212
- Continental
  800-525-0280
- Delta
  800-221-1212
- Delta Express
  866-235-9359
- Frontier
  800-432-1359
- Gulfstream Int'l
  888-871-0530
- JetBlue Airways
  800-538-2583
- LTU International
  866-266-5588
- Midwest Express
  800-452-2022
- Northwest/KLM
  800-225-2525
- Pro Air
  800-939-9551
- Spirit
  800-772-7117
- Sun Country
  800-359-5786
- United/United Express
  800-241-6522
- US Airways
  800-428-4322

nental Connection have six flights a day from Tampa.

International carriers include American, Continental, Delta, LTU, Northwest/KLM and US Airways.

Southwest Florida International is one of the fastest-growing airports in the country. American, American Trans Air, Midwest Express, US Airways and Lynx Air International have all beefed up service. Delta Express recently added a fourth daily flight to Boston, while JetBlue Airways added a second nonstop flight to New York's JFK airport. Frontier Airlines began service here in 2002, with a daily nonstop flight to Denver.

## Renting a car

You'll find six car-rental companies with check-in counters inside the airport. Enterprise and Thrifty don't have airport counters, but run shuttles to their facilities just outside the gates. Always make reservations; cars are often sold out, especially in season. Rental car buses are across the street from the main terminal.

You can rent a car on the islands, too. The Amoco Service Center *(1015 Periwinkle Way, Sanibel; 472-2125)* has Hertz cars. The South Seas Resort *(5611 South Seas Plantation Rd., Captiva; 395-0833)* has an Enterprise office.

## Taxis and limos

Outside the terminal you'll usually find quite a few taxis waiting. But you don't just hail a cab here. Instead, make your arrangements at the ground transportation booth, located between the terminal and parking lot. Taxis have a fixed-fee structure for service to the islands: $40 for the eastern half of Sanibel (as far west as Tarpon Bay Road); $47 for west Sanibel, including West Gulf Drive; and $60 to take you to Captiva.

Shuttle and limo services require advance reservations. You'll pay about the same as a taxi, but the driver will be waiting for you and the vehicles are usually larger and more comfortable.

Most drivers meet their passengers on the ground floor in the baggage claim area. If you arrive in Terminal A, the waiting area is down the escalator and to your right, in front of Baggage Belt Number 1. If you arrive in Terminal B, the area is down the escalator and to your left, in front of Baggage Belt Number 6.

Some services have their drivers meet you outside the terminal beside their vehicle, on the commercial curb across the street. If you're going through customs, meet your driver in the lobby of the International Arrivals building. If you can't find your driver, pick up a white courtesy

phone or stop by the ground transportation booth.

Shuttles and limos serving the islands include:

■ Apple Taxi and Limousine Service *(482-1200 or 800-852-7027)*. A popular van-based service, Apple's rates (for up to three people) are $40 for eastern Sanibel (to Tarpon Bay Road), $47 for western Sanibel, and $54 for Captiva.

■ Sanibel-Captiva Airport Shuttle. *(466-3236)*. This well-known service uses limousines (not stretch). Rates for up to 2 people are $35 to Sanibel, $55 to Captiva. Additional riders are $10 each.

■ Sanibel Island Taxi *(472-4160 or 888-527-7806)*. Rates for up to three people are $35 for eastern Sanibel, $40 for western Sanibel, and $51 for Captiva.

## Page Field

**Page Field** *(501 Danley Dr., Ft. Myers; 936-1443)* caters to charters and private planes, including jets down to two-seaters. It has four runways — the longest is 6,400 feet — and a full maintenance facility, fuel and avionics. Page Field was the area's commercial airport until the early 1980s. It was named the 2002 General Aviation Airport of the Year by the Florida Dept. of Transportation. Budget and Enterprise Rent-A-Car have locations here.

# By car

People often visit Sanibel and Captiva after a trip to Walt Disney World. Most visitors who drive here spend the night before in Orlando. Thirty percent are fellow Florid-

**Welcome to Sanibel**

**Rental cars at Southwest Florida International Airport**

■ Alamo
  800-GO-ALAMO
  Local: 768-2424
■ Avis
  800-230-4898
  Local: 768-2121
■ Budget
  800-227-5945
  Local: 768-1500
■ Dollar
  800-800-3665
  Local: 768-2223
■ Enterprise
  800-736-8222
  Local: 561-2227
■ Hertz
  800-654-3131
  Local: 768-3100
■ National
  800-CAR-RENT
  Local: 768-2100
■ Thrifty
  800-847-4389
  Local: 768-2322

**Distance to Sanibel and Captiva from other Florida cities** (in miles)

| | |
|---|---|
| Clearwater | 145 |
| Daytona | 230 |
| Fort Lauderdale | 155 |
| Gainesville | 250 |
| Jacksonville | 305 |
| Key West | 290 |
| Miami | 158 |
| Ocala | 215 |
| Orlando | 175 |
| Palm Beach | 144 |
| St. Augustine | 270 |
| St. Petersburg | 130 |
| Sarasota | 90 |
| Tallahassee | 375 |
| Tampa | 145 |

**Sanibel is 18 miles west** of Interstate 75, 19 miles west of the airport. That's a 30- to 45-minute drive, depending on traffic.

**Opposite page:** Peaceful island attitudes are irresistible to children

**Keep your eyes peeled** for "Exit 131," the airport exit. Sanibel and Captiva are the top tourist spots in the region, but I-75 signs make no reference to the islands.

ians, most often from the East Coast. No matter where you're driving from, your first step is getting to Interstate 75, and then to Exit 131:

■ **From Orlando or Walt Disney World,** take Interstate 4 south to Tampa, then head south on I-75 to Exit 131. The islands are about 3½ hours from Orlando, 2½ hours from Tampa.

■ **From Atlanta or Tampa,** it's a straight shot down I-75. Driving from Atlanta takes about 10 or 11 hours.

■ **From Fort Lauderdale or Miami,** follow I-75 "north" (you'll actually be heading due west, but the signs will say "I-75 North") out of Fort Lauderdale and across the state, then up past Naples to Exit 131. (I-75 is a toll road from Fort Lauderdale to Naples.)

From the interstate Sanibel is 18 miles away, a 30- to 45-minute drive depending on traffic. Add another half hour to get to Captiva — the only road there is the one through Sanibel. As you drive toward the islands you'll see many real estate "Available" signs that hint at development to come in this area (enjoy looking at those cows grazing along the roadside while you can).

Here's how you get to Sanibel from I-75:

■ **Go west on Daniels Parkway** 2.6 miles to Six Mile Cypress Parkway, also called the Ben C. Pratt Parkway. A few directional signs use a brown triangle to represent Sanibel and a brown circle for Captiva. Except for these, few signs or billboards will mention the islands.

■ **Go left (south) on Six Mile Cypress Parkway** 4.3 miles to Summerlin Road, around the south end of Fort Myers. On your right you'll pass the Lee County Sports Complex, the spring training home of the Minnesota Twins. Stop in for a key-lime ice cream cone at Sun Harvest, an orange juice processing company and store 1½ miles down Six Mile Cypress on your left.

■ **Go left (west) on Summerlin Road** 8.0 miles to the Sanibel Causeway toll plaza. Get out three dollars, the same toll since the causeway opened back in 1963.

■ **Cross the Sanibel Causeway** 3.0 miles to Sanibel. The causeway islands are man-made, built from sand dredged from the bay. The pelicans may fly within inches of your car. They often fly at the same height as your vehicle, and get so close you'll swear they're going to fly right into you. Watch closely and you'll see one spot a fish, suddenly dive-bomb straight into the water, and catch the meal in its pouch. (Turn off your radio and roll down your windows. If a pelican flies close enough, you may be able to hear its wings rustle.)

peace, Love & Dolphins
Sanibel Island

More than 3.1 million vehicles crossed the causeway in 2002, nearly double the traffic of 20 years ago.

Once you're on Sanibel you'll hit a four-way stop at Periwinkle Way. From here the main drag is to the right. But any direction heads to the beach, restaurants and accommodations. Captiva is 10 miles to your right.

**Don't be surprised** if you're delayed for a few minutes by the Sanibel drawbridge (above) opening. Consider it part of the charm of getting here. It opens every 30 minutes (starting at the top of the hour), whenever a boater requests it. The opening and closing takes about five minutes.

The mechanics are controlled by an operator who sits in a tiny control house on the bridge itself. When a boat over 26 feet high (usually a sailboat and its mast) approaches, the captain calls the bridge operator to request an opening, and then waits until the next scheduled time.

The Sanibel drawbridge opens more often than others on the Okeechobee Waterway. Water turbulence around the channel makes it difficult for boats to wait.

And yes, it can get stuck. Still using technology from the 1960s, the bridge sometimes doesn't close all the way. Or it gets locked while it's straight

# By sea

Boating to the islands was the only way to get here until 1963, when the Sanibel Causeway was built. It's still the most scenic and peaceful way to arrive.

Coming in from the north, you'll pass Boca Grande, a getaway for the rich and famous of U.S. society from the Colliers and Vanderbilts of yesterday to the Bushes of today. From the south you'll be charting the same course as Ponce de Leon when he sailed to the islands from Cuba.

You'll spot the Sanibel lighthouse at the east tip of the island, a beacon to sailors for more than a hundred years. If your boat or mast is taller than 26 feet, you'll need to radio the Sanibel drawbridge to open to let you through. It rises on demand at 30-minute intervals from 6 a.m. to 10 p.m., and any time overnight with an hour's notice. The water can be turbulent around the bridge.

Except for the dredged Intercoastal Waterway, San Carlos Bay and Pine Island Sound are shallow. The water is often only a few inches deep, even at high tide. Weekends are crowded with jet skis, flats fishermen, rental boats and more, especially during the winter.

## Marinas

Three marinas on Sanibel and Captiva allow overnight docking. All monitor radio channel 16.

Located near the east end of Sanibel, just east of the causeway, the **Sanibel Marina** *(472-2723)* is tucked in just off the bay, between ICW Mile Markers 2 and 3 (6-foot low-tide depth), on a canal. It takes boats up to 110 feet. The marina has fuel and pump-out, parts and service, showers and restaurant, overnight dock and shore power; bait and fishing equipment; a ramp; boat rentals and charters. Hours are 7 a.m. to 5 p.m. daily. Rates are $1.50 per foot. The manager is Stephannie Peterson.

The **South Seas Resort Bayside Marina** *(472-5111, ext. 3447 or 888-777-3625)* gets lots of good press. Motor Boating & Sailing, Powerboat and Boating World magazines all have recently named it a top yachting destination. Located on the bay side of the northern tip of Captiva, it has 3,600 feet of berthing space and takes boats up to 120 feet. Boaters are allowed to use the resort's barbecue area and gas grills, can take advantage of the resort's recreation program, and can stay in one of the surrounding villas or homes. South Seas has fuel and pump-out (no charge); showers, a restaurant and lodging; overnight dock, shore power, water and cable TV; bait and fishing equipment; a ramp; boat rentals and charters. The marina is open from 8 a.m. to 5:30 p.m. daily. Rates are $2.20 per foot from Thanksgiving through April 30; $1.60 per foot the rest of the year. The dockmaster is John Findley. To get to South Seas from the ICW, head west at Mile Marker 39 (watch for the sign), and proceed 1½ miles west through a privately maintained channel (6-foot low-tide depth). From the Gulf, head through Redfish Pass, which is marked with two green and one red-right-return floating markers (8-foot low-tide depth).

Part of the 'Tween Waters Inn complex, the **'Tween Waters Marina** *(472-5161 or 800-223-5875)* sits midway down Captiva, on Roosevelt Channel just off the bay. It offers fuel and pump-out; showers, a restaurant and lodging; overnight dock and shore power; bait and fishing equipment; a ramp; boat rentals and charters. Rates are $2 per foot from December 24 through April 30 and holidays, and $1.60 per foot the rest of the year. Hotel guests pay $1.20 per foot. From ICW Mile Marker 38, take compass heading 215 one mile to Roosevelt Channel, Marker 2. Follow to Green 19.

up. It can take two hours to crank down by hand.

The control house is manned from 6 a.m. to 10 p.m. When boats come through late at night, a toll-booth operator walks out and opens the bridge for them. In the 1960s the bridge was raised every night and kept up, like the drawbridge of a castle. It was lowered at dawn.

Today the drawbridge is also used to fight crime. Twice in the last few years it has been raised to keep a suspect on the islands.

**Street signs** on the islands come in two colors. A blue sign indicates a public road. An orange sign means the road is private.

**The Sanibel Marina**

# History

*F*or such peaceful islands, Sanibel and Captiva have a wild and woolly past. Half-naked Indians beheaded captives here. Pirates are said to have buried treasure, imprisoned young girls and decapitated a princess. A discredited evangelist started island tourism. But the story of Sanibel and Captiva is also a tale of preservation, of people falling in love with these special lands and fighting to protect their physical and aesthetic beauty.

## Early history

Sanibel and Captiva are young, only 5,000 years old. They began to form about 3000 B.C., when storms created a sandbar about six miles off the coast of today's Florida. Soon mangrove trees grew to hold the sand in place, creating a permanent island. This became Captiva. Sand continued to build up to the south, eventually forming Sanibel. The whole process took 4,500 years. The lighthouse end of Sanibel didn't exist until about 1500.

### Calusa Indians

Calusa ("ka-LOO-sah") Indians had lived in the area the whole time. By 1500 there were 40 Calusa villages in Southwest Florida, about 3,000 people. They moved onto Sanibel and Captiva as the islands were being formed. The Calusa lived off the sea, eating fish and seafood and using shells as tools (such as the ax at right). They built 30-man canoes, strapping two together to travel as far as Mexico. A tall, handsome people, they wore only short deerskin wraps around their waists.

The Calusa's religious practices could be barbaric. As part of the tribe's annual harvest festival, all "nonbelievers" in the village would be sacrificed. First, the Calusa would cut off the victims' heads, then pluck out their eyes. Believing the eyes contained the soul, the tribe would offer them to their Harvest God to eat. (The Calusa worshipped three gods. A second controlled the weather; a third, war.)

The tribe found many reasons to sacrifice someone. When a chief died, his servants would be sacrificed so they could continue to serve him in the spirit world. When a chief's child died, other children would be sacrificed, too, so the young boy or girl would continue to have someone to play with.

All Calusa were required to believe in all aspects of the official religion. To make sure they did, each summer the tribe's shaman would run screaming throughout the village, vividly reminding everyone just who was in charge.

---

**Facing page:** A sleeping lamb marks the 1901 grave of Ann Brainerd. The 10-year-old girl was buried on her favorite spot on Captiva. The area later became the island cemetery.

**Juan Ponce de Leon** landed on Sanibel on June 15, 1513, his last stop on his first voyage to Florida

**Off with her head!** In 1801, pirate José Gaspar raided the ship of the Spanish princess Marie Louise (daughter of King Carlos III), traveling across the Gulf from Mexico. On board were 11 Mexican girls, headed to school at a Spanish convent. Gaspar had his men take the girls to Captiva, where he held them for ransom. He kept the princess for his bride.

But Marie Louise refused to marry Gaspar. He imprisoned her on Useppa, a small island north of Captiva. Years passed, but she never changed her mind. Finally, Gaspar gave up — and chopped off her head.

The princess' body was most likely tossed into Pine Island Sound, but some say she's actually buried in an unmarked grave on Captiva.

# Spanish explorers

Juan Ponce de Leon landed on Sanibel in 1513. On his maiden voyage around today's Florida, he stopped here to clean his ships before heading back to Havana. He named the island "Santa Isybella" after Spain's Queen Isabella, who financed his friend Columbus 21 years earlier ("Santa" is Spanish for "saint").

Ponce returned to settle the area in 1521. Bringing 200 people and 50 horses, he planned to establish the first European settlement in today's United States. But the Calusa attacked, wounding the explorer in his thigh with a poisoned arrow. His ships retreated to Havana, where he soon died.

Other explorers landed in the area, too. The ships of Hernando DeSoto, complete with 640 men, anchored on Sanibel in 1539, but were run off the next day. Pánfilo de Narváez and Alvar Nuñez Cabeza de Vaca (1528), Pedro Menendez de Aviles (1566) and Juan Rodrigues (1688) were all, as Rodrigues wrote, "politely refused."

The Calusa began to include captured Spanish in their beheadings. Spanish priests attempted, and failed, to stop the practice and convert the Indians to Christianity. Jesuit priest Juan Rogel, who landed here briefly in 1566, described the Calusa's rituals as "evil beyond belief."

Five Franciscan friars made one last attempt to convert the Calusa in 1697, when they traveled by themselves to the islands. They landed at night, and cautiously marched into the Calusa village holding candles and crosses. Surprisingly... nothing happened. The Calusa had been scared by the strange sight and had hid in the jungle.

The friars thought they were on to something and marched again the next night. But this time the Calusa were waiting. They attacked the "invaders" and ripped off the Franciscans' clothes. The friars ran naked back to the beach and scurried onto their boats, never to return.

But the Calusa's days were numbered. Spanish slave ships, armed with the latest guns and cannons, captured hundreds in the early 1700s. Others died from European diseases such as yellow fever, tuberculosis and measles. Those that survived joined the Seminoles, a mixed tribe of Creek descendents and escaped African slaves. By 1750, the Calusa nation was gone.

The Spanish never did established themselves here. Spain traded Florida to England in 1763 to regain Cuba, which it had lost in the Seven Years' War. When the American Revolution began in 1776, the world ignored Florida, leaving its coastline open to pirates.

## Pirates and buried treasure

According to legend, two pirates roamed the Sanibel and Captiva waters in the early 1800s. José Gaspar used Captiva as a prison for captured females. Sanibel was the home of Black Caesar and his large stash of treasure.

Gaspar, also known as Gasparilla, was headquartered at Boca Grande, 10 miles north of Captiva. Originally a Spanish naval officer, he stole a navy boat and began a new life plundering merchant ships in the Gulf of Mexico.

Henri Caesar was an escaped African slave in Haiti. He organized a group of ex-slaves and took over a Spanish ship in 1805. A fan of Miami-area pirate Black Caesar, Henri Caesar took that name for himself as well. Lacking any nautical experience, he and his crew raided only smaller ships. But they stockpiled a lot of treasure.

Henri "Black" Caesar sailed to Southwest Florida and met Gaspar. The pirates agreed that Caesar would set up camp on Sanibel. Though Gaspar's headquarters was elaborate, with cannons and servants, Caesar's land base was primitive, just thatch huts guarded by mangy dogs.

The pirates clashed in 1817. During a drunken party, Caesar's crew decided to raid Gaspar's Captiva prison. They killed a guard, and rescued (or, perhaps, abducted) two girls. Furious, Gaspar invaded Sanibel and demanded Caesar surrender the women and leave the island. Vastly overmatched, Caesar immediately set sail, without his treasure. He set up a new camp on Florida's east coast.

Gaspar's reign came to an end in 1822. The U.S. Navy brought a gunboat down to Boca Grande Pass, disguising it as a British merchant ship. When the pirate sailed up to overtake it, the sailors opened fire. Gaspar refused to be taken alive. He wrapped the anchor chain around his waist, pushed the anchor overboard and jumped off.

Tales tell of Gaspar burying 13 casks and chests of gold and silver in the area. Hundreds of his men are said to have buried smaller caches throughout the islands. Legends say Henri "Black" Caesar hid up to $6 million of gold, silver and jewels on Sanibel. But no one's ever found any of it. More than a dozen pirate caches have been found on the Florida west coast, but none on Sanibel or Captiva.

*Note: Pirate lore is notoriously exaggerated. But the U.S. Navy has records of attacking Gaspar, and Henri Caesar's existence is well documented.*

# The Civil War

When the Civil War began in 1861, the Confederate government required that Florida cattle farmers sell their cows

**Shipwrecks.** Here's a partial list of ships that have wrecked off Sanibel:

- The William & Frederick was lost off Sanibel on April 2, 1832, sailing from Apalachicola to Key West.

- The Union captured the Confederate schooner Ida on March 4, 1863. It was run aground on Sanibel and destroyed.

- Sailing on its maiden voyage from Cedar Key to Charlotte Harbor, the 38-ton steamer Huntress was blown off course during a storm, swamped and sank off the coast of Sanibel on Oct. 6, 1873. It contained $4,500 of building materials.

- Sailing from Key West, the 21-ton Sea Bird foundered just east of Sanibel on Aug. 29, 1880. It was a total loss.

- The 207-ton Martha M. Heath hit a shoal and broke apart 2½ miles west of Sanibel on May 5, 1884. Coming from New York, it contained the prefabricated Sanibel lighthouse and coal for its burners (as well as a nearly identical lighthouse for Cape San Blas, Fla.).

- Sailing south from Tampa, the 65-foot, 40-ton freighter Chase was stranded on Sanibel on Jan. 10, 1928.

- The 83-ton freight vessel Athenian burned 25 miles off Sanibel on May 26, 1973.

# What's in a Name?

**Blind Pass.** The Spanish named the cut between Sanibel and Captiva "Boca Ciego," which can mean either "blind" or "shut up." The pass once snaked blindly through the area, reaching the Gulf on the east side of Bowman's Beach. Today the second meaning makes more sense, as this now straight pass often fills with sand.

**Bowman's Beach.** This Sanibel beach was named after Robert Bowman, who attempted, and failed, to homestead on Sanibel in the late 1800s.

**Buck Key.** This small island on the bay side of Captiva was home to many deer before the 1910 hurricane.

**Captiva.** From the original Spanish name, Isle de los Captivas ("Island of the Female Captives"). Legends say pirates held female captives on the island in the 1700s and early 1800s. Other "captivating" tales say Calusa Indians held Juan Ortíz captive here for 11 years in the 1500s and that the Spanish captured Calusa for slaves here.

**Casa Ybel.** "The House of Sanibel." Islanders pronounce it as one word, "CAHS-ah-bel," keeping the "Y" silent. *See Ybel, below.*

**Dixie Beach.** Where the ferry Dixie docked in the 1920s, this beach is on the bay side of Sanibel near the lighthouse. Ironically, Dixie Beach Boulevard does not go to Dixie Beach. Lee County officials named the wrong road.

**Fort Myers.** A U.S. Army outpost, Fort Myers was built along the Caloosahatchee River as one of the first federal bases of the Seminole Indian Wars. It was named in honor of Col. Abraham C. Myers, the son-in-law of the commander of Fort Brooke in Tampa. The city of Fort Myers was incorporated on this spot in 1885.

**Periwinkle Way.** Sanibel's main thoroughfare is named after the flowers the Bailey family planted along the road. County planners wanted to name it Sanibel Boulevard.

**Punta Rassa.** A misspelling of "Punta Rasa," Spanish for "flat point." Where the Sanibel Causeway meets the mainland, this area was a major cattle port in the 19th and early 20th centuries (one day in July 1900, 2,747 head of cattle were shipped from here). Most of the port area is now the Sanibel Harbour Resort & Spa.

**Rabbit Road.** This mid-Sanibel road connects West Gulf Drive with Sanibel-Captiva Road. Years ago, when it was nothing more than a path through the saw grass, it was thick with marsh rabbits. A small street off Rabbit Road is called Bunny Lane.

**Redfish Pass.** Formed by the 1921 hurricane, this pass between Captiva and North Captiva had no name for two years. But in 1923 it became so thick with redfish, fishermen said you couldn't put a hook in the water without catching one.

**Roosevelt Channel.** This channel between Captiva and Buck Key is named after Theodore Roosevelt. He stayed on a houseboat here in 1913, studying rays and sharks.

**San Carlos Bay.** The body of water between Sanibel and the mainland was named after Carlos, the area's Calusa Indian chief. The "San" was added in the 1920s.

**Sanibel.** A contraction and corruption of Santa Isybella ("Saint Isabella"), the name Ponce de Leon gave the island in 1513 in honor of recently deceased Queen Isabella. The Spanish called it San Ybel ("EE-bell") in the 1700s, often simply Ybel. The island was incorporated as "Sanybel" in 1833 and spelled "Sanibel" before the turn of the century.

**Useppa.** This island north of Captiva was named "Josefa" in the early 1800s by fisherman José Caldez who had a boat of that name. Italian fishermen called it "Guiseppe" (Italian for Joseph) in 1870. American mispronunciation led to "Useppa."

**Ybel.** The shorthand version of San Ybel, the spelling of the island in the late 1700s. Point Ybel (where the Sanibel lighthouse is), then, means "the point of Sanibel."

to the Rebel Army. It paid $8 to $10 a head, in unstable Confederate dollars. Trouble was, Cuba was already buying Florida cattle at $30 a head — in Spanish gold.

Farmers from Tampa to Miami continued to sell to Cuba, bringing their cattle to the stockyard at Punta Rassa, which held thousands of cows. The Confederates responded by building a naval station on Sanibel at Point Ybel (where the lighthouse stands today), and blocking Cuban boats from entering or leaving local waters.

The Union, however, had many area sympathizers. It took control of the Southwest Florida coast within months, and used the Sanibel facility to block Confederate-allied supply ships headed north (a quarter of the 23 vessels captured were British). The U.S.S. Rosalie, a 45-foot sailboat with a shallow 3½-foot draft and a single cannon, seized the British schooner Director here in 1863, loaded with a cargo of salt and rum headed for New Orleans.

# Settlers arrive

## Magic beans

In 1862 the U.S. passed the Homestead Act. It allowed any citizen (i.e., Northerner) to claim up to 160 acres of selected land as long as he or she farmed it for five years.

When he heard the news, Union soldier William Allen got an idea. Stationed on Key West, he noticed how effectively Army doctors used castor oil to treat yellow fever. When the war ended, Allen thought, he could file a homesteading claim in Florida, grow castor beans, and get rich.

After the South surrendered, Allen found his spot: Sanibel. Not that far from his contacts on Key West, the island's east end had just been opened for homesteading.

In 1866, Allen and his brother, George, set up a castor-bean farm on the same ground as today's Tarpon Tale Inn. Within weeks the beans were growing like crazy. The Allens received the title to the land in 1871. They were set for life, or so it seemed. On Oct. 6, 1873, a hurricane covered Sanibel with 5 feet of water. Their crops and equipment ruined, the Allens had to abandon their homestead.

Their castor beans, ironically, are still here. Some seeds survived the storm, and today the beans grow wild.

## Sanibel lights up

After the Civil War, Cuba continued to buy Florida cattle. San Carlos Bay and the port of Punta Rassa were getting busier every day. But many steamers came in at night, and navigating the notoriously shallow water was a risky

**Right place, wrong time.** Sanibel became "Sanybel," one of Florida's first planned developments, in 1833. The New York-based Florida Land Co. mapped "the garden island of Florida" into a subtropical farming community, where 50 families would live and work. Sanybel's east end was to be a large village, with a town square, parks and 50 homesites. The rest of the island was divided into 50 parallel tracts, each running from the Gulf to the bay. Five hundred dollars got you a city lot *and* a country farm.

As settlers moved in, they planted sugar cane, sisal, hemp and pineapple. They also met some Indians (a few still lived on the islands) and, unlike the Spanish, got along well with the natives.

But that friendliness cost them their town. Hearing of Indian sympathizers on the island, the feds declared a mandatory evacuation of Sanybel when it launched its War of Indian Removal in 1835. That summer, while the farmers were gone, a hurricane hit the island. The unprotected homes, crops — and dreams — washed away.

**For more historic photos** check out "Sanibel's Story," by Betty Anholt, available at island bookstores

proposition. After the 21-ton Sea Bird wrecked in the bay on Aug. 29, 1880, the U.S. decided to aid the merchants by erecting a navigation lighthouse on Sanibel.

The 104-foot lighthouse was made by the Phoenix Iron Co. in New Jersey (the company that built the cannon that fired the first shot at Gettysburg). Built in large sections, it was an early example of prefab construction. The design featured an open frame, like that of an oil derrick, so strong winds could blow right through the legs. Phoenix Iron simultaneously built a nearly identical lighthouse for Cape San Blas, in the Florida panhandle.

Both were shipped to Florida on a schooner, and fell overboard when the ship broke apart as it struck a shoal two miles off Sanibel. Except for two small brackets, however, both lighthouses were completely recovered.

The Sanibel light was lit on Aug. 20, 1884.

The first light burned coal. Each evening the lighthouse keeper carried the coal, as well as a 5-gallon can of kerosene, inside the narrow metal tube and up the 127 spiral steps, and lit the burner with a match. At dawn he climbed up again and blew it out.

The light was a fixed white beam that varied with a brighter flash every two minutes. It could be seen 16 miles out at sea. (The lighthouse was converted to electricity in 1962. Today's automated system produces two grouped flashes every 10 seconds.)

## Early homesteaders

Federal officials celebrated the new lighthouse by opening nearly the entire island to homesteading (the east end, as far west as today's Bailey Road, was kept in government hands for decades). The first American settler was William Reed, who moved here with his son from Maine in 1887. Frank Bailey and his family homesteaded a year later. By 1889 100 Americans were on the island — 40 families living in just 21 homes. (The population would stay under 300 for 65 years, until the first small subdivision was built in 1954.)

Captiva was settled by accident — literally. Austrian shipwreck victim William Binder washed up on a Captiva beach in 1885. He spent 10 days on the island recovering from his wounds, and fell in love with the place. Legends say he then swam to the mainland and immediately filed a homesteading claim.

## Fish tales

The Sanibel area was put on the national map on March 12, 1885. New York tourist W. H. Wood caught a tar-

**Facing page:** Bolted together nearly 120 years ago, a network of girders and cables keeps the lighthouse standing

**The Coast Guard** decided the lighthouse was no longer needed in 1972, as Punta Rassa's days as a port were over. Islanders saved the structure by getting it put on the National Register of Historic Places. Today it still operates, flashing twice every 10 seconds.

**Captiva's 10-year-old landowner.** Ann Brainerd moved with her family from Canada to Buck Key, a small bay island next to Captiva, in 1895. Six years later, at age 10, she told William Binder, Captiva's main landowner, how this one piece of his land, less than an acre, was the prettiest spot she had ever seen. Charmed, Binder said he'd sell it to her for a small gold coin she was carrying. Ann agreed.

Tragically, she stepped on a rusty nail just a few days later, and died from tetanus. Her family buried her on her land, which today is the Captiva cemetery. Islanders place seashells on her lamb-topped tombstone (page 42) to honor her memory. Ann's family is buried next to her, and William Binder is just a few steps away, toward the parking lot.

pon in San Carlos Bay with a rod and reel — a feat thought to be impossible. Until then, fishermen had only caught tarpon with awkward hooks and chains, or occasionally a harpoon. Wood caught the 93-pound, 5-foot 9-inch fish after a 27-minute battle. Later, he caught a second tarpon weighing 117 pounds.

The news spread throughout the country: now anyone could catch this huge, amazing fish. Sporting magazine Forest and Stream regaled Wood's accomplishment. New York reel manufacturers Julius and Edward vom Hofe came to the area to perfect a new saltwater-resistant tarpon reel. Soon the "Silver King" became the most sought-after fish in Florida.

# Paradise on earth

In the late 1800s Sanibel was even prettier than today. With all-native vegetation, the island was like a large subtropical park, with long vistas and open wetlands. The interior was filled with long grass, wildflowers and clumps of sabal palms. The weather was great, the beaches terrific, the wildlife incredible. As Northerners soon learned, it was an ideal place for a vacation.

## The Promised Land

Island tourism got its start when an unorthodox Presbyterian evangelist moved to Sanibel in 1889. From Kentucky, 63-year-old Rev. George Barnes stumbled upon Sanibel by accident, while in nearby Punta Gorda visiting friends.

**Hooking tarpon.** Early islanders caught tarpon with clumsy shark hooks and chain lines.

**Though most everyone** pronounces Sanibel as "san-a-bell," the first homesteaders called the island "san-a-bull." Their descendants still use this pronunciation today. Today, mispronunciations heard at hotel reservation desks include "Santa-bell" and, believe it or not, "Sans-a-belt."

**Facing page:** Rod-and-reel fishing meant anyone could catch a tarpon. Here, Florida Heitman displays her 185-pound catch, circa 1905. Florida was the daughter of a prominent Fort Myers businessman.

Taking him out for a tour of San Carlos Bay, Barnes' friends didn't realize the tide was going out. The boat ran aground off Sanibel. Stuck in the sand until high tide, Barnes and his friends decided to wade over to the island and look around.

As he explored the island, Barnes suddenly thought that God had planned the mishap for his benefit, that God had led him to his own Promised Land. Barnes filed a homesteading claim, and moved to Sanibel with his wife and grown children.

In Kentucky, Barnes had been tried for heresy. His nontraditional beliefs mixed Christianity with Hinduism, which he had learned traveling in India. So Barnes decided to build his own church, the nondenominational Church of the Four Gospels. The optimistic reverend put in pews to seat 300, three times the island population (and nearly enough for all of Fort Myers' 349 residents). He put a large cross on top to attract sailors.

Still with plenty of room on his property, Barnes and his son, William, next built a 30-room inn. Barnes named it "The Sisters" because his unmarried daughters, Georgia and Marie, had their rooms there. For dinner, the reverend's wife, Jean, served Indian cuisine.

Well-known as the "Mountain Evangelist," Rev. Barnes continued to travel, preaching to thousands at each stop. He loved to work tales of the island into his sermons.

## Barnes' believers

"It's paradise on earth!" Rev. Barnes proclaimed at a Kentucky revival meeting in the summer of 1895. In the crowd were Will and Harriet Matthews. Will, an accountant, had always dreamed of becoming a farmer.

The reverend's tale was spellbinding. Sanibel sounded like the perfect spot to fulfill Will's dreams, so he packed up his family and headed south. He and Harriet moved in at The Sisters before the year was out, and soon purchased an island farm.

But once they bought their farm, the Matthews nearly bought *the* farm. Having no experience growing crops, Will watched his dream quickly die. To make a living, the couple took on boarders in their home.

Barnes renamed his inn Casa Ybel in 1903. The Matthews daughter, Charlotta, named their place the Island Inn in 1936. Both resorts still operate today.

**Rev. Barnes' wife, Jean,** poses with her grandson

**Facing page:** Jean Barnes stands in front of the Church of the Four Gospels (1889). Just as the church was completed, the Barnes' grandson (above) died. Rev. Barnes buried his grandson next to the church, dedicating it to the boy's memory.

**William Barnes** holds an indigo snake, 1903

SANIBEL HISTORICAL COMMITTEE

**Wet and wild.** Women's beach wear in the Victorian era, like the "swimsuits" in this 1911 Casa Ybel photo, were, in essence, short dresses. These loose-fitting outfits had a pronounced feminine silhouette, and were not designed to get wet. At the time, getting in the water was considered improper, even scandalous. But these free-spirited women didn't care. Notice the two older men appear to disapprove.

**A typical Matthews dinner** featured an oyster appetizer; followed by fresh fish caught by the guests; complemented with tomatoes, peppers and other vegetables from island farms; topped off with key lime pie

## A Victorian vacationland

Within no time Sanibel became a popular destination for wealthy Easterners, who came for weeks at a time. Businessmen came to escape the tensions of the industrial age. Sportsmen came for the game. The elderly came for the warm salty air. More than anything, guests came to relax.

A 1904 Casa Ybel brochure explained the appeal: *"Here one may be thoroughly rested. With plenty to amuse him, without turning a hand to amuse himself, one may loaf to his heart's, or body's, content. To watch the bathers; to stroll idly on the beach; to sit on the pier and watch the fishers haul in their prizes — these be recreations which re-create.*

*"The somnolent breezes rustling the palms and the steady swishing monotone from the beach will make him sleepy long before he is tired. He will retire at an unconscionably early hour to a night of dreamless slumber. It is the almost universal testimony of island visitors that they 'sleep like a log.' Many go to bed soon after dinner, because they can't keep awake."*

Families loved it here. Children could play safely outdoors all winter. The beaches made clean playgrounds, and, unlike the beaches of the Florida east coast, they had no undertow, giant waves or sudden dropoffs.

## Fish, fowl and frills

Many guests went fishing, with guides arranged by the inns. "On Sanibel the angler can revel in piscatorial abandon," wrote Camping and Cruising in Florida in 1902, "and cover himself with fish scales."

Shelling became one of Sanibel's greatest attractions, not just to the women and children, but to nearly all the men as well. Initially scoffing at the mania for picking up "worthless shells," a man would typically come back from his first beach trip with both pockets bulging and both hands full. Guests displayed their best finds at the annual Casa Ybel Shell Day.

The inns took their guests on mule-drawn wagon rides along the beach. Longer trips went to the lighthouse or Blind Pass, with oysters served out of the shell for lunch. Some visitors shipped down horseless carriages and drove them along the shore. Organized activities included tennis, croquet and dancing. At Casa Ybel, a corner of the reading room was reserved for the "flirtatiously inclined."

This being the Victorian era, a proper sense of decorum was always important. Women wore formal dresses at all times, and usually elaborate beach attire. Dinners at the inns were coat-and-tie affairs, with no alcohol served. "Casa Ybel is a clean, wholesome place," wrote Manager William Barnes, "with no bar, no gambling, no so-called 'high living,' but rather sane enjoyment amid congenial surroundings."

Traveling to Sanibel was an adventure in itself. From the north, you took a train to Lakeland, Fla., then caught a second train down the coast (travelers often complained about the drunken, pistol-carrying locals onboard). At Punta Gorda you hopped on a steamboat for a six-hour trip to the Sanibel dock. Finally, you climbed onto a mule-drawn wagon for the 40-minute ride to your inn.

**Hunting was a popular activity** for early island visitors. Instead of using blinds and decoys, guests would simply walk down the beach, shooting gulls as they bobbed in the surf. Inland, hunters would approach ducks on their hands and knees, and crawl within range. Some guests took day trips to Punta Rassa to hunt quail, turkey and deer. Some guests even shot large wading birds, collecting their feathers for women's hats.

**Overleaf:** Casa Ybel hunters with turkey, deer, rabbit, and, at far right, an alligator belly skin.

**A mule-drawn wagon** takes visitors from the Sanibel steamer dock to the Matthews inn, 1910

ISLAND INN

**Teddy Roosevelt** came to Captiva three times between 1913 and 1916 to fish and study wildlife

**Previous pages:** A manta ray caught at the Casa Ybel dock, 1911.

**The Sanibel Packing Co.,** circa 1900

# Farming

## Fields of gold

Homesteading on Sanibel in the 1880s, farmers grew tons of tomatoes and limes, as well as eggplant, cucumbers, watermelon, radishes, peppers and bananas. They had a nine-month growing season, October to June.

But it wasn't easy. Just as the crops would ripen the summer heat would burn them up. Mosquitoes and "no-see-ums" made farmhands miserable. Drinking water tasted like sulfur. A rare deep freeze hit the island in the winter of 1898, and many fields were wiped out. (Icicles hung from the palms and a few snowflakes were seen, the only snow in Sanibel history.)

And you could only grow food for yourself; there was no way to get crops to a mainland market.

Then Connecticut businessman Bradley Plant built a railroad down to Punta Gorda, Fla., and began running steam ships down to Sanibel. Now island farmers could sell their crops nationwide.

Each morning a steamer arrived at the Sanibel wharf. A commission merchant would hop off, shake hands with the farmers, examine their produce and cut deals. Soon Sanibel tomatoes were everywhere. They were especially popular in New York grocery stores.

Sanibel became an active small town. The Sanibel Baptist Church (now the Colonial Bank) opened in 1909.

FLORIDA STATE ARCHIVES

Kids went to school at the one-room Sanibel School (now the Old Schoolhouse Theater). The Sanibel wharf was the center of island life. Kids packed produce at the Sanibel Packing Co., earning 4 cents per crate, three dollars a day.

A trip to Fort Myers took three days: one to take the noon steamer, one to do business, one to catch the morning steamer back.

When a 1910 hurricane leveled the Barnes church, farmers replaced it with the nondenominational Sanibel Community Church (still in operation). Islanders donated the land and held bake sales to raise money for materials. Volunteers built the new church when they could spare time from their fields, finishing it in 1914. Some pews were salvaged from the Church of the Four Gospels. (Rev. Barnes died in 1908. Legend has it he is buried in an unmarked grave at the Sanibel cemetery, just down the road from his Promised Land.)

Captiva grew, too. It built a schoolhouse and opened the Snyder School, a summer camp for wealthy boys.

But the thriving towns were not to last. That same year the U.S. entered World War I, and most young island men left to fight. Potash, vital for growing vegetables in sandy soil, was commandeered by the government for military purposes. Meanwhile paved roads had come to the mainland, giving farmers there a huge competitive advantage in getting their crops to market.

Two hurricanes dealt the final blows. Most farmland was ruined by a 1921 storm, which covered Sanibel and Captiva with saltwater. The remaining fields, and the wharf, were wiped out by the tremendous 1926 hurricane, when a 14-foot storm surge swamped the islands.

**Shallow-draft steamboats** (including the Uneeda, above, 1911) made commercial farming possible

**'Remember the Maine!'** Working for the International Ocean Telegraph Co., George Schultz ran Sanibel's cable relay hut. It connected an ocean-floor telegraph cable from Key West with another to Punta Rassa. On Feb. 15, 1898, he received a message from Key West: "At 9:40 Tuesday the U.S. Battleship Maine was blown up in Havana Harbor." Schultz relayed it to the mainland, which sent it to Washington. The incident started the Spanish-American War. Today, the site of the hut is marked by a small plaque. Look for it just off the road, just before the lighthouse.

FLORIDA STATE ARCHIVES

**Captiva school children,** 1912. The one-room school was built in 1901 by the island's first settler, William Binder. Today it's the Chapel by the Sea.

**The Shark Factory.** The Hydenoil ("hide-and-oil") Products Co. operated a shark rendering plant on Sanibel in the 1920s, at the site of today's Sanibel Marina. It made use of nearly the entire creature. The liver was processed into shark oil and vitamins. The meat and intestines made good fertilizer and soap. The cartilage became glue, the fins were sold for soup. The tanned skin became "ocean leather," a product still sold in Florida today. Carcasses piled up outside, and a windmill propelled the stench throughout the island's east end. To the relief of many, Hydenoil went bankrupt a few years later.

**Facing page:** Ruins of the 1920s dock of Bailey's General Store, down the shore from Bailey Road

## Coconuts and key limes

Now nearly deserted, island land became quite a bargain. That caught the attention of Fort Myers entrepreneur Clarence Chadwick. He had just struck it rich as the inventor of forgery-proof paper for bank checks and of the automatic check-writing machine.

Chadwick figured the islands were still fine for farming, as long as he grew salt-tolerant crops. He purchased the north end of Captiva and created a large working plantation, growing coconuts and limes. Soon he became one of the largest key lime distributors in the world.

But another hurricane hit in 1935. The islands were again covered with water, and most of Chadwick's lime trees were ruined. Noticing how tourism had replaced farming on Sanibel, Chadwick decided to do the same. He rechristened his land as the South Seas Plantation vacation village (now the South Seas Resort).

## Famous visitors

Automobile ferry service to Sanibel began in 1926. The ferry carried seven cars and a handful of passengers, making four trips per day. Thomas Edison and Henry Ford were regulars. Looking for new rubber sources, they searched for exotic plants to take back to Edison's winter laboratory in Fort Myers.

With hurricanes stirring up the Gulf floor every few years, "rare" shells were everywhere. Visitors would carry flour sacks to the beach and fill them with Florida cones and olives, as hundreds lay on the sandbars. Scientists from Harvard and the Smithsonian Institution visited, gathering shells for study and field-identification books.

More tourists came each year. New inns and restaurants opened. Plans were made for a causeway to Pine Island, which was already connected to the mainland. Poet Edna St. Vincent Millay vacationed on Sanibel. Charles and Anne Lindbergh honeymooned on Captiva in 1929.

Then the stock market crashed.

# An isolated world

Tourism nearly disappeared during the Great Depression, and the islands reverted back to an isolated world. The few residents lived off the land. Many ate alligators, sea turtles and gopher tortoises. Some homes were abandoned, then taken over by poor black families. The Baptist Church became the Sanibel School for Colored Children.

To socialize islanders gathered at the Sanibel Community House. A mix of upper-crust transplanted Yankees and down-home Florida crackers, they held Shakespeare readings one night, square dancing the next. But it was all by kerosene lamp. Electricity wouldn't reach the islands until 1941.

## Bombs and bullets

Few visitors came to the islands during World War II, as the ferries were requisitioned for troop use. But it wasn't quiet here. Waters just off Sanibel became B-24 artillery and bombing ranges. For targets, an armored barge was anchored about three miles off the lighthouse, while a 30-by-30-foot platform sat about two miles off Bowman's Beach. An Army plane would buzz boaters before each bombing run, giving them the signal to leave. A few stray bullets hit Sanibel roofs and rainwater tanks.

Beachcombers reported seeing periscopes in the water — supposedly German subs hunting U.S. supply barges. The Coast Guard stationed a detachment at Casa Ybel, and built a spotting tower next to the lighthouse.

Only 75 people lived on the islands during the war. All were photographed and fingerprinted. Today a few artillery shells still wash up on Bowman's Beach.

## Early developers get Dinged

The state of Florida made the islands a state wildlife refuge in 1930. But ten years later it planned to sell 2,000 acres of Sanibel, almost a third of the island, to developers (at just 25 cents to $1 an acre).

Jay Darling came to the island's rescue.

A frequent visitor, he was the former head of the U.S. Biological Survey (today's Fish and Wildlife Service) and a Pulitzer Prize-winning syndicated political cartoonist for the Des Moines (Iowa) Register. His cartoons, often focused on conservation topics, were carried by 130 U.S. newspapers. He signed his work "D'ing," a contraction of his last name.

Incensed by the state's plan (and the World War II bombing runs), Darling arranged for the federal government to lease the land, which became the Sanibel National Wildlife Refuge in 1945. Today it forms the core of the J.N. "Ding" Darling National Wildlife Refuge.

SANIBEL HISTORICAL COMMITTEE

**Prohibition was not enforced.** Moonshine was made from sugar cane. Passing Cuban fishermen stopped to trade rum and acquadente, a potent liquor. Above, lighthouse keeper Roscoe McLane (left) buys liquor from an island bootlegger.

**Facing page:** Island Inn manager Jane Terrill with a captured alligator, 1939

**"Ding" Darling** (below) lived in an over-water home that still stands off Captiva (overleaf)

J.N. "DING" DARLING FOUNDATION

FLORIDA STATE ARCHIVES / FRANCIS P. JOHNSON

**Honeymooners** play shuffleboard at a Sanibel resort, January 1957

**Cubans left the area in 1959,** when Fidel Castro took power. They had fished here since 1871.

Until 1889 up to 150 Cubans lived on Sanibel year-round. Their "fish ranches" each had a group of cottages and sheds, as well as a larger building to salt and store mullet. The buildings were made without nails, just palm fronds wrapped around mangrove frames. The guides and workers lived here. One Cuban fish ranch was near the site of today's Sea Horse Shops on Periwinkle Way.

The Cubans moved off the island in 1889, when Sanibel was opened to homesteading. But they continued to fish the area for 70 years.

# Developers move in

The tourists returned after the war. More inns opened along the beaches. As visitors would drive off the ferry, they'd be met by innkeepers handing out brochures. The charming islands were more popular than ever.

After mosquito control came to the islands in 1953, outside developers were again back in force. Having failed to buy up the refuge land a decade earlier, this time they were after everything else.

With little to stop them, developers began dredging the wetlands, piling up the spoil to create roads and homesites. The east end of Sanibel was sliced up into canals. A St. Petersburg corporation made plans to fill in Tarpon Bay.

"The back country of the island offers unusual opportunities for development," the Fort Myers News-Press reported. "Hundreds of acres are available for subdivisions and homes. The bay side of the island is overgrown with giant mangroves, which, if cleared and landscaped, would provide the South Seas setting for luxurious estates."

"Ding" Darling died while plans for the Sanibel Causeway were being reviewed. Strong islander opposition didn't stop Lee County, and the causeway was built in 1963. But it didn't go to Pine Island, as once planned. Developer Hugo Lindgren convinced the county to build it straight from the mainland, across the bay, directly into his new Sanibel subdivision. (Incredibly shortsighted, the decision ensured that Fort Myers and Punta Rassa, with the southernmost bay on the Florida west coast and a history of Cuban trade, could never again be major ports.)

The county zoned the island for maximum development potential. In 1967, it announced that all non-refuge areas of Sanibel would be developed. Forget the "heaven on earth" stuff, the county said, high-rise condos would be built throughout the island. Plans called for 90,000 residents, a density equal to Miami Beach. And county planners didn't forget Captiva and the out islands —a four-lane highway would be built straight through them all, connecting Sanibel to Boca Grande.

With the county in their pockets, developers had a field day. They cut and burned native vegetation and dredged and filled wetlands. Too impatient for a sewer system, they plopped down septic tanks by each new building. Raw sewage began to leak into the remaining waters.

The natural Sanibel of "Ding" Darling was disappearing. The spiritual Sanibel of Rev. Barnes was being forgotten. (Sold, ignored and falling apart, his Casa Ybel would be torn down in the late 1970s, replaced by new buildings.) In their place came a growing concrete and blacktop jungle of subdivisions, strip centers and parking lots.

But there was still hope.

A grassroots conservation movement was gaining strength, and more people were appreciating the islands' natural qualities. Taking over the mission "Ding" Darling had begun, the Sanibel-Captiva Conservation Foundation was firmly established. Most tourists were nature lovers; shelling was more popular than ever, and with the opening of Wildlife Drive visitors were now coming for the birds as well as the beaches.

"The residents of Sanibel and Captiva are trying to get zoning restrictions that would prevent the building of high rises on either island," one islander wrote to the Sanibel-Captiva Islander in 1969. "We are opposed almost entirely by speculative landowners — not residents — whose purpose seems to be to make money fast and move on — leaving us with the unhappy results."

County officials, however, remained devotees of development. Island leaders began to realize they had to take control of their destiny. If they could stop the developers, they could preserve much of Sanibel's character while securing their tourist economy.

ISLAND INN

**Shown here preparing for the 1949 Shell Fair** with her grandson, Harriet Matthews ran the Island Inn from 1900 to 1950

**Anne Lindbergh** published "Gift from the Sea," a Captiva-inspired collection of eight essays about serenity and the meaning of a woman's life, in 1955. The book is still an island best-seller.

**Sanibel school kids** have class at the beach, 1948

FLORIDA STATE ARCHIVES

# Island Originals

**Sam and Francis Bailey,** 2002

Sam and Francis Bailey know Sanibel. They were born here. Grew up here. And, at 79 and 81 years old, are still here, running Bailey's General Store.

Their father, Frank Bailey, moved to the island with his parents from up north in 1894. His dad was retired, and his mom wanted a warmer climate. Sanibel seemed an ideal spot to relocate, as long as someone in the family could earn a living. That job fell to Frank. Just 21, he became a farmer, growing watermelons to sell to steamer merchants headed to Cuba, Key West and New Orleans.

Business grew. At 26, Frank opened a dockside packing and shipping business, the Sanibel Packing Co. As a sideline, he bought out the island's lone retail store, which he renamed Bailey's General Store. When the farming boom hit the islands that same year (1899), Frank became Sanibel's Main Man — the one person everyone in the tiny island village knew. He soon married and started a family.

Sons Francis, John and Sam had an isolated, subtropical life few can even dream of. As young boys, they'd go fishing at least once a week. Francis remembers the morning "I caught a needle fish, John caught a big shell, and Sam caught his big toe on a fish hook!"

They'd swim in the Gulf nearly every day. But forget swimsuits — these kids just tossed off their clothes and waded in. "Only once did some fishermen in a boat happen to see us," Francis recalls, "and one of the fishermen turned out to be a fisher-woman!"

The boys went to the old one-room Sanibel School through eighth grade. There were 32 students, one teacher. To get away from things, Francis would ask to use the outhouse, then while away a few minutes outside listening to the meadowlarks sing.

As young adults the Baileys became as well known as their father. In 1951 Sam got the swamp cabbage for the Casa Ybel 4th of July fish fry, chopping down a dozen palms to feed the 50 or so people. Later Francis became a civic leader, serving on the original Sanibel City Council.

John Bailey passed away a few years ago, but Francis and Sam still run Bailey's General Store, now more than 100 years old. What's its secret?

"I think of it not as the Bailey family store," Francis says, "but as the peoples' store, the island's store." Sam agrees. "We believe in the island. So the island believes in us."

Sam misses the freedom of the old days, especially the skinny-dipping and the fishing anywhere and everywhere. Francis resents some of the newcomers, the ones that "come in, spend a day, and think they're experts on everything.

"But most of the people here want the same thing we old-timers have always wanted. And that is to protect and preserve the island."

**Sam, Francis and John Bailey,** 1931

SANIBEL HISTORICAL COMMITTEE

ISLAND INN

# Sanibel takes control

On Nov. 5, 1974, residents voted to incorporate. The island of Sanibel became the city of Sanibel. The new government, under mayor Porter Goss (now a U.S. congressman) issued a moratorium on building permits. The 1976 Sanibel Plan allowed construction to resume, but limited development to 7,800 dwelling units (later increased to 9,000). New buildings had to be far off the beach, and no taller than 45 feet. The plan also protected wildlife and vegetation. Developers sued, but Sanibel prevailed, arguing that an overcrowded island could be a death trap in a hurricane. The islanders had their island back.

## The problems of paradise

"Sanibel shall remain a barrier island sanctuary and a small-town community," says the island's 1997 Vision Statement. "It shall be developed only to the extent to which it retains its quality of sanctuary. It will serve as an attraction only to the extent to which it retains its qualities as a sanctuary and community." But creating such a Utopia has brought Sanibel a new threat: gentrification. With property values soaring, the island is changing, not always for the better.

"Before, younger people and people with limited incomes could come to Sanibel, fall in love with it, and move here," lifelong resident Francis Bailey says. "But now many ho-

**Dude, where's my grouper?** Lost or tossed overboard by smugglers offshore, many bales of marijuana floated up on island beaches during the 1970s. Locals called it "square grouper." Teens (and some adults) collected the bootleg bounty, dried it out in microwave ovens, and used it to make brownies. In these photos from 1977, beachgoers surround, then carry off, bales that washed up behind the Island Inn.

ISLAND INN

# Big Mac Attack

Once you get accustomed to the islands' unique beaches, weather and wildlife, you begin to notice something else is different here, too. There's no McDonald's.

The fast-food giant tried to come to Sanibel in 1993. But residents said no. They fought off Big Mac — a rare feat — by organizing quickly, getting tons of publicity and finding McDonald's Achilles' heel. Here's how it happened:

McDonald's announced plans to build here on Dec. 8, 1992. It paid $571,000 for an acre of land on Periwinkle Way (across from Bailey's General Store, where the SunTrust Bank sits today). The news alarmed islanders. Within days a grassroots group organized (naming itself McSpoil) and publicized McDonald's plan.

## McSPOIL
## NO McDONALD'S ON SANIBEL

The island was united in its opposition. Hotel owners didn't want to damage Sanibel's "get-away-from-it-all" atmosphere. Restaurant owners didn't want the competition. Even kids didn't want Ronald and his pals. In a poll at the island elementary school, 53 percent of the children said they wanted McDonald's to stay away. "Our students feel as though they are the keepers of the island," explained then-principal Barbara Ward.

Tourists were the most vocal opponents. They flooded Sanibel newspapers with letters.

"A true vacation spot is a place you can escape from one's normal lifestyle, a place to take it easy and relax," wrote a visitor from Pittsburgh. "Fast food should remain in the fast lane back home. A McDonald's on Sanibel will change what the island has to offer."

"McDonald's is in airports, the subways, hospitals, college and high-school cafeterias, stadiums. Dear God, please, don't they have enough?" wrote a visitor from Kansas. "Must even Sanibel be covered with cups and cartons, straws, bags and Happy Meals? I can see the osprey nests in Ding Darling now — built from Big Mac cartons and apple pie boxes."

"I am a 14-year-old girl from Atlanta," another tourist wrote. "I have been coming to Sanibel and Captiva with my family for nine years. One of the reasons I love the islands so much is because they are not very commercialized. Living in Atlanta, I eat at McDonald's pretty often. Believe me, it is not that great. In fact, it's not even good."

The Associated Press covered the story, and newspapers across the country gave it space.

McDonald's ignored the commotion. "This is a vocal minority that only appears to be a majority," a spokesman said. But McSpoil had a smart strategy: Don't try to kill the entire McDonald's monster. Just kill its profit center — the drive-through window. The group petitioned the city of Sanibel to ban drive-through restaurants.

The city commissioned two independent studies; both said allowing drive-throughs would be a mistake. "Sanibel needs to be very particular about the land use mix that it permits," one report said. "The island markets itself as 'unique.' If it has all the normal strip commercial uses, that sense of uniqueness is lost."

Sanibel officials agreed. The drive-through ban became law in August, 1993.

McDonald's fought the law for two years, then announced it would concede and build the unit without a drive-through. But suddenly, just before Christmas, 1995, McDonald's withdrew its application. A spokesman said, "Public opinion had nothing to do with it."

Sanibel lawmakers went even further in 1996, passing a complete ban on what it called "formula" restaurants — those with three or more locations that have the same or similar name, menu, uniforms and exterior.

tels have long minimum stays, so we get less young and middle-class people right off the bat. For most who do come, our housing prices make it too hard to move here."

The result? The island is becoming a monoculture, dominated by wealthy retirees, most of which only live here half the year. Today most Sanibel homes (57 percent) sit vacant from April to October. New construction is geared exclusively to second-home buyers.

Though middle-aged families still make up a good part of the population, young adults are few and far between. In the 10 years from 1990 to 2000, the island's 18–34 population dropped by nearly half (41 percent) while the 65+ crowd grew by 26 percent (U.S. Census data).

"Diversity makes a city strong," Bailey says, "but gentrification works against diversity."

Unincorporated Captiva has been transformed. Most of its cottages, bars and restaurants have been torn down, replaced by trophy vacation estates. Captiva's median home price was $1.5 million in 2002, when Worth magazine ranked it No. 20 on its list of the 250 Richest Towns in the U.S.

"Sanibel and Captiva are a great experiment," says former mayor Mark "Bird" Westall. "When you protect the environment and limit human habitation, property values go up. But then people come here not just for the nature, but also for the exclusivity and value of the place."

**A Captiva waterfront cottage** is demolished. Developers get around building ordinances by leaving a small part of the old structure in place, calling the creation of the new, multi-million-dollar home (such as the one below) a "renovation."

**Historic buildings.** The **1896 Bailey house** is still the private home of the family. It's on Periwinkle Way in front of Donax Street. The **1928 Sanibel Community House** *(2173 Periwinkle Way; 472-2155)* is still the island's meeting place. The **1909 Colonial Bank** *(520 Tarpon Bay Rd.; 472-1314)* was first a Baptist Church, later a black school and church. One of Sanibel's oldest surviving homes, the **1891 George Cooper House** *(630 Tarpon Bay Rd.)* is now part of the Olde Sanibel shops. Captiva's **1921 Island Store** *(11500 Andy Rosse Ln.; 472-2374)* is a old rooming house once owned by "Ding" Darling.

**George Cooper House**

**Island Store**

# Historical sites and attractions

The **Sanibel Historical Village and Museum** *(850 Dunlop Rd., Sanibel; 472-4648)* is a collection of six restored island buildings from the early 20th century, filled with intriguing artifacts. Well worth a stop, it's the best spot to get a first-hand look at the island's past. See our Diversions chapter for more information.

You can walk up to the 1884 **Sanibel lighthouse** *(east end of Periwinkle Way)* but it's not open to the public. Island employees live in the keeper's quarters. Two nearby historical markers show the sites of the World War II **submarine spotting tower** (on the road, just north of the lighthouse) and the 1867 **telegraph cable relay hut** (where Periwinkle forks). The beach area is the unmarked site of the 1861 **Civil War naval station.**

As you walk the Shell Mound Trail in the J.N. "Ding" Darling National Wildlife Refuge, look for a huge pile of shells overgrown by vegetation. This is a **Calusa Indian shell mound,** where the tribe tossed leftover shells.

Remains of Sanibel's 1927–1963 **ferry landing** are west of the fishing pier (look for a small filled-in canal and pilings). This was the dropping-off point for visitors until the causeway made ferries obsolete. Just west are the locations of the 1800 **Allen castor bean farm** (at today's Brennen's Tarpon Tale Inn), an 1871 **Cuban fish ranch** (directly across Periwinkle Way) and the 1923 **Hydenoil shark plant** (today's Sanibel Marina). Two charming 1940s resorts worth a look are the **Seaside Inn** *(541 East Gulf Dr., Sanibel; 472-1400)* and the **Gulf Breeze Cottages** *(1081 Shell Basket Ln., Sanibel; off Nerita St., which connects Middle and East Gulf Drs., 472-1626).*

The lobby of a tiny **Bank of America** branch *(1037 Periwinkle Way, Sanibel; 472-5575)* is decorated with historical photos. Just down the street is the 1917 **Sanibel Community Church** *(1740 Periwinkle Way, Sanibel; 472-2684)* and the 1896 **Old Schoolhouse Theater** *(1095 Periwinkle Way, Sanibel; 472-6862),* a one-room schoolhouse for grades 1 through 8 until 1963.

Forty-one million dollars in gold, silver and emerald treasure from an old Spanish shipwreck is on display at **Mel Fisher's Sanibel Treasure Co.** *(2353 Periwinkle Way, Sanibel; 472-6862).* The exhibit offers a fascinating glimpse of the Spanish galleons that once sailed past the islands. The artifacts are from the 1622 wreck of the Atocha, found near the Florida Keys in 1985 (the richest treasure find since King Tut's tomb). The exhibit is open Monday through Saturday 10 a.m. to 6 p.m. Admission is $5 for adults and $3.50 for children. Kids under 5 are free.

Sites along West Gulf Drive include **Casa Ybel** *(2255 West Gulf Dr., Sanibel; 472-3145),* a 1970s-era resort built on the site of the original 1889 inn; and the **Island Inn** *(3111 West Gulf Dr., Sanibel; 472-1561),* still going strong after 100 years (check out the photo albums in the lobby).

Two little-known Sanibel spots also bring history to life. Drive down to the bay end of Bailey Road (off Periwinkle Way, just west of the causeway) to the site of the 1899 **Matthews Wharf** then walk up the shore (down the closed section of the road, now crumbling into the bay) to the locations of the 1927 **Bailey's General Store** and **Miss Charlotta's Tearoom,** identified with historical markers (the buildings are now at the Sanibel Historical Village). **Remains of the store dock** still stand.

Time stands still on **Woodring Road** (head left at the end of Dixie Beach Road, also off Periwinkle), where simple country ways still prevail. Drive with your windows down and listen for the crowing roosters.

Captiva has its share of interesting historic sites, too. The **Old Captiva House** *(at the 'Tween Waters Inn, 15951 Captiva Dr., Captiva; 472-5161)* has original drawings by "Ding" Darling. Charles and Anne Lindbergh ate here often. The **Chapel by the Sea** *(adjacent to the Captiva cemetery, 11580 Chapin Ln., Captiva; 472-1646)* was built in 1901. Church services (including an unforgettable candle-lit Christmas Eve event) are still held here seasonally. For another dose of true Florida character shake hands with the Jensen brothers at **Jensen's Twin Palms Resort and Marina** *(15107 Captiva Dr., Captiva; 472-5800).* A few feet away is **McCarthy's Marina** *(15041 Captiva Dr., Captiva; 472-5200),* with more colorful characters. The **Captiva History House** *(at the entrance to the South Seas Resort, near Chadwick's restaurant, Captiva; 472-5111)* is one of the original worker cottages from the resort's days as a key lime plantation. Today it displays old photographs and memorabilia. The museum is open five days a week; admission is free. Historical tours of the resort depart from here Tuesdays and Thursdays at 3 p.m.

The island's native **Calusa** are the subject of a new artifact-filled exhibit at the Bailey-Matthews Shell Museum

The **Sanibel Cemetery** is not visible from the road. You'll find the tiny piece of land in Gulfside City Park, alongside the bike path that runs between Middle Gulf Drive and Algiers Drive. County records show 26 people buried here, about twice the number of marked graves. The lovely **Captiva Cemetery** is a shady spot next to the Chapel by the Sea. It contains the graves of first settler William Binder and other island pioneers. Headstones marked "C.S.A." identify Civil War soldiers who served the Confederate States of America.

# Hurricanes

Twelve hurricanes struck Sanibel and Captiva from 1870 to 1960. None have hit since. (Does the word "due" come to mind?)

A hurricane is a large rotating system of wind. It forms out of a mass of thunderstorms in warm water far out at sea. It builds slowly. When the wind begins to rotate in a closed circle, the storm is labeled a tropical depression. When sustained winds reach 39 mph, it's called a tropical storm. When wind speeds reach 74 mph, the storm becomes a hurricane. In the Northern Hemisphere, hurricanes always spin counterclockwise.

A strong hurricane can devastate a coastal community. Winds can blow out windows and then blow off roofs. Typically 6 to 8 inches of rain falls at speeds up to 100 mph. Sometimes the storm's collision with land creates tornadoes and whirling vortices, with their own counterclockwise spinning winds of up to 200 mph. But the real damage comes from the storm surge — a literal rising of the sea whipped up by the strong winds. The water can rise up to 20 feet, and it comes up in just a few hours.

Weather officials began naming hurricanes in 1950. Unless retired, the names are recycled every six years. The names for the 2003 season include Ana, Bill, Claudette and Danny. In 2004 the first four storms will be Alex, Bonnie, Charley and Danielle. There are 21 names each year (the letters "Q," "U," "X," "Y," and "Z" are not used).

Hurricane season is officially June through November. But since 1900, every hurricane that has hit the islands has come in September or October.

Here's a recap of those storms:

■ **Oct. 17, 1910.** A large section of land east of the Sanibel lighthouse washed away in this hurricane, and the Church of the Four Gospels at Casa Ybel was destroyed. The barometric pressure dropped to 28.40 inches. A lone white-tailed deer wandered around the lighthouse afterward, the last deer ever seen on the island.

■ **Oct. 25, 1921.** This hurricane covered the islands with a few inches of saltwater.

■ **Sept. 19, 1926.** This hurricane brought a 14-foot storm surge to Sanibel, ending commercial farming. It broke Captiva into two parts, creating Redfish Pass. The storm came across the state from Miami, where it turned that area's real estate boom to bust. At the time it was the most severe hurricane in U.S. history.

■ **Sept. 3, 1935.** It rained for nine straight days before this storm hit. Water was armpit-deep on Bailey Road, waist-deep in the middle of Sanibel. "It was a plain of water stretching the width of the island," recalls Sam Bailey, then 11.

■ **Oct. 18, 1944.** Wind gusts reached 100 mph during this storm, which came straight north from Cuba. All the burrowing owls on Sanibel were killed. Quail, once common, disappeared. Two-thirds of the Casa Ybel cottages were tossed off their foundations. A Cuban fishing boat in San Carlos Bay tried to make it to Sanibel and safety, but was blown onto a grassy flat (near where the center causeway island is today). The crew drowned. A few days after the storm government surveyors accidentally started a large fire on Sanibel, when they lit a palm frond to defend themselves against wasps.

■ **Sept. 17, 1947.** Winds reached 110 mph. Parts of the islands were six feet underwater. The lighthouse keeper said he looked down from his tower and saw no green.

■ **Sept. 10, 1960.** Hurricane Donna was the killer storm people fear. Fortunately it hit in September (when few tourists were on the island), and in 1960, when the islands had less than 600 residents. The most destructive hurricane in Florida's history until Andrew in 1992, Donna spun up the west coast without losing speed. The eye came across at Bonita Beach. Barrier islands from Sanibel to Gasparilla (facing page) were hit hard.

Winds reached 121 mph. The Fort Myers News-Press (below) reported that Australian pines "fell like ten pins" across Periwinkle Way in stacks up to 15 feet high, making it impossible for cars to get to the ferry. Coast Guard helicopters made last-minute evacuations, landing in 60 mph winds. The 6-foot storm surge made officials fear Sanibel would be cut in two: the island had new man-made canals throughout the east end.

Here's how one resident described the storm: "Our neighbor's dock crashed into our house. Acting as a battering ram, it was propelled by each successive wave, finally forcing down a wall. It churned inside the children's bedrooms. Then Donna broke in through the roof, through the windows and through the front door, exposing the entire house and furnishings. Our belongings took flight. Some pieces were found around the post office. Others sailed to the lighthouse. Many, of course, were never seen again."

With no way to leave, 38 people crammed into the Bailey home on Periwinkle Way for safety. "Even there," one said later, "the bay quietly crept to the back yard and gradually rose. The palm trees bent double. We mopped and mopped as the rainwater came at the house horizontally. It sneaked under the doors, around the windows, over the sills. There was no gaiety, no laughter, no drinking, no partying. Most of us were terrified."

About half of the homes on Sanibel were damaged. Many had their roofs torn off. Some were without electricity for 26 days. The island did not split in two, but most of the east end was underwater. The next day President Eisenhower declared all of Lee County a disaster area.

FORT MYERS NEWS-PRESS

**FEROCIOUS HURRICANE CAUSES HUGE DAMAGE, 3 DEATHS HERE**

121-Mile Winds Rake Area Toppling Trees, Buildings; No Grave Injuries Reported

Donna Was Here

# Beaches

Stroll along the shore. Slowly take in the changing beauty of the Gulf and sky, and the changeless beauty of the land. Or lie at the water's edge, and be soothed by the slow, rhythmic wash of the surf. Whatever you do, a few hours on the beaches of Sanibel and Captiva will refresh your mind and renew your spirit.

Our beaches are wild, as nature intended. Tropical birds and sandpipers stroll alongside you. Pelicans glide overhead; dolphins cruise offshore. Buildings are kept far away, tucked behind the palms and sea oats. The sand is never raked, so shells, seaweed and sea life wash up and back with the tide.

The water, most often, is calm. The waves are gentle, and curl and break slowly. There's rarely an undertow; never a heavy surge. Offshore disturbances are evident only by a quick tumble of small waves. With a pair of binoculars you can often see an upheaval at the horizon, while only its miniature is at your feet.

The sea floor has a gradual slope. In many places you can wade out 500 feet before it's over your head, even at high tide. There are no holes or sudden dropoffs. The bottom is always clean white sand. And you can swim year-round — the Gulf averages 71 degrees in winter, 84 in summer.

Island beaches aren't ruled by boom boxes and beer. Our beach music is the natural symphony of gulls and surf. Our drug of choice is the purest intoxicant of all — total, complete relaxation. And, no, you don't have to hold your stomach in. No one does, and no one cares.

## Gulf beaches

The southern and western shores of Sanibel and Captiva are actually one continuous 16-mile beach. But the curving shoreline creates six distinct areas. Each has its own public access point, with a parking lot and, in most cases, basic restrooms.

The narrow **Lighthouse Beach** *(at the east end of Periwinkle Way)* is the easiest beach to get to from the causeway, and the most crowded on the islands. During season, the parking lot fills by 10 a.m. Boardwalks run out to the beach, through arching mangrove roots that often form canopies overhead. You can clearly see Ft. Myers Beach from here, three miles across the bay. Be careful swimming; the strong, swift current can carry you out to sea. But this is a great shelling spot, the best place in the world to find the tiny wentletrap. While you're here walk up to the still-operating lighthouse and wander down

---

**Facing page:** Waves wash ashore on Turner Beach, the steepest beach on the islands

the shady Gnarly Woods nature trail, a jungle of palms, sea grapes and other tropical foliage. The trail is hard sand, perfect for bikes and joggers. A separate parking lot serves the adjacent fishing pier.

**Gulfside City Park** *(east of the Casa Ybel Resort, off Casa Ybel Rd. at the end of Algiers Dr.)* features a long, shaded picnic area. A portion of refuge land borders the dunes here, distancing the beach from the resorts that line the rest of this area. The Gulfside Park Preserve hiking trail is within walking distance, off the bike path along Algiers Drive.

There's plenty of room to stretch out at the **Tarpon Bay Road Beach** *(Tarpon Bay Rd. at West Gulf Dr.)*. This wide beach has good shelling and a surprising amount of wildlife. The parking lot, with special spots for recreational vehicles, is a short hike away on Tarpon Bay Road. Walking to the beach is safe from traffic; just use the bike path. The beach entrance has restrooms, a water fountain and a small outdoor shower.

Farther down West Gulf Drive are the seven **West Gulf Beach Access Points.** Past Rabbit Road, these remote beaches are accessible to visitors only by foot or bicycle. Parking is by resident-permit only.

One of the best beaches in Florida, **Bowman's Beach** *(five miles west of Tarpon Bay Rd., off Sanibel-Captiva Rd. at the end of Bowman's Beach Rd.)* has no hotels, homes or other development; it's just beach, beach and more beach. Two shady lots have ample parking, again with special spots for RVs. A sand path takes you through Bowman's Beach Park, over a footbridge and out to the water. The uncrowded beach runs for a mile in both directions.

The park is the island's best spot for picnics and birthday parties, with dozens of picnic tables, scattered in three distinct spots, most with a barbecue grill (few people find the ones across the west bridge, off to the left). Facilities include large restrooms, changing booths, a bike rack, two overhead showers, two foot showers and a faucet with a hose near a canoe launching spot.

A crowd gathers every night to watch the sunset at **Turner Beach** *(at the divide between Sanibel and Captiva, alongside Sanibel-Captiva Rd.)*. Actually two distinct beaches, Turner Beach is divided by Blind Pass, the narrow cut that separates Sanibel and Captiva. (Often the pass is closed, but plans are to keep it open.) Each side has a parking lot and Port-A-Potty restrooms. Big and wide, Turner Beach is popular with fishermen and shellers. The gray, packed sand is filled with tiny shells. On the Sanibel side, there's often a two-foot shelf of shells about 20 yards from the water. Swimming is dangerous

**Get a tide chart** at island grocery stores or marinas. Tide times change daily, and the printed times are for only one particular spot (usually the Sanibel lighthouse). Tides come later for points farther west or north.

**Hidden workout.** Once you cross the footbridge on the path to Bowman's Beach, watch for a shady path that veers right (west). It goes for nearly a mile. Along the way are a series of exercise stations, with instructions for both adults and children.

**You can see Naples** from the Lighthouse Beach. The city's high-rise condos are barely visible, just before the horizon.

**Islanders call Gulfside City Park 'Algiers Beach.'** The Algiers was an old ferryboat, brought ashore here in the 1950s and converted to a faux-steamship home. Later abandoned, the boat was demolished in 1980, and the land was converted to a park. Rumor has it that a few pieces of the Algiers are still back in the woods.

**Facing page:** With black-eyed susans swaying in the breeze, Bowman's Beach shows off its natural beauty

# Nude No More

Sanibel native Sam Bailey, 79, says he and his brothers used to go skinny-dipping at the beach all the time. "We'd strip off our clothes as we walked, and toss them into the grass when we got to the dunes." Growing up at the family homestead on Periwinkle Way, the beach was just a short walk out Donax Street.

"There wasn't anything brazen about it," says his brother Francis, 81. "Sometimes we'd just be walking along the beach and decide to shuck our clothes and cool off."

Other islanders carried on this tradition. Talk to a Sanibel resident long enough, especially over a couple of beers, and eventually you'll hear a tale about skinny-dipping back in his or her younger days. The popular spot in the 1970s and 1980s was Bowman's Beach, especially at the remote western end at Silver Key. Sure, it was against the law. But it was discreet, innocent, and harmless. Island police looked the other way.

But those carefree times are gone.

In the 1990s, the open-minded attitude on Sanibel began to get national publicity. Web sites touted Bowman's Beach as an "official" nude beach. Some said it was a gay beach. Visitors began coming to the Silver Key area specifically because of its nude or gay reputation. Locals and visiting families began to stay away. Stories of lewd exhibitionism and sexual aggression began to appear in island papers.

Then tragedy struck. Late one evening in 1998 an elderly woman went for a walk in the woods at Bowman's and was attacked by a nude man. The incident outraged island residents, and though the attacker was never directly associated with the nudist crowd, the free-spirited days of old were clearly over. The Sanibel police began routine ATV patrols of all beach areas. They also began enforcing the anti-nudity regulations — laws that never really seemed right for the islands before. The awful stories went away, and Bowman's again became known for its natural — instead of *au naturel* — attractions.

Today there are no areas where public nudity is allowed on the islands, officially or unofficially. Don't expect officers to look the other way anymore. They are under orders to arrest nude sunbathers.

on the Captiva section; the water gets deep quickly and there's a strong undertow.

Another great sunset beach, **Captiva Beach** *(at the end of Captiva Dr., Captiva)* is the northernmost public access point on Captiva, bordering the South Seas Resort. The parking lot here is tiny (maybe a dozen spots), with no restrooms or facilities. Don't be intimidated by the South Seas beach chairs you see here; the entire beach is public land, open to all. The best time here is the 4th of July, when South Seas launches fireworks over the Gulf.

# Bay beaches

The **Sanibel Causeway** beaches *(on three man-made islands along both sides of the road)* are fine for swimming, fishing and picnicking. Windsurfers love it here. The water is shallow, so even young kids can splash around without fear. You can park your car anywhere you like, at the water's edge. Bring a chair to watch the windsurfers, boats and dolphins, or to watch the sun set over Sanibel.

The bay side of Sanibel is generally covered by mangroves, but there are some sandy areas. The north end of **Buttonwood Drive** (near the lighthouse) has a skinny stretch of sand (barely walkable); ditto for the end of **Dixie Beach Road.** Your best bet: the end of **Bailey Road,** next to the causeway. This shady spot is popular with boaters. Captiva's only bay beaches are small, man-made areas at the 'Tween Waters Inn and the South Seas Resort.

**The beach scenes** for the 2002 movie "Sweet Home Alabama" were filmed on Captiva

**Beach parking** is 75 cents per hour on Captiva. It's $2 an hour on Sanibel.

**Away from it all** on a peaceful island beach

# Beach Reads

We asked the folks at Island Book Nook, Macintosh Books and Sanibel Island Bookshop for their recommendations on what to read at the beach. Their top choices were:

- **"Gift From the Sea,"** Anne Morrow Lindbergh. This uplifting classic addresses the beauty of nature and the meaning of life. Inspired by the author's visits to Captiva.
- **"The Beach House,"** James Patterson and Peter De Jonge. A short, steamy thriller.
- **"The No. 1 Ladies' Detective Agency,"** Alexander McCall Smith. A mystery starring Botswana's one and only lady private detective, Precious Ramotswe.
- **Anything by local author Randy Wayne White.**

Their other choices for a good beach read:

- **"Balzac and the Little Chinese Seamstress,"** Dai Sijie. The story of two Chinese urban teens sent to a small village for reeducation during Mao's Cultural Revolution.
- **"The Beach House,"** Mary Alice Monroe. A novel that takes place in the Low Country of the East Coast, involving sea turtles and restoring a beach house.
- **"Beach Music,"** Pat Conroy. A widower's search for a family secret, taking him from World War II through the 1960s, and into the American South.
- **"Big Trouble,"** Dave Barry. This mystery novel set in Miami will make you laugh.
- **"Body & Soul,"** Frank Conroy. Coming-of-age story of a child prodigy pianist.
- **"Bridge of Terebithia,"** Katherine Paterson. Children's book explores death.
- **"Colony,"** Anne Rivers Siddons. Intergenerational tale set in an elite enclave in Maine.
- **"Forever: A Novel,"** Pete Hamill. The story of a peasant in eighteenth-century Ireland who gains eternal life in New York City and experiences Sept. 11, 2001.
- **"Hemingway on Fishing,"** Ernest Hemingway, Jack Hemingway, Nick Lyons. A collection of the author's writings on fishing.
- **"Hornet Flight,"** Ken Follett. Tale of amateur spies pursued by Nazi collaborators in occupied Denmark in 1941.
- **"The Lost Continent: Travels in Small-Town America,"** Bill Bryson. A funny and cynical travelogue through small towns in 46 states.
- **"The Old Man and the Sea,"** Ernest Hemingway. The tale of a Cuban fisherman and his battle with a giant marlin out in the Gulf.
- **"One Thousand White Women: The Journals of May Dodd,"** Jim Fergus. Fictional account of the 1875 treaty that sent women to be the brides of Cheyenne warriors.
- **"The Orchid Thief,"** Susan Orlean. Non-fiction story about the passion surrounding the strange world of an orchid hunter.
- **"The Secret Life of Bees,"** Sue Monk Kidd. A coming-of-age Southern Gothic story set in the 1960s.
- **"The Shell Seekers,"** Rosamunde Pilcher. A novel set in London and Cornwall, post-World War II, telling the story of three generations of one family.
- **"To the Lighthouse,"** Virginia Woolf. The story of the Ramsay family during visits to their summer home on the Isle of Skye in Scotland.
- **"Too Close to the Falls,"** Catherine Gildiner. Clinical psychologist Gildiner's memoir of growing up in 1950s New York, near Niagara Falls.
- **Any of the mysteries by Carl Hiaasen, John D. MacDonald, Tim Dorsey, Laurence Shames, James W. Hall, Elmore Leonard and Edna Buchanan.** Many of these take place along Florida coastlines.

**Facing page:** Olivia Horning, 4, jumps for joy on Captiva

# Beach sunsets

Each evening people gather along the shore, awaiting the show. Nearly everyone brings a camera. But photographs don't do a sunset justice. The panorama is just too wide, the vibrant colors just too subtle. And it's not a static event. The sky continually changes colors as the sun goes down. When the sun's on its last gasp — when it's just a tiny sliver of bright gold — the light flattens out and spreads across the horizon. The clouds turn a bright silver just after the sun sets. Keep your eyes peeled for the elusive green flash right at the horizon as the sun dips below the edge. It's real, but rare, most likely on a cloudless sky.

The secret of a sunset is some simple science. As the sun goes down, its light passes through more air. This filters out the blue color in the sun's rays, which changes the white sunlight to gold. At dusk the sky turns orange and red because the dust in our air reflects these colors.

Some evenings the islands turn pink. When the sky is clear to the west, but cloudy above, the clouds reflect the reddish light straight down, diluting it to a surreal rosy cast. It happens rarely, usually in the summer.

About a half hour after the sun disappears, turn around and watch the eastern sky for something just as interesting — a dark purple haze rising from the east. This is the earth's shadow. When the shadow circles around to cover the entire sky, it becomes dark.

Of course there really is no such thing as the sun "setting." During a sunset, the sun is standing relatively still.

**Watching the sunset** on Turner Beach

**Sunset times** (p.m.)

| MONTH | 1ST DAY | LAST DAY |
|---|---|---|
| January | 5:46 | 6:09 |
| February | 6:10 | 6:28 |
| March | 6:29 | 6:44 |
| April | 7:45 | 7:59 |
| May | 8:00 | 8:16 |
| June | 8:17 | 8:25 |
| July | 8:25 | 8:15 |
| August | 8:15 | 7:48 |
| Sept. | 7:47 | 7:15 |
| October | 7:14 | 5:45 |
| Nov. | 5:45 | 5:34 |
| Dec. | 5:34 | 5:46 |

**To make a beach towel comfortable,** sculpt the sand to your body before you lay it out: Make a sand pillow; dig spots for your elbows, heels and bottom.

**Facing page:** Ohio's Lauren and Abby Simon escape from a friend

The action is the earth rotating. The lands west of us rise up in relation to the sun, blocking our view of it. What we are really watching is an "earth-rise."

# Tips for beach fun

Besides the obvious — shelling, swimming, sunbathing — what else can you do at the beach? Here are some ideas:

## Thirteen beach games

A Sanibel or Captiva beach is a natural game field. Almost any spot is wide, flat and uncrowded. There's no better place to play catch. Frisbee's good, too. Resorts often set up nets for pick-up volleyball games. More fun:

**1.** It's great for groups, but even two people can have fun with a **scavenger hunt.** Each person gets a list of 10 beach objects to collect within, say, 30 minutes. Whoever gets the most wins. Here's a good list: 1) Pen shell. 2) Egg case. 3) Sponge or coral. 4) Piece of driftwood. 5) An orange shell. 6) A man-made object. 7) A striped shell. 8) Part of a sand dollar. 9) A coconut. 10) A feather. Our Shelling chapter has other possible items.

**2. Touch football** is easy to organize. All you need is something that resembles a football, like a coconut. Just find a good stretch of uncrowded beach and draw a couple of goal lines in the sand.

**3.** Can't find a football? Try **touch with no ball.** Each team lines up as usual. But before each play, the offensive team announces which of its players is the "scorer." Only this player can score; the others serve as blockers and interference. Of course, the play ends as soon as the defense touches the scorer. Plays start with a loud, pretend "Hike!"

**4.** A game of **beach darts** also requires no special equipment. Draw six concentric circles in the sand, and give each one a point value. That's your dart board. For darts, each player uses a different color or type of shell, with three darts per player. Players take turns tossing their darts at the board, keeping score in the sand.

**5. Checkers** is easy to improvise. Draw the game board in the sand, and use clam or scallop shells as the playing pieces. For a king, top the shell with a matching half.

**6.** Bring some plastic cups to the beach to make a **bowling** alley. First, fill 10 cups with sand. Then create a bowling-pin triangle by turning each cup upside down. Put one "pin" in front, two in the second row, three in the third, and four in the back. Draw a line in the sand about 6 to 8 feet in front of the pins. Players take turns rolling a tennis ball (or, again, that coconut) from the

## Sunsets

*Sunsets blaze with*
*    unimaginable colors,*
*Stunning everyone with*
*    beauty and brightness.*
*On fire, the sun*
*    slides down,*
*Down like a broken*
*    egg yolk.*

*Clouds surround the flash,*
*Turning peach to a purple*
*That could never be*
*    expressed with paint.*

*The colors run together*
*    like rain on a window,*
*Creating illusions for*
*    the human eye,*
*Everything glowing with*
*    the intensity of it all.*

*I have lived here for*
*    fourteen years*
*And every evening*
*    my breath is still*
*    taken from me.*

— Sanibel native Emily Compton, 14

### Eleven ways to relax at the beach

1. Watch the sunrise.
2. Watch the sunset.
3. Take a long walk.
4. Read.
5. Play cards.
6. Sleep.
7. Fish.
8. Jog.
9. Have a picnic.
10. Look for dolphins.
11. Sit in a chair at the surfline, and let the waves wash over your legs.

**Facing page:** Hunting for lost coins with a waterproof metal detector

line to knock over as many pins as possible. Each player gets two tries at a time. Keep score in the sand.

**7.** Play sand **tic-tac-toe** by using pen shells to draw the grid to mark the X's and O's. (Got a lot of people? Do a super-size version, with people as X's and O's.)

**8. Hopscotch** is easy to sketch out, too. For fun, players can use shells or other beach finds as markers to toss.

**9.** To play **King of the Castle** mark out a rectangular field, about the size of a basketball court. Divide it into two halves, with a square at each end. One team starts on each side. Taking turns, each team attempts to steal the "ball" (a coconut works great) from its opponent's square, and pass or run it to its own square. Each successful trip earns one point. The rules: Your opponents can tackle (touch) you on their half of the field — your team loses the ball and you personally must go off the field and do 20 push ups. But you can't be touched on your half of the field. If you are, the offender does 20 push ups.

**10.** Want to get wet? Play **Balloon toss.** Actually, few people get soaked playing this (the sand absorbs the water), but the game does put a smile on everyone's face. Fill up balloons with water at a beach restroom (or bring them with you in a Hefty bag). Players divide into two-person teams. Teammates face each other, standing five steps apart, and begin tossing a water balloon back and forth. But after each catch, that player takes one step back. A team is out when one of its players fails to catch its balloon. The last team left is the winner.

**11.** Play **What's that cloud?** with children. You'll be surprised how imaginative they can be. It's the simplest game of all: Just lie on a blanket, stare at the sky, and decide what each of the clouds above looks like.

**12.** Got a beach ball and a towel? That's all you need for **Towel toss,** a simple game young kids love. Divide your group into two-person teams. Have each set of teammates face each other, holding their towel between them. Then put the ball in the center of the towel. Each team pumps their towel to toss their ball in the air, catching it as it returns. The winner is the team that does the most tosses without missing the ball (or, for younger kids, the team that tosses its ball the highest).

**13.** And, if you're an aging baby boomer: Bring a bingo game and a large towel to the beach. Set it up and, just like Frankie and Annette, it's **Beach blanket bingo!**

## More ideas for families

As kids play in the surf, their smiles are as big as the sun. But if you want to help plan their fun (or want to relive

**What to bring to the beach.** Figuring out what to pack for the beach may seem like a no-brainer: a swimsuit and a towel. But don't forget sunscreen, a cap (or hat) and polarized sunglasses. Other ideas:

- Money for parking.
- A cooler with drinks.
- A book or magazine.
- Beach shoes.
- Your camera and film.
- A snorkel and mask.
- Sand toys for kids (pails and shovels should be at the top of your list).
- A big towel or quilt.
- A beach umbrella.
- Beach chairs.

If you drive, bring a few bottles of tap water with you in the car. Use them to wash off your feet when you return.

What not to bring: a radio or boom box. No one uses them here; they clash with the back-to-nature ambience.

Many stores sell beach supplies; resorts often provide equipment for guests. You can rent beach goods from Island Rental Service (472-9789), Sanibel Rental Service (2246 Periwinkle Way, Sanibel; 472-5777) and Jim's Rentals (11534 Andy Rosse Ln., Captiva; 472-1296).

**Facing page:** Packed up after a day at Turner Beach, Massachusetts visitors Mary Beth Cromer and David Gourley are all smiles

**Joey's snack boat** pulls up to Captiva to sell hot dogs and ice cream

**Artist John Torina** paints a Captiva beach scene. His work hangs in galleries in New Orleans, Memphis, and Atlanta.

your own childhood, at least for an afternoon) here are some things to keep in mind:

First, remember that kids love to get dirty and wet. They want to dig in the sand, drizzle it through their fingers or build a sand castle. They want to lay on a raft or play on a boogie board. Older kids want to ride a skim board along the surf line, and, if they waves are big, try their luck with a surfboard. Once the thrills wear off, a child may want to fly a kite.

Four more activities for kids of any age:

■ **Bury someone in the sand.** Talk your spouse, parent or partner into laying flat on their back and letting you cover up everything but their head. Then you draw them a new body — perhaps a muscle man, a mermaid, a dolphin or a giant octopus. Decorate it with clothes and accessories, using shells, seaweed and other beach finds. Take a picture for a souvenir. (An alternate method: Dig a knee-deep hole. Have your subject stand in it and fill it back in. Sculpt some shoes around their knees.)

■ **Pole vault.** Get a long stick to use as a pole. Run along the surf, leap in the air, and fall on the wet sand.

■ **Make art in the sand.** Draw a flower or a face. Sculpt an alligator or mermaid. Decorate it with shells. Use seaweed for hair, moon snails for eyes, pen shells for a crown.

■ **Write a message in the sand.** Tell the world who you love, what you think, where you're from, or why

**The sand** off Buttonwood Dr. (left) is powdery, like an ashtray. Bowman's Beach (middle) is rougher. Captiva's beaches (right) have been renourished with coarser sand from offshore.

# Beach Science

Beaches have three distinct zones. The **intertidal surf zone** is along the water, where the waves break on the shore. Snails, crabs, clams and sand fleas live here. Small fish swim up here to feed. Birds dine here too, darting in and out with the surf. Too dry for sea life but too salty for plants, the **middle beach** is a sand bank. Mother Nature deposits and withdraws sand from here, piling it up during one storm, carrying it back to sea during another. Sea turtles nest on the middle beach, which keeps their eggs safe from the saltwater that can destroy them. The **dunes** are the low ridges of sand at the top of the beach. They protect the islands from storm surges. The plants here have roots that grow into a tangled net, which keeps the sand from eroding when the sea rises to this height. The dunes are home to lizards, snakes, tortoises and rabbits (and millions of prickly, painful sand spurs).

**Sea foam** is common on Bowman's Beach when Clam Bayou, an estuary a mile west, is open to the Gulf. It's created when plant debris dissolves into the sea. The material alters the composition of the water just enough to allow bubbles to form during a strong wind.

**Tides** are created by the gravity of the moon. As the earth rotates, its deepest water (in the southwest Pacific) comes in line with the moon's pull. A small amount is pulled closer to the moon, and moves out around the globe, rising and falling in most areas twice a day. The amount of "drainage" varies; around here it's generally one to two feet. Gulf tides are more complicated: we don't always have two a day. The openings around Cuba bring in Atlantic waters, which are on a different tide schedule than Gulf seas. The Gulf and Atlantic tides occasionally cancel each other out, resulting in no tide at all.

**Red tide** is produced by an overabundance of a reddish, single-celled organism (*Karenia brevis*). Outbreaks cause coughing spells, sore throats, rashes and irritating breathing problems in humans, as well as the death of fish and other marine life, which get cast up onto the shore to decay. "Red" tides can be red, green, purple, brown or no color at all.

**How to build a sand castle.** Here are six steps to make it photo-worthy:

1. Be prepared. Bring buckets, small shovels or spades, plastic knives and spoons and a spray bottle.

2. Pick a spot far from the water so that the tide doesn't wash away your work before it's finished. Pour several buckets of water on your spot, then firmly pack a sand pile a few feet high, soaking it with several buckets of water. This will be the base for your castle.

3. Use wet sand. You need lots of water to glue the sand together and let you mold it into shapes.

4. Build the main tower by first making a big pancake of wet sand several inches thick. Gently add it to your base and blend it in. Then make the next pancake, slightly smaller. Repeat until your tower is the height you want.

5. Cluster small towers around the central one in a pattern; make them anchor points for your walls. Make "dribble towers" with nearly liquid sand, dribbling it between your fingers. Scoop up wet

*Continued on next page…*

you're here. (Or follow the lead of our daughter. A thoughtful, sensitive girl — from a family of writers — she loves to scrawl "Boo-yah!")

## Nine ways to enjoy beach nature

**1. Go beachcombing.** Walk along the shore and hunt for sea whips, sea pork and other strange creations that have washed up from the sea (see the last section of our Shelling chapter for photos and descriptions).

**2. Bring your binoculars.** You'll be able to see dozens of birds up close.

**3. Snorkel.** Put on a mask and snorkel (or just a mask) and explore right at the edge of the surf, where the waves hit. Goggles work great, too. Note: Spit on the inside of your mask or goggles (and rub) to keep it cloud-free.

**4. Watch the water.** You may see a dolphin arc out of the waves, or the silvery flash of passing tarpon.

**5. Go to the beach at dawn.** You'll see the natural world waking up.

**6. Go at night.** The tranquil evening beach is a world of its own. Bring a flashlight to see crabs scurry across the sand. Point the light steadily at the water to attract fish and other swimming life. If you're out just after dusk, turn off the light and splash the water and you may see star-shaped pin points of phosphorescent light (caused by single-celled organisms called Noctiluca scintillans). In the summer and early fall, loggerhead turtles climb onto the beach at night to lay eggs. "I love walking on the beach in the middle of the night," says Brianne Meyers, 22, who grew up here. "There's no one else around, and it's very quiet and peaceful."

**7. Make a sea-floor scanner.** Starting with a large plastic soda bottle, cut off the tapered portion and the bottom, so you are left with just the middle section. Stretch a piece of plastic wrap over one end and secure it with an elastic band. When you push the bottle through the water's surface, you'll have a clear view of any objects, or creatures, sitting on the sand below.

**8. Make a giant magnifying lens** by suspending a puddle of water on a piece of plastic wrap. Use it to explore tiny wonders of the beach, from multi-colored grains of sand to microscopic insects floating on the water.

**9. Join a naturalist** from Tarpon Bay Explorers *(900 Tarpon Bay Rd., Sanibel; 472-8900)* on a walk along the shore of the Perry Tract of the J.N. "Ding" Darling National Wildlife Refuge, adjacent to Gulfside City Park. Walks are at 8:30 a.m. Tuesday and Friday. The cost is $5 per person (children 5 and under free).

*Continued from last page…*

sand with both hands and squeeze out the water to make a wall. Make a high wall by stacking one clump on another, thick at the base, narrow as it rises. For an arch, gently tunnel your way through at the base. Enlarge and shape the opening into an arch by shaving off thin layers of sand. Use plastic knives to make ramps, steep for staircases or sloping for walkways. Carve steps with a straight-edged tool. 6. Decorate your castle with shells and other objects (pen shells make good drawbridges). Keep your work from drying out by gently misting the castle walls and fine details with a spray bottle.

**Catching mole crabs**
on Captiva

# Stay legal, stay safe

**1. No island beach has a lifeguard;** you swim at your own risk.

**2. Alcohol is allowed on Sanibel beaches** during the day (one hour before sunrise to one hour after sunset) from Dec. 15 to May 15, and at all hours the rest of the year. Alcohol is illegal all year on Captiva beaches and the Sanibel Causeway.

**3. Pets are allowed on Sanibel** beaches if leashed or under the control of the owner. No pets are allowed on the beaches of Captiva or the Sanibel Causeway.

**4. Birds will eat your snacks.** Keep them hidden. Gulls love to attack chip bags and cookie boxes, especially when you're not looking.

**5. Keep an eye on your kids.** Young children can get lost on the island beaches, and sometimes become dehydrated or seriously sunburned. If they wander out of sight of their parents, they can forget which way they came from (easy to do, since the natural wilderness has no landmarks). If your child gets lost, call the Sanibel Police at 472-3111. On Captiva call the Lee Co. Sheriff at 477-1200.

**6. Thieves may be watching you when you park.** Put your valuables in the trunk *before* you get to the parking lot. Serious crime is rare on the islands, but thefts from beach parking lots are common. Thieves wait in vans with dark windows, watching until they see people put purses or other valuables into their rental car trunk. Once the victims go off to the beach, the thieves break into the trunk.

# Dawn at Bowman's Beach

### By Julie Neal

My daughter and I go to Bowman's Beach every morning at dawn to walk our puppy. (I'd go anyway, just to get shells). It's a short hike from our home, down a sand trail that winds through sea grape and palms.

Today we leave early, 15 minutes before dawn. On the way we hear birds call in the low light. The whirrr of red-bellied woodpeckers. Chirping cardinals. The soft who-whooing of mourning doves.

It's light now, but the sun isn't up yet. We walk across the weathered footbridge over Old Blind Pass (above). The faded sign in the middle says no fishing or crabbing allowed. Micaela, 9, says it's because everything here is so wild, it shouldn't be caught.

This morning we see a small alligator under the bridge. The water is so clear you can see the gator's whole body — the long tail, the dangling dark clawed feet. The ridges and bumps on its back are still sharp and well-defined. The lab's ears lift up. I keep his leash tight. Only 4 months old, Bear's never seen an alligator before. But he sees this one. Their eyes lock. The gator sinks below the surface and disappears.

As we step off the bridge, we see a motionless green heron in the mangroves. The gold edges of its emerald wings hide it in the grasses and roots.

Now we're on the final stretch, the white sand path that leads straight to the beach. As always, it's covered with raccoon tracks. The upper dunes here are a blooming desert. There are cactus, wildflowers, scrubby low grasses and plenty of bare sand. Black-eyed susans sway in the light breeze. You can hear the surf from here. It roars like a highway.

About 30 feet from the end of the path, Micaela and I notice a big hole. Just then, an armadillo sneaks out in front of us. He looks like a big mouse with armor. He sees us, and scurries into the hole. Bear is sniffing the sand on the other side and misses him.

Finally we're at the beach. Everything's the same color. The sky blends into the water, which blends into the sand. It's low tide, so the beach is as wide as a parking lot. Micaela and Bear go romping off toward the water.

Each morning there are new messages written in the sand. Today I learn it's MIKE N CARRIE 4-EVER. There are new sculptures, too. I nearly step on someone's daisy, made of pen-shell petals with a moon snail for the center. I count five sand castles, most still in good shape.

The sun comes up. The sky becomes striped in pink and purple, silver and bright blue. Gulls, terns and plovers are feeding at water's edge. The sandpipers move impossibly fast, skitting along the surf line. I pick up a fighting conch, but it feels too heavy. Then I see one stalked eye peeking out at me. I lay it back down.

As usual, there are shells everywhere. My feet crunch with each step.

Micaela and Bear are up ahead. She sprints along the surf, yelling with abandon, splashing in her worn beach shoes. Bear romps along her side.

It's hard to be in a hurry. I keep stopping to look for shells, convinced I see junonias tumbling in the water.

Then I see something that's not an illusion. Five hundred feet offshore, hundreds of pelicans are diving in the water, feeding. Not just a few, hundreds. They're in a straight line that streches for miles in each direction, parallel to the beach.

Bear is ripping apart dead pen shells. It's become his morning ritual. He trots from shell to shell, pounces on each one, and shakes it until it breaks apart.

Don't tell my vet, but he usually eats what's inside.

We see a big plastic bag bobbing in the surf. It's stuffed full, ready to burst. Then we notice it's not trash. It's a jellyfish, 18 inches in diameter.

Micaela uses a stick and turns it over. We examine it from every angle. We look at the transparent insides, the frilly tentacles. The solid body is like soft plastic. We find another jellyfish a few feet away.

We don't let Bear touch them. But our restraint just makes him crazy. He runs full speed in circles, then frantically digs a hole. He barks at the hole. I soon learn that a pen shell makes a great pooper scooper.

We walk to the end of the beach, where dozens of Australian pines have fallen over and the erosion has created a 4-foot sand cliff. To me, the mass of branches and roots looks like a great spot to rest.

But not to my daughter and her puppy; they don't even slow down. Bear leaps like a deer over the low branches, and scoots under the high ones. Micaela climbs up onto the biggest tree and shimmies out over the water. I think of my first-aid kit, way back home.

She shimmies back off the tree — disaster averted — and climbs the sand cliff. Bear tries to follow, but can't make it all the way up. Again, he runs in circles and madly digs a hole. He tries again, again, and again. Finally, his hind legs straining, he makes it up. He is so happy he becomes one big wiggle.

Heading back, Micaela again races Bear down the shore. She's at full speed; he's trotting right behind her. His paws leave huge prints in the sand.

Micaela tries to skip shells in the water. Then she finds two palm-size cockles and makes castanets. She dances the flamenco in the waves. Meanwhile, Bear has pounced on a dead crab. Micaela tries to take it from him, but he's playing keep-away. He crouches in front of her, bottom in the air, luring her closer. Then he bounds off.

Almost back to the walkway, Micaela finds a perfect white sand dollar. I find another one nearby, this one pale honey brown. And I find two beautiful shells, a rose petal tellin (my first ever) and a buttercup.

I carefully put them all in my pocket.

My shoes sploosh as I walk. I can feel the fragile sand dollars in my pocket.

We pass a family in bright new vacation clothes. An engrossed little girl is putting shells in a net, oblivious to her smiling mom taking her picture.

Final tally for the morning: one alligator, one green heron, one armadillo, a live Florida fighting conch, two jellyfish, a buttercup, a rose petal tellin, two sand dollars.

One smiling daughter. One sleepy Bear.

We walk back home. Bear's happy face is sugared with sand. As she gets ready for school, Micaela hums and plays with her shell castanets. She's in no hurry.

I gingerly tug out the sand dollars from my wet pocket.

They're still perfect.

# Shelling

*I*t is perhaps a more fortunate destiny to have a taste for collecting shells," wrote author Robert Louis Stevenson, "than to be born a millionaire."

Looking for shells, you escape from the headaches back home. You move with the shore birds, hunting for treasure as they hunt for food. You occasionally look up and see a pelican, a dolphin.

The only problem is that you can't stop. The shells are everywhere. You always know a rare find — maybe a junonia — could be just a few steps away. Anything is possible, so why stop right this minute? "Yeah, I'm coming... Just a second..."

The design and detailing of these gifts from the sea can equal that of the prettiest flower or butterfly. But you can keep these treasures. Most are conveniently sized to fit in your pocket, and, later, that vase in your living room.

Sanibel is the best place in the Western Hemisphere to collect shells. The island lies perpendicular to the mainland, sticking out in the Gulf like a roadblock. Deepwater shells that would normally roll right by, instead roll right up. Many shell beds line the island's coast, bringing in tons of local specimens. Best of all, the sea floor here has a gentle slope. Waves stay small, so many shells wash up intact.

Experts say the only better shelling spots *in the world* are the Sulu Islands of the Philippines and Jeffrey's Bay on the southeast tip of South Africa.

## Tips for good shelling

Want to shell like an islander? We asked 200 Sanibel residents for their shelling secrets. Here are their 12 most common tips:

**1. Go at dawn.** You'll get first choice of everything that washed up overnight.

**2. Go at low tide.** The moon's gravity pulls the water off the beach usually twice a day. This exposes acres of sea bottom and thousands of additional shells. The amount the water recedes varies with each tide. The lowest of low tides is during a full moon.

**3. Go after a storm.** Big waves loosen shells from the sea floor and bring in treasures from far away. (If you're here right after a big storm, and there's a full moon, and low tide comes at dawn — you've hit the jackpot!)

**4. Bring a container.** Chances are you'll find dozens of good shells, more than will fit in your hand. Stuff a plastic grocery bag in your pocket, or bring a bucket (cut off the top of a milk jug, but leave the handle, and you'll have a bucket with a grip). Small net bags work, but smell if they're not washed. Forget a paper bag; wet shells will break through it.

---

**Facing page:** Large lightning whelks are sometimes waiting for early-morning shellers

**Above:** Most shellers love to show off their treasures. **Below:** Getting down close to the sand, North Carolina's Katelyn Horning, 12, finds tiny shells on Captiva Beach. **Facing page:** Delicate rose petal tellins are a colorful find.

**5. Bring a sand dollar baggie.** Sand dollars are fragile. They'll break apart if you mix them in with shells.

**6. Wear a hat.** Going shelling is an easy way to burn your head. Some crazy devoted shellers even wear hats at night — miner's hats, complete with lights.

**7. Wear shoes.** Sneakers, beach shoes, sandals, whatever can get wet will work. Shells hurt to walk on; shards from broken shells can sting. Pen shells can cut your feet.

**8. Slow down.** Move at a snail's pace (sorry). Stand still and stare at the sand. Often a shell will be too small to see with one glance. Perhaps the surf will uncover a hidden treasure at your feet. Squat down to see small shells. You may see a real beauty camouflaged in the sand.

**9. Look at the surf break.** A few feet out in the water there's often a dropoff, a few inches to a foot high, where the waves break. Round shells such as nutmegs, cones and olives get trapped at the bottom of this edge. Older surf breaks are exposed on the beach.

**10. Stick your face in the water.** Put on a diving mask and a swimming-pool snorkel, and search in the first few feet of water. You'll find the shells no one else sees.

**11. Talk with other shellers.** Ask what they have found and where the good spots are. Most shellers love to talk, and will share their secrets.

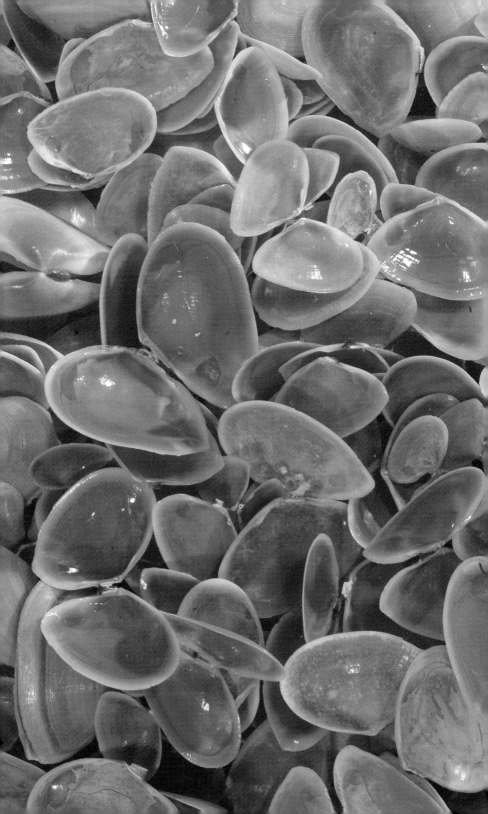

### The Song of the Sea

Put a big shell up to your ear and you'll hear the Song of the Sea. The sound of the surf has been trapped inside the shell, to live forever!

That's the legend. The truth is less romantic.

What you hear is the amplified sounds of the room — the hum of the air conditioner, for example — or area you're standing in. Nearly every place has at least a little movement of air. This breeze rotates inside the shell, amplifing the sound waves to create that "rushing wave" effect. You can hear the same sound by holding a drinking glass up to your ear.

Listen to a shell in a closet, where the air is still and there are lots of clothes to muffle the sound, and you will hear almost nothing. But then take it out to your living room, and — *voilá!* — the Song of the Sea returns.

**Strands of shells** are still accepted as currency in the Soloman Islands and Papua New Guinea, near Australia. A six-foot strand is worth about $11. Called "tabu," these shells often hold their value better than paper currency.

**Facing page:** Viewed from the top, a lightning whelk reveals its circular growth pattern

**12. Rinse your shells.** Wash them off in the Gulf. Or better still, in a sink or bathtub back in your room. Beach shells may look clean, but inside there's often sandy muck that may start to reek in a day or two.

**13. Respect the law.** Live shelling is illegal on the islands. Included in the ban are sand dollars, starfish and sea urchins. The fine is up to $500 for the first offense.

# More shelling fun

**1. Look for small shells.** Go out once and only collect shells less than an inch long. Bring a pill bottle to put them in.

**2. Have a treasure hunt.** Before you start shelling, make a list of 10 shells to hunt for with your friends or family. Compare your finds back at your beach umbrella.

**3. Separate your collections.** When you get home, separate your shells by species, putting each into a separate bottle. You'll end up with a lettered olive bottle, a fighting conch bottle... a whole collection for your shelves.

**4. Dig for coquinas.** Sit down a foot or two from the surf. Dig down a few inches and scoop up a big handful of sand. Dozens of multicolored little coquinas may frantically burrow toward your skin. (Kids love this.)

# Shelling charters

For even better shelling, hire a guide with a boat. You'll travel out to islands and sand flats accessible only by water. This will increase your odds of a rare find (these beaches get fewer shells, but far fewer shellers), and you'll have a pro helping you out. Call for reservations well in advance.

■ Up to four passengers can join **Capt. Mike Fuery,** author of the "New Florida Shelling Guide," for a three-hour trip to Cayo Costa and Johnson Shoals. He leaves 'Tween Waters *(466-3649)* at 7:30 a.m.

■ Native Floridian **Capt. Joe Burnsed** leaves from the Castaways *(472-8658)* for North Captiva and Cayo Costa. He also offers lunch trips to Cabbage Key, Boca Grande and North Captiva. Group rates available.

■ You can combine a shelling and fishing trip at **Memorable Charters.** Capt. Russ *(boat: 336-8377, home: 549-1426)* departs from the dock at Punta Rassa, at the east end of the Sanibel Causeway. This charter is popular with families.

■ The **Sanibel Island Cruise Line** *(472-5799)* uses large boats to keep per-person rates more affordable. The boats have private heads (restrooms), coolers and ice. Cruises last from two hours to all day.

# Shell Science

A shell is an exterior skeleton. It protects the soft, vulnerable body of the mollusk inside ("mollusk" means "soft-bodied"). Two types of mollusk shells are common on Sanibel and Captiva beaches:

1) A mollusk with a hinged shell, such as a scallop or clam, is called a **bivalve.** It has two sides, or "valves." The animal stays inside, protecting itself with strong muscles that keep its hinge shut. The vast majority of shells on the beach are bivalves.

2) A mollusk with a single-piece shell, such as a conch or whelk, is a **univalve** — it has only one "side." With few exceptions, a univalve can come outside its shell, at least a little bit. It stays safe by withdrawing inside and sealing its shell opening with a "door," called an operculum, that's attached to its foot.

Many univalves eat bivalves. The univalve will grab its hinged relative with its foot, drill a hole into its prey's shell with its file-like teeth, and eat the meat. Some univalves do it differently, injecting a muscle-relaxing chemical into the bivalve, then prying it open and munching away.

## Growth and life

Most mollusks are born with a tiny shell. As the animal grows, it secretes calcium carbonate onto its shell, which hardens to create more shell.

The shell becomes a historical record of the animal's life. Many shells have scars — healed-over breaks and chips — from battles with predators. Others have color variations, due to changes in diet or water quality. Older mollusks often have thick, dull shells.

## Shape, color and shine

For each species of mollusk, the shape of its shell has evolved to make it better suited to its environment. Mollusks that need lots of camouflage have developed spiny or irregular shells, which let them catch and hang onto all sorts of encrusting small creatures and plant life. Burrowing mollusks have shells that move through wet sand easily: smooth, slender, and tapered.

The color of a shell can vary within the same species. Shells from the clear waters of the Caribbean will usually have brighter colors, or more contrast, than the same shell from murkier Florida waters. The diet of the mollusk can affect its shell color, too. Some pigments, such as the yellows and reds of beta carotene, help strengthen the shell.

Some shells are polished by the animal living inside. A portion of the mollusk's body slides up around the shell, like a cape, to help the animal crawl or feed. Rubbing its shell as it moves, the mollusk cleans and shines the surface.

## Record setters

The giant clam of the southwest Pacific is the world's largest mollusk; the biggest ever found measured 4 feet, 7 inches, and weighed 734 pounds. Giant clams have been used as children's bathtubs and baptismal fonts.

Second place belongs to the Australian trumpet, at 2 feet, 6 inches. The largest American mollusk is the Florida horse conch. It can be up to 2 feet long.

The smallest adult shell comes from the species Ammonicera rota. It's just two-hundreds of an inch long. You could fit about 35 across the tip of your thumb.

# What you'll find

## Arks

These thick shells are often covered with a dark, hairy muck, called a periostracum. Many wash up unbroken. Arks are some of the few bivalves to have hemoglobin, a substance that moves oxygen through an animal's tissues. It colors the live animal red.

**Cut-ribbed ark**

The National Marine Fisheries Service is working on a way to commercially farm the **cut-ribbed ark** *(Anadara floridana, 1 to 3 inches)*. The **mossy ark** *(Arca imbricata, 1.5 to 3.25 inches)* is served on tables from the southeastern United States to Brazil. The warm-weather **ponderous ark** *(Noetia ponderosa, 1.5 to 2.75 inches)* is found only in the southern United States. But fossilized shells have been recovered as far north as Massachusetts, implying that the weather was much warmer there long ago.

**Mossy ark**

The **transverse ark** *(Anadara transversa, 1 to 3 inches)* is closely related to the larger eared ark of the West Indies and Brazil.

A **turkey wing** *(Arca zebra, 1.75 to 3.5 inches)* is easy to identify by its turkey-like coloring and long hinge. You can tell it apart from the mossy arc by its stripes and the lack of beads along its ribs. The inside of the shell has scars that look like tooth marks.

## Augers, ceriths, horn shells

These small, thick shells look like pointed dunce caps. They have multiple whorls, usually with beads and ribs. The **common American auger** *(Terebra dislocata, 1.25 to 2.5 inches)* looks like a tiny drill. The live **Florida cerith** *(Cerithium atratum, 1 to 2 inches)* is sometimes used to scavenge and clean up aquariums. The aptly-name **ladder horn shell** *(Cerithidea scalariformis, 0.75 to 1.25 inches)* has ribs that look like a ladder, and a mouth that looks like a horn.

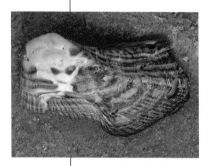

**Ponderous ark**

**Sew security.** Most arks (as well as jewel boxes, jingle shells and pen shells) sew themselves onto undersea rocks offshore. They create a flexible anchor chain called a byssus ("BISS-us"). The threads break apart during a storm.

## Bittersweets

Bittersweet clams look similar to arks, but are more round.

The **comb bittersweet** *(Glycymeris pectinata, 0.5 to 1.25 inches)* has concentric zigzag lines which run across its prominent ribs. The **giant bittersweet** *(Glycymeris*

**Transverse ark**

**Turkey wing**

**Common American auger**

**Florida cerith**

**Ladder horn shell**

**Comb bittersweet**

**Giant bittersweet**

**Spectral bittersweet**

*americana, 2 to 4.25 inches)* is the largest member of this group. The **spectral bittersweet** *(Glycymeris spectralis, 0.5 to 1.25 inches)* is the newcomer here. It wasn't identified until 1952. (The comb was named in 1791; the giant in 1829.)

## Clams

They're called clams because they clam up, closing their shells tight. The Old English "clamm" meant "bond."

An **angel wing** *(Cyrtopleura costata, 4 to 8 inches)* rarely washes up intact. A delicate bracket that holds the two halves together usually breaks apart in the surf. The shell may have a touch of pink on its interior. An angel wing is a boring clam. It digs into mud on the sea floor by rocking back and forth. The much smaller **fallen angel wing** *(Barnea truncata, 1.25 to 2.75 inches)* sometimes bores into driftwood. The more prosaic name for the **false angel wing** *(Petricolaria pholadiformis, 1.5 to 2.25 inches)* is the truncate borer.

**Angel wing**

The soft pattern of the **calico clam** *(Macrocallista maculata, 1.5 to 3.5 inches)* makes it look out of focus.

Tiny **coquinas** ("ko-KEE-nahs") *(Donax variabilis, 0.5 to 1 inch)* live just beneath the beach surface, moving with the surf line. When exposed by a wave they quickly burrow back in the sand — doing the "Dance of the Coquinas" — to hide from snacking birds. Each day they stroll up and down the beach, following the tide. Usually striped, the shells can be purple, red, white or yellow outside; often a different color inside. Coquinas are common here from July through October.

**Fallen angel wing**

The **chione elevata** *(Chione elevata, 0.5 to 1.5 inches)* and the **cross-barred venus** *(Chione cancellata, 1 to 1.75 inches)* look similar. But the chione elevata has small zigzag marks, while the venus has a cross-hatched pattern and a purple-tinged interior.

Remember 45s? Then you'll like to find **channeled duck clams** *(Raeta plicatella, 1.5 to 3.25 inches)*, **disk dosinia** *(Dosinia discus, 1.75 to 3 inches)* and **elegant dosinia** *(Dosinia elegans, 1.75 to 3 inches)*. Their circular ridges look like grooves of a phonograph record.

The grooved **imperial venus** *(Chione latilirata, 0.5 to 1.5 inches)* lives from the southeastern U.S. to Brazil. The **lady-in-waiting venus** *(Puberella intapurpurea, 0.5 to 1.5 inches)* has small ruffled spines on its ridges. The **princess venus** *(Periglypta listeri, 1 to 2 inches)* has closely spaced concentric ridges.

The **purplish semele** *(Semele purpurascens, 0.5 to 1.5 inches)* is a colorful cousin of the white Atlantic semele.

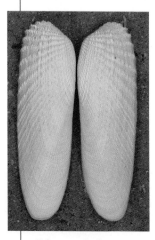

**False angel wing**

Calico clam

Chione elevata

Coquina

Cross-barred venus

Channeled duck clam

Disk dosinia

Elegant dosinia

Imperial venus

**Lady-in-waiting venus**

**Princess venus**

**Purplish semele**

**Southern quahog**

**Sunray venus**

**Atlantic surf clam**

**Atlantic strawberry cockle**

**Common egg cockle**

**Giant Atlantic cockle**

**Morton's egg cockle**

**Florida prickly cockle**

**Spiny paper cockle**

A **southern quahog** ("COH-hog") *(Mercenaria campechiensis, 2.75 to 6 inches)* makes a great car-key holder for your kitchen. The **sunray venus** *(Macrocallista nimbosa, 3 to 6 inches)* is one of the most colorful local clams. The triangular **Atlantic surf clam** *(Spisula solidissima, 1.75 to 7 inches)* uses its strong foot to jump away from predators.

## Cockles

A cockle is shaped like a heart — twice. Each half resembles a heart when viewed from the top. And the whole shell is heart-shaped when viewed from the side. Often as large as clams, most cockles also can be identified by their prominent ribs.

The **Atlantic strawberry cockle** *(Americardia media, 0.75 to 2 inches)* has reddish spots. Like the Atlantic surf clam, the **common egg cockle** *(Laevicardium laevigatum, 1.25 to 3 inches)* can use its foot to jump quite a distance. The **giant Atlantic cockle** *(Dinocardium robustum, 2.25 to 5.25 inches)* is the largest cockle in Florida.

The tiny **Morton's egg cockle** *(Laevicardium mortoni, 0.5 to 1 inch)* has an oval shape. Unlike most shells, the inside is more vividly colored than the outside. If you are lucky enough to find both halves of the shell, notice the interiors' matching, delicate concentric circles.

The **Florida prickly cockle** *(Trachycardium egmontianum, 1.25 to 2.75 inches)* has sharp, ridged spines along its ribs. Coloration varies, but usually the outside is whitish with irregular brown splotches; the inside often has a purple tinge. The **spiny paper cockle** *(Papyridea soleniformis, 1 to 2 inches)* is spotted brown and white.

The **Van Hyning's cockle** *(Dinocardium robustum vanhyningi, 2.25 to 6 inches)* is unique to Southwest Florida, a variation of the giant Atlantic cockle. Its dark chestnut stripes, prominent ribs, and pink interior make it a memorable find.

The **yellow cockle** *(Trachycardium muricatum, 1.25 to 2.5 inches)* has a delicate pale yellow color inside and out, often with reddish splotches on the outside.

## Conchs

These curving, spiraled univalves are the shells you hold up to your ear to hear the Song of the Sea. Conch is pronounced "kawnk," not "kawnch."

The **crown conch** (*Melongena corona, 1 to 8 inches*), or king's crown conch, lives in mud flats, such as those at the refuge's Red Mangrove Overlook (a no-shelling area). Look for one at low tide, camouflaged by a covering of mud and slime. Or check the mangrove roots, where the conch climbs to eat oysters. It can breathe out of the water, as it carries a "to go" supply of water in its shell.

Pick up a live **Florida fighting conch** (*Strombus alatus, 2.75 to 4.25 inches*) and it may fight you. It might even draw blood as it beats your hand with its foot. Place it upside down and it will turn itself over. These carnivorous mollusks live hundreds of yards offshore, but come near the beach during breeding season. If you see one, notice its bright blue eyes, located on half-inch stalks.

The **Florida horse conch** (*Pleuroploca gigantea, 4 to 24 inches*) is one of the largest shells anywhere. But large ones are rare. Half-inch, young conchs are common on Captiva. The shell is orange outside (bright orange or yellow when young), and red or brown inside. The **hawk-wing conch** (*Strombus raninus, 1.75 to 4.5 inches*) resembles warty frog skin. In its scientific name, "raninus" comes from rana, Latin for "little frog."

## Cones

A live cone stabs its prey with poison-tipped harpoons, each the size of the tip of a ballpoint pen, that grow from its teeth. But don't worry. The poison in American cones is not dangerous to man.

Some folks (apparently some who have never been to China) say the orderly, dark-scribbled pattern on an **alphabet cone** (*Conus spurius atlanticus, 1.75 to 3 inches*) resembles the Chinese alphabet. The similar, but smaller, **Florida cone** (*Conus floridanus, 1.25 to 2 inches*) is especially common here in southwest Florida.

**Van Hyning's cockle**

**Yellow cockle**

**Crown conch**

**Florida fighting conch**

**Hawk-wing conch**

**Alphabet cone**

**Florida cone**

**Buttercup lucine**

**Chalky buttercup lucine**

**Florida lucine**

**Thick lucine**

**Tiger lucine**

**Florida horse conch**

**Colorful Atlantic natica**

**Atlantic baby's ear**

**Atlantic moon snail**

**Caribbean milk moon**

**Maculated ear moon**

**Purple sea snail**

**Apple murex**

## Lucines

These clam-like mollusks are sometimes called hatchet shells, although they are more round than hatchet-shaped.

The deep-yellow interior of the **buttercup lucine** *(Anodontia alba, 1.25 to 2.5 inches)* makes it a favorite with shellcrafters. The inside of the **chalky buttercup lucine** *(Anodontia philippiana, 2.5 to 4.25 inches)* is far less yellow. The **Florida lucine** *(Lucina floridana, 0.75 to 1.25 inches)* has pronounced grooves and ridges. The **thick lucine** *(Lucina pectinata, 1.5 to 2.75 inches)* is often found near mangrove trees. The misnamed **tiger lucine** *(Codakia orbicularis, 2 to 3.75 inches)* was once confused with the Codakia tigerina from the Pacific and Indian oceans. It's known in the West Indies by the Spanish name "almeja."

## Moons

Moon snails have inspired man, and woman, for centuries. Georgia O'Keefe painted them. Anne Morrow Lindbergh wrote poems about them.

The **Atlantic baby's ear** *(Sinum perspectivum, 1 to 2 inches)* has an opening so wide you can see the entire inner shell. The white shell may have yellow or tan accents.

A live **Atlantic moon snail** *(Neverita duplicata, 1 to 3 inches),* or shark's eye, secretes a corrosive acid onto a clam shell to soften it up, then bores into it. It can eat several clams a day. The dead shell is harmless.

The **Caribbean milk moon** *(Polinices lacteus, 0.5 to 1.5 inches)* is named for its creamy color. Lacteus is Latin for "milk."

The **maculated ear moon** *(Sinum maculatum, 1 to 2 inches)* is similar, but brown or with brown spots.

A live **colorful Atlantic natica** *(Natica canrena, 1 to 2.5 inches)* has a broad foot as colorfully patterned as its shell. The **purple sea snail** *(Janthina janthina, 1 to 1.5 inches)* floats in the open ocean, clinging upside down on a raft of bubbles. The carnivorous mollusk is often found with jellyfish and Portuguese man-of-war, on which it feeds.

## Murex

These carnivores are known for their spines and ridges. A live murex anesthetizes its victim (usually a clam) with a smelly yellow poison, which turns purple in the sun. Ancient royalty, including Antony and Cleopatra, used this rare liquid to dye their robes, giving us the color "royal purple."

The **apple murex** *(Phyllonotus pomum, 2 to 4.75 inches)* is the most common murex on the islands. The sturdy, bumpy shell washes up in fine shape. A good spot to find a live one is on the beach side of a sandbar. It likes to dig in muddy sand. The delicate **Florida lace murex** *(Chicoreus florifer dilectus, 1 to 3.25 inches)* has tiny spines and other frills that break easily in the surf.

**Florida lace murex**

## Mussels

Mussels thrive in brackish waters, and often live in beds of Spartina grass. The **chestnut mussel** *(Lioberus castaneus, 0.5 to 1 inch)* anchors onto small shells in turtle grasses. The **hooked mussel** *(Ischadium recurvum, 1 to 2.75 inches)* is likely to be found attached to oyster beds just below the low-tide line. The most common mussel in the Gulf, the **scorched mussel** *(Hormomya exusta, 0.5 to 1.75 inches)* has a distinctive metallic purple interior. The brown periostracum easily flakes off of the fully-grown **Southern horse mussel** *(Modiolus squamosus, 1.5 to 3 inches)*, revealing the growth rings beneath. The **Southern ribbed mussel** *(Geukensia granosissima, 2 to 5 inches)* has closely-spaced ribs and an iridescent, creamy interior.

**Chestnut mussel**

**Hooked mussel**

## Olives and bubbles

Olives and bubbles have glossy shells. That's because the live animal is bigger than its shell. A portion of the snail is always rubbing the outside of its shell, keeping it polished. The shell's opening extends its entire length.

The **common bubble shell** *(Bulla umbilicata, 0.5 to 1.25 inches)* is thin and fragile. A **lettered olive** *(Oliva sayana, 1.75 to 3 inches)* is covered with markings that look like crudely drawn letters. Most on the beach are unbroken. The rare, yellow **golden olive** is a variation of

**Should I stay or should I go?** An adult oyster doesn't travel. It attaches itself to a hard surface and lives its life there. But a scallop actually swims, up to a few minutes at a time, fleeing predators and finding feeding areas. It moves by squirting water out of its shell.

**Scorched mussels**

**Southern horse mussel**

**Southern ribbed mussel**

**Common bubble shell**

**Lettered olive**

**Very small dwarf olive**

**Eastern oyster**

**Rock oyster**

the lettered olive, not a separate species. The **very small dwarf olive** *(Olivella pusilla, 0.25 to 0.5 inch)* is common on the islands.

## Oysters

An oyster attaches itself to a rock, shell or other hard surface, always with its left valve. Some use a glue so strong it takes a chisel to remove them. If it's not crowded, an **Eastern oyster** *(Crassostrea virginica, 2 to 8 inches)* can live to be 20 years old. It starts out as a male, changes sex several times, and ends up as a female. The yellow, orange or pink **rock oyster** *(Chama macerophylla, 2 to 5 inches)* has long, frilly projections.

## Pen shells

Pen shells are everywhere on the beaches. Dark, spiny and brittle, they are ignored by most shellers. But take time to pick one up and notice the inside. It's lined with an iridescent nacre, the same material an oyster uses to make a pearl. The live animal sticks itself straight down in the sand. Slipper shells, oysters, barnacles or other creatures often cover the exposed area. Baby murex and banded tulips often hide inside, even in dead shells. Pen shells have strong hinges, so it's easy to find both sides still connected.

The **saw-toothed pen shell** *(Atrina serrata, 6 to 12 inches)* can cut your feet. The **stiff pen shell** *(Atrina rigida, 5 to 11 inches)* has the more reflective nacre.

## Scallops

You've seen the distinctive shape of a scallop thousands of times. It's the symbol of the Shell Oil Co. A live scallop can swim freely. It moves by opening its shell and clamping it shut, over and over again, squirting out jets of water. It often can dart out of the way of a sea star, its main predator.

Scallops have rows of blue eyes that line the shell opening. They can sense light, but can't see in the conventional sense.

**Bay scallops** *(Argopecten irradians, 2 to 3 inches)* are served in some upscale restaurants. But most places use **calico scallops**

**Saw-toothed pen shell**

**Stiff pen shell**

**Bay scallop**

**Calico scallop**

**Lion's paw**

**Rough scallop**

**Zigzag scallop**

**Rose petal tellin**

*(Argopecten gibbus, 1.2 to 3 inches).* Calico scallops come in a seemingly infinite number of patterns and colors. Some are simply one vivid color, such as orange or yellow.

The **lion's paw** *(Lyropecten nodosus, 2 to 3.5 inches)* is the largest American scallop. It has seven to nine ribs covered with large, hollow knobs and bumps. Most are dark red or dark orange; some are yellow. The live animal lives far out at sea in depths up to 100 feet, so intact beach finds are rare.

Small spines along the ribs give the **rough scallop** *(Aequipecten muscosus, 0.75 to 1.5 inches)* its name. Yellow variations, called **lemon pectens,** are sought by collectors.

You can use the flat top of a **zigzag scallop** *(Pecten ziczac, 1.2 to 2.8 inches)* as a necklace centerpiece. It looks like a fan, with small ribs. It may have a decorative zigzag pattern.

## Tellins

Clam-like tellins have delicate, petal-shaped shells. Tellins are favorites among collectors and are often used in shell-craft.

The lovely **rose petal tellin** *(Tellina lineata, 0.5 to 2 inches)* looks similar to a coquina. But it's much bigger, and harder to find. Many shellcrafters use it to form flower petals. Colors range from yellowish, with faint pink rays, to a deep rose. The similar **shiny dwarf tellin** *(Tellina nitens, 0.5 to 1.75 inches)* is a paler pink, sometimes pearly white. The large **sunrise tellin** *(Tellina radiata, 2 to 4.5 inches)* has radiating yellow and peach on its interior.

## Tulips

Look for tulips during the winter. Live specimens will be tucked into the sand at low tide. Pick one up and it will extend its foot and thrash about, searching for a way to right itself. The **banded tulip** *(Fasciolaria lilium, 1.6 to 4.8 inches)* is popular with collectors. It's usually gray, but some have tan, green or orange tints or accents. The less common **true tulip** *(Fasciolaria tulipa, 3.6 to 8 inches)* has a darker color. It's sometimes nearly black, and often has a green or red tint.

**Shiny dwarf tellin**

**Sunrise tellin**

**Banded tulip**

**True tulip**

**American star shell**

**Chestnut turban**

**Channeled whelk**

**Lightning whelk**

**Pear whelk**

**Fargo's worm shell**

**West Indian worm shell**

**Variable worm shell rock**

## Turbans

Bumpy, beaded turban shells are cone shaped, with a pointed top. The **American star shell** (*Astraea tecta americana, 0.75 to 1.75 inches*) is found among rocks or turtle grass at the low-tide level. The **chestnut turban** (*Turbo castanea, 1 to 1.75 inches*) was named for its resemblance to a prickly chestnut seed. It lives under rocks in shallow water.

## Whelks

Nearly 200 species of whelks are found in North American waters. The species that wash onto Sanibel and Captiva beaches are thick and sturdy. Whelks can often be found unbroken, and make great souvenirs.

A live whelk eats clams and other bivalves. It usually pries them apart. But sometimes a whelk will break a shell open by whacking it against its own shell. Then the whelk sticks its "tongue" — a bizarre tube with teeth at the end — into the prey to feed.

The large, tan **channeled whelk** (*Busycon canaliculatum, 3.5 to 7.5 inches*) has a gray periostracum, often with tiny hairs. The **lightning whelk** (*Busycon contrarium, 2.5 to 16 inches*) is the only shell in Florida that spirals to the left. Streaks on the sides of younger specimens look like flashes of lightning. The smooth **pear whelk** (*Busycon spiratum, 2.5 to 5.5 inches*) has the same shape as the common fig. But the pear whelk has a thicker shell, with no cross-hatching.

## Worm shells

A worm shell was home to a mollusk, not a worm. The tube-shaped coils are tightly wound at the base, then expand into wide, loose circles. When alive, the animal moved about freely in the water.

Not identified until 1951, **Fargo's worm shell** (*Vermicularia fargoi, 1.5 to 3 inches*) forms a tight spiral. The similar **West Indian worm shell** (*Vermicularia spirata, 1 to 5 inches*) has a shorter spiral. **Variable worm shells** (*Petaloconchus varians, less than 1/16 inch*) live in mass colonies called worm rocks.

## Other shells

Some Sanibel and Captiva shells — often the most unusual — fit in no particular category.

The **Atlantic hair triton** *(Cymatium pileare, 1.5 to 4 inches)* has a hairy covering to protect it from boring sponges. The shell itself is colored like a giraffe. It's one of the few mollusks found in both the Pacific and Atlantic oceans.

**Atlantic hair triton**

Hard-core shellers ignore the common **broad-ribbed cardita** *(Carditamera floridana, 0.75 to 1.25 inches)*. But shell-crafters love it — the shell makes the feet for their shell critters. Carditas are whitish with heavy ribs in black or chestnut. It was formerly called the Florida cardita.

**Broad-ribbed cardita**

The **common fig** *(Ficus communis, 3 to 4 inches)* is fragile. Few make it to the beaches intact. Similar in shape to a pear whelk, the fig has distinctive crosshatching.

The flat-bottomed **common American sundial** *(Architectonica nobilis, 1 to 2.5 inches)* has beautiful beaded spirals. Leonardo da Vinci is said to have used one to design a spiral staircase.

**Common fig**

The **Florida spiny jewel box** *(Arcinella cornuta, 1 to 2.5 inches)* is often worn down by the sea. A whole shell forms a circle.

**Jingle shells** *(Anomia simplex, 0.75 to 2.25 inches)* are soft and flaky. A handful will jingle if you shake them. A scar inside each shell, where the mollusk was attached, is said to resemble a baby's foot, sometimes even with a heel and toes. The similar, but thicker **Atlantic false jingle** *(Pododesmus rudis, 1.25 to 2.25 inches)* has a dull gray or pinkish-white color.

Find a **junonia** *(Scaphella junonia, 2.5 to 4.5 inches)* and you'll get your picture in an island newspaper — it's that special. Long the symbol of Sanibel, this prized shell decorates signs and menus throughout the island. The live shell lives in deep water, miles off-shore, so it usually takes a good storm to wash one up onto the beach. But the one you find may be planted. Rumors say the Chamber of Commerce sometimes places store-bought junonias on the beach, to keep those pictures coming.

**Common Am. sundial**

**Overleaf:** Junonia

**Florida spiny jewel box**

**Jingle shell**

**Atlantic false jingle**

**Atlantic kitten's paw**

**Common nutmeg**

**Scotch bonnet**

**Atlantic slipper shell**

**Angulate wentletraps**

You'll usually find only the top half of an **Atlantic kitten's paw** *(Plicatula gibbosa, 0.5 to 1 inch)* or "cat's paw." The bottom glues itself onto other shells and rocks, and stays put after the mollusk dies.

Many **common nutmegs** *(Cancellaria reticulata, 1 to 2.25 inches)* have scars from crab attacks. They live in water 20 to 30 feet deep. Look for these beaded, brown or white shells at the surf line, or perhaps out on a sandbar.

A **Scotch bonnet** *(Phalium granulatum, 1 to 3.75 inches)* looks like a pilgrim woman's hat. The shell has a bulging shape, with a flat shield next to its opening.

An **Atlantic slipper shell** *(Crepidula fornicata, 0.75 to 2.5 inches)* looks like a shoe, or a small boat with a seat (other names for it include boat shell, canoe and quarterdeck). The one-piece shell also resembles half of a bivalve.

The tiny **angulate wentletrap** *(Epitonium angulatum, 0.25 to 1 inch)* is known as the Staircase Shell. The rib pattern looks like a winding stairway. In fact, the German word "wendel-treppe" means "spiral staircase."

You won't find an **angulate periwinkle** *(Littorina angulifera, 1 to 1.6 inches)* at the beach. This tree snail lives on the roots and branches of mangrove trees. It climbs up at high tide, eating lichens off the branches, then eases back down at low tide. The snail lays its eggs into the water. A good place to spot an angulate periwinkle is at the Red Mangrove Overlook in the J.N. "Ding" Darling National Wildlife Refuge. The shell often has a pale periwinkle-blue tip. *Note: No collecting of any type is allowed in the refuge, so finding a specimen you can keep is a challenge.*

**A kitten's paw** is not a scallop (though it looks like one) and not related to the larger lion's paw.

**Lighthouse Beach** is known as the best spot in the world to find an angulate wentletrap. Look in the debris at the high-tide line.

**Man, I feel like a woman.** Slipper shells live in stacks, up to eight high. When they mate, the sex organs of a male extend down the stack until it finds a female. If there are no females, a male near the bottom will change himself into one.

**The angulate periwinkle** is a tree snail. It lives on the roots and branches of mangrove trees.

**Crucifix shell**

**Dead man's fingers**

**Lightning whelk egg case**

# Other beach finds

## Crucifix shell

Not really a shell at all, the **crucifix shell** is actually the skull of the gafftopsail catfish *(Bagre marinus)*, or sailcat, the fish Christian scholars say Jesus used to feed the masses. Viewed from the bottom, the skull is said to resemble Christ on the Cross, including the spear wound. Finding one is said to bring good luck, especially if it rattles. That represents the sound of gamblers throwing dice, trying to win Christ's garments (it's actually from two small bones inside the skull which helped the live fish keep its equilibrium).

## Dead man's fingers sponge

When it feeds, the **dead man's fingers** sponge *(Codium fragile)* resembles a decomposing human hand. Tiny polyps emerge from the sponge to filter food from the water, giving the animal's "fingers" a fuzzy appearance.

## Egg cases

The odd-shaped egg cases of skates and snails protect developing eggs from small predators. Each also helps keep its species spread throughout its habitat, as it tumbles with the waves into new breeding grounds. The egg case of a **lightning whelk** is a series of flat disks, attached like the bellows of an accordion. Whelks secrete them a disk at a time. The longer the string, the older, and larger, the whelk that made it. Each disk incubates 20 to 100 mollusks, each the size of a pinhead. Newborns eat each other for food. Generally only one per disk survives to maturity. The **Atlantic moon snail** lays its eggs into a leathery sand collar. Brittle pieces wash up on the beach. Whole collars, full of live eggs, are common in the flats. **Tulip** egg cases attached themselves to clam and pen shells. Laid in clumps, they look like small megaphones. The **skate**, a relative of the stingray, creates a "mermaid purse," an egg case that looks like a small, black handbag. It averages 3 inches long, about 1½ inches wide, with two inward-curving horns (purse "handles") at each end. Hold one up to the sun and you may see a single embryo inside. (Unlike skates, stingrays give birth to live young.)

## Parchment tube worm

Those 5-inch-long sandy tubes littering the beach are the casings of the **parchment tube worm** *(Chaetopterus pergamentaceus)*. The long-gone animal buried itself in wet sand in a "U," with both ends sticking out. As water flowed through the tube, the worm ate microscopic particles of food that washed in. One or two pea-sized crabs *(Pinnixa chaetopterana)* lived in the tube, too.

Like a firefly, a live parchment tube worm glows in the dark. If you're on the beach in the evening, watch for its flashing blue light.

## Sand dollar

A **sand dollar** *(Mellita quinquiesperforata)* is not a shell. It's the complete remains of a type of sea urchin. Turn one over and you can see its tiny hairs, called cilia, which it uses to direct food to its centrally-located mouth. The cilia move in a wave-like pattern.

Many sand dollars live in the beach tidal zone — the area between high and low tide. The sturdy animal breaks apart easily after death. Live sand dollars are brown; dead ones are light tan or gray. To make one white, soak it in a 50-50 mix of bleach and water.

The animal has a five-point flower pattern on its top, with sets of large and small holes. The five large holes let food pass down to the mouth and help the animal burrow in the sand. Eggs or sperm are released from the five small holes in the center, called gonopores. Inside the "petals" are small slits where the sand dollar breathes.

The patterns have religious significance for many Christians. Four of the large holes symbolize the hands and feet of Christ. The top flower resembles a poinsettia, the traditional Christmas flower, while the bottom pattern is similar to an Easter lily. The teeth — the hard pieces you find when you break open a dead specimen — are said to be tiny doves.

**Tulip egg case**

**Skate egg case**

**Parchment tube worm**

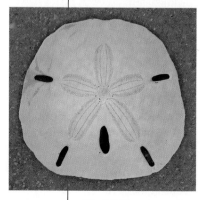

**Sand dollar**

**Sargassum weed**

**Sea horse**

**Sea pork**

**Starfish** can be the bane of the oyster industry. They infest beds, eating everything. Oystermen once raked and ripped them up, tossing the pieces into the sea. But each piece, if it included part of the animal's central disk, then grew into a separate, identical starfish.

## Sargassum weed

Each piece of **sargassum weed** *(Sargassum natans)* holds a colony of tiny creatures that has traveled over a thousand miles to get here. It's from the Sargasso Sea, a mass of free-floating seaweed in the Atlantic, south of Bermuda. Small crabs, shrimp and fish, each different than our own, cling to it as it washes around Florida and into the Gulf. For camouflage, many have evolved to look like parts of the weed, which is kept afloat by air sacs on its stems. *Columbus spotted the Sargasso Sea in 1492. He thought he'd found land.*

## Sea horse

Is there anything stranger than a **sea horse** *(Hippocampus hudsonius)?* This small pipefish has the head of a horse, the tail of a monkey, and the pouch of a kangaroo. Its body has prickly, spiny plates instead of scales. And to top it off, the male gives birth!

Simply put, she has the eggs, but he has the uterus. The female injects her eggs into the male, in a slotted pouch below his stomach. He fertilizes the eggs as they come through, then incubates them in a placenta-like material. They hatch a week later, as dad pushes out a few at a time, through a series of labor-like spasms that can last for days.

A sea horse doesn't act much like a fish, either. It swims upright, using its back fin as a tail. It feeds by wrapping its tail around sea grass and sucking off the plankton.

Most beach finds are 3 or 4 inches long. At low tide live sea horses are on sandbars.

## Sea pork

This blob mystifies everyone. Many people think it's a jellyfish. To us, it always looked like a brain, perhaps the result of some gruesome mutiny at sea. In fact, it's **sea pork** *(Ascidian sp.),* a harmless slab of gelatin. Each is a large commune full of hundreds of tiny sea creatures. To see them, slice off a piece and look at it closely in the sun.

## Sea star (starfish)

The arms of a sea star come in handy. They help it feed, pulling apart oysters and other mollusks. They help it travel, becoming legs that crawl. They protect it, too: When a sea star is threatened, an arm will fall off. As the predator eats the arm, the rest crawls away. Later, a new arm grows back. The **brown spiny sea star** *(Echinaster spinulosus)* has five thick, rounded arms. The top has blunt spines; the underside hundreds of sucker-tube feet. The larger **nine-pointed star** *(Luida senegalensis)* has thin arms. The **short-spined brittle star** (*Ophioderma brevispinum*) is just a few inches long.

**Sea urchin**

## Sea urchin

A **sea urchin** *(Lytechinus variegatus)* is a round animal small enough to hold in your hand. Short spines cover its body. It eats seaweed; its mouth, on the underside of its body, has five powerful teeth. You'll often find a sea urchin holding onto a rock or shell with its tube feet. It's related to a sand dollar.

**Sea whip**

## Sea whip

The slender **sea whip** *(Leptogorgia virgulata)* looks like a tiny, wire tree. But it's an animal, also known as the soft or horny coral. A small shell (generally an Atlantic winged oyster) is usually attached to one end of this flexible animal, and the whole creature is often covered with polyps. Most sea whips here are red or purple. A few are yellow.

**The brown spiny sea star** is the creature most people associate with the word "starfish"

# Wildlife

S anibel, Captiva and the surrounding waters are a sanctuary for wildlife. The combination of freshwater and saltwater environments provides food and shelter for hundreds of different animals, including representatives of over 40 percent of Florida's endangered species. And it's being protected. Most of Sanibel is conservation land, while nearly all of Pine Island Sound is a state aquatic preserve.

Alligators, birds, dolphins, manatees, spoonbills, stingrays — they're all here, and relatively easy to see. "The wildlife is incredible," says Eric Carlsson, visiting from Sweden. "I've seen many birds at the refuge, and many raccoons, even in the daytime." Adds New Hampshire's Tom Lamarck, on vacation with his family: "We saw dolphins hunting for fish up on Captiva, and a huge family of stingrays at the beach. Then we saw spoonbills flying overhead by the school."

## Birds

Whether you're a hard-core life lister or just a casual observer, looking for birds on Sanibel and Captiva is a guaranteed pleasure. Serious birders, armed with decades of experience and a $1,000 pair of binoculars, can spot up to 230 species of birds here, including stilts, cuckoos and hummingbirds. But our main attractions — the wading birds, osprey and pelicans — are easy for anyone to find and enjoy. "We told our travel agent we love birds, and she recommended Sanibel," says Colleen Redmond, from Hartford, Conn. "We haven't been disappointed!"

### Wading Birds

These long-legged birds feed in shallow water. Look for them along mangrove shorelines and often at the beach, especially at low tide.

#### EGRETS AND HERONS

A **great blue heron** *(Ardea herodias)* is the tallest bird on the islands. The largest American heron, it can reach a standing height of over 4 feet. Great blues rarely feed together and protect their territories vigorously, sometimes fighting to the death. *Avg. length:* 46 inches. *Avg. wingspan:* 72 inches. *Avg. weight:* 5.3 pounds. *Lifespan:* up to 21 years. *Appearance:* Slate-gray body tinged with blue; dark blue wingtips visible in flight; yellow bill; black plumes on head; pinkish-gray neck; gray legs.

The **great egret** *(Ardea alba)* is the largest white wading bird on the islands. An adult

---

**Facing page:** A little blue heron rests in the mangroves at the "Ding" Darling wildlife refuge

can stand more than 3 feet tall. Great egrets have little fear of man, and are common even at crowded beaches. *Avg. length:* 39 inches. *Avg. wingspan:* 51 inches. *Avg. weight:* 1.9 pounds. *Lifespan:* up to 22 years. *Appearance:* White, tall and slim; bright-yellow bill; S-shaped neck; black legs and feet.

The **green heron** *(Butorides virescens)* is tough to see. It usually stays in the shadows, crouched on mangrove roots at the edge of the water. Quite a sophisticated fisherman, it places bait — seeds, insects, flowers, twigs — on top of the water. When a curious crab or fish ventures up for a look, the green heron grabs its meal. When threatened, the green heron can stretch its neck straight up and down to camouflage itself as a long reed or tall piece of grass. Formerly called the green-backed heron and the little green heron. *Avg. length:* 18 inches. *Avg. wingspan:* 26 inches. *Avg. weight:* 7 ounces. *Lifespan:* up to 5 years. *Appearance:* Small and stocky; dark, irides-cent green back with gold markings; white undersides; greenish black crown; dark-brown neck; brown bill; orange legs.

The **little blue heron** *(Egretta caerulea)* is the only wading bird here that's a solid color besides white. Little blue herons often feed with tricolored herons. *Avg. length:* 24 inches. *Avg. wingspan:* 40 inches. *Avg. weight:* 12 ounces. *Lifespan:* up to 12 years. *Appearance:* Slate-blue body (purplish head during breed-ing season); light-gray bill (blue during breed-ing season) tipped in black; pale-green legs. *Juvenile:* White; pale-gray bill, tipped in black. *A Florida Species of Special Concern.*

The islands' two night herons are the only area birds with year-round plumes. Despite their names, both species feed during the day.

The **black-crowned night-heron** *(Nycticorax nycticorax)* is notorious for snack-ing on the eggs, and chicks, of other wading birds. *Avg. length:* 25 inches. *Avg. wingspan:* 44 inches. *Avg. weight:* 1.9 pounds. *Lifespan:* up to 16 years. *Appearance:* Stocky, pale gray body; white face with black crown; white plume; dark gray bill; large red eyes; yellow legs. *Juvenile:* Brown-ish-gray with large white spots; no plumes; yellowish bill.

The **yellow-crowned night-heron** *(Nyctanassa violacea)* rarely eats fish. Instead, it munches on mangrove tree crabs

**Great blue heron**

DAVID MEARDON

**Green heron**

**Black-crowned night-heron**

**Facing page:** Great egret

**Overleaf:** Yellow-crowned night-heron

DAVID MEARDON

**Reddish egret**

**Tricolored heron**

**The cattle egret** is a newcomer to the United States, emigrating from Latin America in the 1950s

the way kids gobble popcorn. *Avg. length:* 24 inches. *Avg. wingspan:* 42 inches. *Avg. weight:* 1.5 pounds. *Lifespan:* up to 16 years. *Appearance:* Stocky gray body; black and white head with pale-yellow plumes; gray bill; red eyes; yellow legs. *Juvenile:* Brown with tiny white spots; no plumes; dark bill.

The rarest wading bird here is the **reddish egret** *(Egretta rufescens)*. It fishes like it's drunk, lurching about with its wings spread. *Avg. length:* 30 inches. *Avg. wingspan:* 46 inches. *Avg. weight:* 1 pound. *Lifespan:* up to 15 years. *Appearance:* Slate-gray body; dusky, shaggy rose head and neck; gray legs and feet; pink bill with black tip. *Juvenile:* Chalky gray. *A Florida Species of Special Concern.*

The **snowy egret** *(Egretta thula)* is the only island bird with black legs and yellow feet, earning it the nickname "Golden Slippers." It feeds by sprinting about in shallow water, causing fish to dart out into the open, and by raking its toes through the water, flushing out insects and small vertebrates from the sand. *Avg. length:* 24 inches. *Avg. wingspan:* 41 inches. *Avg. weight:* 13 ounces. *Lifespan:* up to 22 years. *Appearance:* White, slim; black bill with yellow near the eyes; black legs; yellow feet. *A Florida Species of Special Concern. (Photo on pages 2 and 3.)*

The **tricolored heron** *(Egretta tricolor)* is easy to distinguish by the white stripe down the front of its neck. Birders also speak of its "white pants," its white belly and rump. Formerly called the Louisiana heron. *Avg. length:* 26 inches. *Avg. wingspan:* 36 inches. *Avg. weight:* 13 ounces. *Lifespan:* up to 15 years. *Appearance:* Slender, blue-gray body; white belly; white and yellow stripe down throat; yellow bill; yellow legs. White plumes on head and blue bill during breeding season. *Juvenile:* Reddish head, neck and body. *A Florida Species of Special Concern.*

Finally, we can't ignore the **cattle egret** *(Bubulcus ibis)*, a humble bird that, despite its egret genes, never feeds near water. The birds got their "cattle" name because, on the mainland, they stay near cows to catch the insects flushed from grazing. Look for one searching for insects along a road. *Avg. length:* 20 inches. *Avg. wingspan:* 36 inches. *Avg. weight:* 12 ounces. *Lifespan:* up to 17 years. *Appearance:* White, with pale orange patches on the chest, back and top of the head during breeding; short yellow bill; black legs. *Juvenile:* Similar to adult except bill is black.

NATIONAL ARCHIVES AND RECORD ADMINISTRATION/USFWS

# Fine-feathered fiend

Feathers on ladies' hats were the rage in post-Victorian society, but they spelled death to many species of colonial nesting birds. They also spawned the creation of the National Wildlife Refuge System, a battery of federal and state laws, and numerous private organizations including the National Audubon Society, all of which aimed to halt the decline in egrets, herons, terns, and songbirds whose feathers were prized for fashion.

As recounted by the National Audubon Society, the outcry began in Massachusetts – from women – in 1896. "Politically correct" ladies of the time refused to buy or wear feather-bedecked hats and clothing made from birds. They formed the Massachusetts Audubon Society. Pennsylvania conservationists followed suit. By 1899, 15 other states had citizen-based Audubon societies.

The New York State Audubon Plumage Law in 1910 banned the sale of plumes from all native birds in the Empire State, a credit to the pressure brought on state governments by incensed residents. The federal government followed in 1918 with the Federal Migratory Bird Treaty Act, which aimed to protect migratory birds throughout the North American continental flyways. It led to agreements with Great Britain (for Canada), Mexico, Japan, and the Soviet Union to conserve species that transcended arbitrary political boundaries.

The legal wild bird trade was dead. Residual trading in bird parts and feathers was confined to the netherworld of poachers and denizens of the underworld. And photos such as the one above were reduced to quaint relics of a bygone era, along with those of zeppelins and horseless carriages.

— *U.S. Fish and Wildlife Service*

# Ibis

The **white ibis** *(Eudocimus albus)* has a downcurved bill about as long as its legs. It often hangs out in gangs, strolling mud flats, beaches, even parking lots. An ibis feeds by probing sand or mud with its bill, hunting small fish, crabs, frogs, shrimp, insects and snakes. Get close and you'll hear it grunt. In the refuge, look for ibis roosting on the south side of Indigo Trail. *Avg. length:* 25 inches. *Avg. wingspan:* 38 inches. *Avg. weight:* 2 pounds. *Lifespan:* up to 16 years. *Appearance:* White body; red or orange downcurved bill; red legs; black-tipped wings. *Juvenile:* Mottled-brown and white body; paler legs and bill. *A Florida Species of Special Concern.*

**Roseate spoonbill**

# Spoonbill

The **roseate spoonbill** *(Ajaia ajaia)* is known for its pink feathers. But look closely and you'll see a range of colors, from pale pink to deep red on its body, to orange on its tail. A spoonbill feeds by dipping its partly-opened

**Wood stork**

bill in the water and swinging it from side to side, feeling for small fish, shellfish, insects and shrimp. Spoonbills roost in the refuge across from the observation tower, or farther down Wildlife Drive on the left, at the Three Islands area. Most stay on the islands from March through September, spending the winter near the Everglades. *Avg. length:* 32 inches. *Avg. wingspan:* 50 inches. *Avg. weight:* 3.3 pounds. *Lifespan:* up to 7 years. *Appearance:* Pale-pink to vivid-pink body; orange tail; gray featherless head; gray spatula-shaped bill; red eyes; red legs. Related to an ibis. Often mistaken for a flamingo. *Juvenile:* Pale, whitish body. *A Florida Species of Special Concern.*

# Stork

The **wood stork** *(Mycteria americana)* looks like it flew out of a Dr. Seuss book. Visually, it's a haphazard collection of other animals. The stork's bald, too-big head is that of a vulture. The rough and wrinkled neck resembles an elephant. The body, at least, looks like a wading bird — specifically an ibis, with the same brilliant white feathers and stunning black accents.

The bird's real story is not funny at all. The wood stork is one of the most endangered birds on the islands. There are only about 2,500 pairs left, in less than 20 colonies.

**A secret birdwatching** spot is the gazebo behind the Sanibel City Hall

**Need binoculars?** The refuge visitors center loans them to guests, free

**To see the most wildlife,** go out in the morning at low tide. Pick up a tide chart at an island marina.

**A spoonbill's bill** shuts automatically when a fish swims into it, letting the bird catch food it can't see

**Facing page:** A white ibis flaps its wings as it hunts fish along a Sanibel beach

**Herring gull (juvenile)**

**Laughing gull**

**Ring-billed gull**

**Western sandpiper**

The last surviving American stork, it lives in only a few spots in Florida, including on Sanibel and Captiva. The reason is simple: A wood stork can only live in areas that are teeming with fish, and there are few of those left. It's not an efficient fisher — it feeds by feel, wading through the water with its beak open, waiting for a small fish to swim in. (The bill snaps shut in 25 milliseconds, one of the fastest actions in the animal kingdom.) Raising a newborn is especially tough. To feed themselves and two chicks, the parents must catch 50 to 100 fish a day.

Storks keep their young cool by dribbling water over their infants' heads. In flight, they climb thousands of feet, then soar for miles. As they descend they dive, roll and turn. *Avg. length:* 40 inches. *Avg. wingspan:* 61 inches. *Avg. weight:* 5.3 pounds. *Lifespan:* up to 10 years (breeding begins at 4 years). *Appearance:* White body with bald, blackish-gray head, black-edged wings; downcurved, thick, dark-gray bill; gray legs with yellow feet. *A U.S. and Florida Endangered Species.*

## Shore birds

### GULLS

The **herring gull** *(Larus argentatus)* is the largest gull on the beaches, and the only one with the pink legs. An adult has a bright red spot on its lower bill, which may serve as a target for chicks to peck at for food. *Avg. length:* 25 inches. *Avg. wingspan:* 58 inches. *Avg. weight:* 2.5 pounds. *Lifespan:* up to 28 years. *Appearance:* Mostly white. *Juvenile:* Uniform dark brown (only in the eastern U.S.), then mottled and brownish with age.

The call of a **laughing gull** *(Larus atricilla)* sounds like, well, a laugh. *Avg. length:* 16.5 inches. *Avg. wingspan:* 40 inches. *Avg. weight:* 11 ounces. *Lifespan:* up to 19 years. *Appearance:* White body with gray wings; black tail with white spots; black and reddish bill; black head in summer; distinctive white circles around eyes. *Juvenile:* Tan and white.

The most common gull here is the **ring-billed gull** *(Larus delawarensis),* probably the

No. 1 gull in North America. *Avg. length:* 17.5 inches. *Avg. wingspan:* 48 inches. *Avg. weight:* 1.1 pounds. *Lifespan:* up to 20 years. *Appearance:* White body, pale-gray wings; yellow bill with broad black ring; pale eyes; yellow legs. *Juvenile:* Mottled brown and white.

**Royal tern**

## OTHER SHORE BIRDS

A 2001 survey found less than 400 pairs of the **American oystercatcher** *(Haematopus palliatus)* in Florida. It pries open the shells of oysters and clams, using its bill as a chisel. *Avg. length:* 17.5 inches. *Avg. wingspan:* 32 inches. *Avg. weight:* 1.4 pounds. *Lifespan:* up to 14 years. *Appearance:* Brown back, wings; black head; white belly; bright orange bill; black eyes rimmed with red and yellow; yellow legs. *A Florida Species of Special Concern.*

The **black-bellied plover** *(Pluvialis squatarola)* is the largest plover. *Avg. length:* 11.5 inches. *Avg. wingspan:* 29 inches. *Avg. weight:* 8 ounces. *Lifespan:* up to 9 years. *Appearance:* Drab gray with white belly; black chin and belly in the April–September breeding season; black armpits; white tail. *Juvenile:* Similar to non-breeding adult except more pronounced streaked breast.

Sanibel is home to 12 percent of all the **southeastern snowy plovers** *(Charadrius alexandrinus tenuirostris)* in Florida. In 2002 22 pairs hatched 35 chicks here (mostly on the western half of Bowman's Beach); only 180 pairs live in the state. This rare bird feeds in the dunes, not at the water's edge. Chicks are so small they can hide behind seashells. *Avg. length:* 6.25 inches *Avg. wingspan:* 17 inches. *Avg. weight:* 1.4 ounces. *Lifespan:* up to 3 years. *Appearance:* Sandy upper parts, white belly, black patches above wings; thin black bill; gray legs. *Juvenile:* Similar to adult but less distinct. *A Florida Threatened Species.*

The **western sandpiper** *(Calidris mauri)* darts in and out of the breaking waves, quickly probing for food between crashes. *Avg. length:* 6.5 inches. *Avg. wingspan:* 14 inches. *Avg. weight:* 0.9 ounce. *Lifespan:* up to 10 years. *Appearance:* White belly with gray to reddish spots on back and wings; pale face; gray bill curving slightly downward; black legs. *Juvenile:* Similar to adult except paler and less distinct. Often mistaken for the semipalmated sandpiper.

**Ruddy turnstone**

**Willet**

**Heap o' peeps.** The smaller shore birds are difficult to identify, even for veteran birders. Many observers call them all simply "peeps" or "LBJs" ("Little Brown Jobs").

**Overview:** An American oystercatcher

## Love birds

- A male great egret will sit on his mate's eggs for a short period. The pair show affection by caressing with their heads.

- A male reddish egret courts a female by raising his wings and walking in circles around her.

- A male snowy egret courts by extending his neck toward the sky, then flying in a circle and tumbling to the ground.

- Little blue herons flirt by wrapping their necks around each other.

- Male black-crowned night-herons repeatedly bow to their intended, hissing at the lowest point in each bow.

- When yellow-crowned night-herons build a nest, the male gathers each stick, one at a time, and presents it to the female. If (and only if) she likes it, she adds it to the nest.

- Courting spoonbills give sticks to each other.

- A male royal tern courts a female by doing an elaborate aerial ballet with a fish in his bill. If the female approves, he lands and gives her the fish.

- Willet pairs take turns incubating their eggs, bowing to each other as they switch off.

- Bald eagles, osprey and many hawks mate for life. They can use the same nest for decades.

Steamlined **royal terns** *(Sterna maxima)* are social birds, hanging around together in groups. *Avg. length:* 20 inches. *Avg. wingspan:* 41 inches. *Avg. weight:* 1 pound. *Lifespan:* up to 15 years. *Appearance:* White, with pale gray wings, back and tail; black cap with crest; bright orange-red bill; black legs. *Juvenile:* Wings and back are mottled white and gray; yellowish bill.

Whoever named the **sandwich tern** *(Sterna sandvicensis)* must have been running out of ideas. Supposedly, the yellow tip on its bill is mustard, as if the bird has just eaten a sandwich. *Avg. length:* 15 inches. *Avg. wingspan:* 34 inches. *Avg. weight:* 7 ounces. *Lifespan:* up to 10 years. *Appearance:* Similar to a gull. Mostly white with pale gray top and wings. Long black bill slightly tipped with pale yellow. Black eye stripe; black cap. Black legs and feet. Deeply forked white tail. *Juvenile:* Paler heads; tails less forked.

The **ruddy turnstone** *(Arenaria interpres)* turns over "stones" (rocks, shells and debris) to find food. *Avg. length:* 9.5 inches. *Avg. wingspan:* 21 inches. *Avg. weight:* 3.9 ounces. *Lifespan:* up to 20 years. *Appearance:* White body; brown/black/white calico wings, head and chest; dark gray bib on chest; gray bill; ruddy-orange legs. *Juvenile:* Like adult except lighter colors, with rusty-edged feathers.

The **willet** *(Catoptrophorus semipalmatus)* is the islands' largest shorebird, standing more than a foot high. Its name is the sound of its call: "will-it." *Avg. length:* 15 inches. *Avg. wingspan:* 26 inches. *Avg. weight:* 8 ounces. *Lifespan:* up to 9 years. *Appearance:* Stocky tan and white body with white belly; gray bill tipped with black; gray legs; striking black-and-white coloring on wings visible only in flight.

## Anhinga and cormorant

The **anhinga** *(Anhinga anhinga)* catches fish by swimming underwater. It stabs its prey with its bill, then comes to the surface, tosses the fish in the air and swallows. Its bill has fine, inward-sloping grooves so the fish can't escape.

An anhinga eats almost nothing but fish, though it sometimes snacks on frogs, snakes and baby alligators.

You'll see it in brackish water throughout the islands. Look for it at the J.N. "Ding" Darling National Wildlife Refuge along the dike ditches by Wildlife Drive, especially near culverts. Also look in tree branches a few feet above the water, where they spread their wings out wide to dry after fishing. An anhinga's feathers don't repel moisture, which helps it dive through the water.

Nicknamed the snake bird, an anhinga's thin bill, head and neck resemble a snake when it raises its head out of the water. It's also known as the water turkey, because its tail looks like that of a turkey when it fans out to dry. The name "anhinga" comes from the Tupi people of Brazil; it means devil bird or evil spirit. *Avg. length:* 35 inches. *Avg. wingspan:* 45 inches. *Avg. weight:* 2.7 pounds. *Lifespan:* up to 10 years. *Appearance:* Black body; yellow pointed bill; long neck; black legs. Males: Black head and neck. Females: Tan head and neck. *Juvenile:* All look like females until the third year.

The similar **double-crested cormorant** *(Phalacrocorax auritus)* has a hooked bill. It usually grabs (instead of spears) its fish. The "double-crested" name refers to two small head tufts that appear during the breeding season. *Avg. length:* 33 inches. *Avg. wingspan:* 52 inches. *Avg. weight:* 3.7 pounds. *Lifespan:* up to 23 years. *Appearance:* Black duck-like body; orange, hooked bill and jowls.

## Eagles and hawks

It's true: Eagles and hawks really are "eagle-eyed." Their eyesight is up to eight times sharper than a human's. They can spot a rabbit a mile away. They have a rough upbringing: in a nest, the strongest sibling may even kill the weaker chicks. One egg hatches a day or two ahead of the others. The oldest chick fights off the others for food, sometimes violently. (As parents, the female is usually larger than her mate. The greater size helps her produce large eggs and defend her young from predators.)

The national symbol of the United States, the **bald eagle** *(Haliaeetus leucocephalus)* can fly up to 40 mph and reach speeds of 100 mph in a dive. It can even swim, using a movement similar to a butterfly stroke. It's not above stealing prey from other birds, even in flight. It sometimes feeds on dead animals.

Its nests are the largest of any bird in North America. A pair will reuse the same nest each year, and continually make it bigger. The nests can be up to 10 feet wide. Florida has more bald eagles than any other state; about a dozen live on Sanibel, Captiva and the neighboring islands. By the way, this use of the word "bald" comes from the Old English "balde," which means white, a reference to the bird's head. *Avg. length:* 31 inches. *Avg.*

**Anhinga**

**Double-crested cormorant**

**Osprey**

DAVID MEARDON

**Bald eagle**

DAVID MEARDON

**Red-shouldered hawks**

*wingspan:* 80 inches. *Avg. weight:* 9.5 pounds. *Appearance:* Dark-brown body; solid-white head; yellow bill; yellow feet. *Juvenile:* All brown; head feathers whiten with age. *Lifespan:* over 30 years in the wild. *A U.S. and Florida Threatened Species.*

An **osprey** *(Pandion haliaetus)* eats almost nothing but fish. This fish hawk snatches its prey from the water's surface (some have drowned by hooking into too big of a fish and getting pulled underwater). It eats its meal head first, usually while perched in a tree.

Osprey prepare their nests in December and January, sometimes adding in dolls, towels, hats and other found objects. After the young are born, only the male fishes. He eats the head and tail of his catch himself, then brings the nutrient-rich middle section back to the family. Adults teach their young to fish. Today there are 75 to 80 osprey nests on Sanibel and Captiva, up from 35 in 1979.

*Avg. length:* 23 inches. *Avg. wingspan:* 63 inches. *Avg. weight:* 3.5 pounds. *Lifespan:* up to 25 years. *Appearance:* Dark-brown body above with flecks of white; white chest and belly; distinctive dark eye stripe; gray feet. Females: Brown spots on chest.

Seemingly faded from the sun, the **red-shouldered hawks** *(Buteo lineatus)* here are paler than those up north. *Avg. length:* 17 inches. *Avg. wingspan:* 40 inches. *Avg. weight:* 1.4 pounds. *Lifespan:* up to 22 years. *Appearance:* Reddish chest and shoulders; pale-gray head and back, dark tail with narrow white bands; yellow legs. *Juvenile:* Streaky brown and white on back and wings; pale chest and belly.

## Pelicans

A **brown pelican** *(Pelecanus occidentalis)* is an icon of the islands. You'll see hundreds along the Sanibel Causeway, just off the beaches, and at any marina.

It feeds by gliding over the sea, constantly watching for fish down below. When it sees one it dives at full speed, crashing into the waves. In fact, its whole body is built for that purpose. A brown pelican's chest is full of air sacks, which inflate during a dive to cushion the impact. Its bones are hollow, making the bird so light it can fly and dive for hours without getting tired. Its pouch can hold an average of three gallons of water, so it can catch many fish on each dive.

It doesn't swallow its catch right away. First it sits for a moment and lets the water drain out of its pouch. But it always swallows before taking off again.

On a hot day a brown pelican will pant like a dog, flapping its pouch to cool itself. But it can live only where temperatures are above freezing. Its pouch and feet get frostbitten easily.

**A juvenile** brown pelican has a furry brown head

*A wonderful bird*
*is the pelican,*
*His bill can hold more*
*than his belican.*
*He can take in his beak*
*Food enough for a week;*
*But I'm damned if I see*
*how the helican!*

*— Dixon Lanier Merritt*
*(sometimes incorrectly*
*attributed to Ogden Nash)*

**A brown pelican** turns gray as it matures. It has a yellow head in the winter.

**When you see someone else looking for birds,** join in. Birders are usually friendly and helpful, willing to share their knowledge. We were all beginners once. If all else fails, just go to the refuge with your binoculars. Someone is sure to strike up a conversation and they might lead you to a whole new group of birding buddies.

**A white pelican is a migrating bird.** It is only in Florida during the winter. It flies here from mountain lakes in Canada, Minnesota, Montana and Utah. (When flying, it looks similar to a wood stork. Both are large and white with striking black-edged wings.)

**White pelicans**

*Avg. length:* 51 inches. *Avg. wingspan:* 79 inches, smallest of any pelican species. *Avg. weight:* 8.2 pounds. *Lifespan:* up to 30 years in captivity; in the wild only 10 percent live to be 10. *Appearance:* Distinctive pouch; grayish-brown body; dark-gray legs; orange and yellow bill; yellow cap in winter; dark-brown stripe on back of neck in breeding season (Dec.–Aug.). 1-year-old: Brown neck and wings, white belly. 2-year-old: Gray, lighter neck, darker stomach. *A Florida Species of Special Concern.*

A **white pelican** *(Pelecanus erythrorhynchos)* is huge. Its average wingspan is 108 inches — that's nine feet! In fact, it has the second largest wingspan of any bird in North America, just behind the California condor.

Unlike its brown cousin, a white pelican doesn't dive for its food. Floating on the surface of the water, a group of white pelicans works together like a team of cattle ranchers. They surround a school of fish and herd it into a small circle in shallow water, making the fish easy to catch.

You can see white pelicans on Sanibel between November and March. They are not as approachable as brown pelicans, and shy away from people. But a large flock usually gathers at the refuge, in an impoundment about halfway down Wildlife Drive. Look to your left about a hundred feet off the road. You can't miss it — other cars will probably already be stopped there.

*Avg. length:* 62 inches. *Avg. wingspan:* 108 inches. *Avg. weight:* 16.4 pounds. *Lifespan:* up to 12 years. *Appearance:* Distinctive pouch; white body; pink, yellow and orange bill; black-edged wings; orange legs.

DAVID MEARDON

# Other island birds

The **American coot** *(Fulica americana)* is a small duck with a white bill. Look for it in a freshwater impoundment or roadside canal of the refuge. *Avg. length:* 15.5 inches. *Avg. wingspan:* 24 inches. *Avg. weight:* 1.4 pounds. *Lifespan:* up to 9 years. *Appearance:* Small, dark gray-black body; black head; white bill. *Juvenile:* Dull, gray-brown body.

**Common moorhen**

The elusive **mangrove cuckoo** *(Coccyzus minor)* is here year-round, but difficult to see as it sneaks through the mangroves. It's the ultimate sighting for island birders. "My ornithological dream is to find the mangrove cuckoo," says Joanne Beagan, from the Jersey Shore. "He's in there somewhere!" *Avg. length:* 12 inches. *Avg. wingspan:* 17 inches. *Avg. weight:* 2.3 ounces. *Lifespan:* up to 10 years. *Appearance:* Medium-brown top; buffy belly; black tail with large white spots; black eye stripe; downcurved bill black on top, yellow below.

A **common moorhen** *(Gallinula chloropus)* is slightly smaller than the American coot, and has a red bill. *Avg. length:* 14 inches. *Avg. wingspan:* 21 inches. *Avg. weight:* 11 ounces. *Lifespan:* up to 11 years. *Appearance:* Small, dark blue-gray duck-like body; black head; red or orange bill. *Juvenile:* Drab gray bill.

A **turkey vulture** *(Cathartes aura)* has some crude behaviors. It eats dead animals, either fresh or "aged," sticking its head deep inside a carcass. Its digestive system can kill most any virus and bacteria in the food it eats. When threatened it vomits, repulsing the attacker with the odor. Look for turkey vultures soaring overhead in a group, or roosting together in dead trees, especially along Sanibel-Captiva Road. Turkey vultures don't build nests, but rather lay their eggs beside shrubs and bushes. Unlike most birds, they have a strong sense of smell. *Avg. length:* 26 inches. *Avg. wingspan:* 67 inches. *Avg. weight:* 4 pounds. *Lifespan:* up to 5 years in the wild; up to 17 in captivity. *Appearance:* Large brown body with bold red head, like a turkey; silvery-edged feathers. *Juvenile:* Grayish head.

The **pileated** ("PILL-ee-ated") **woodpecker** *(Dryocopus pileatus)* is the largest woodpecker in North America. Digging in a tree (or a house) for insects, it makes a rectangular hole. Adults over 40 may remember the famous cartoon pileated, Woody Woodpecker. *Avg. length:* 16.5 inches. *Avg. wingspan:* 29 inches. *Avg. weight:* 10 ounces. *Lifespan:* up to 9 years. *Appearance:* Black body with bright-red crested head; white under wings; stripes on face and neck; black eye stripe.

**Coots** take a long time to take flight. They run along the surface of the water to build speed.

**Both the American coot and common moorhen** pump their heads back and forth when they swim

**In North America,** mangrove cuckoos are only found along the Southwest Florida coast and the Florida Keys.

**'Ding' Darling is one of only four** U.S. national wildlife refuges (out of 540) where the common moorhen lives year-round

**Cherokee Indians** called the turkey vulture the "peace eagle." It doesn't screech (it has no voice box) or kill (its claws and beak can't tear live flesh).

**The feet of a pileated woodpecker** have two toes pointing forward, and two pointing backward

JOHN AND KAREN HOLLINGSWORTH/USFWS

**An eastern tiger swallowtail butterfly** shares a thistle with a bee

**There is no such thing as a mosquito 'bite.'** The insect can't open its jaw. A female (never a male) pierces your skin with her stinger, spits in the wound, then sucks your blood.

**Monarch caterpillars**

PETER J. BRYANT/BPS

# Insects

### BUTTERFLIES

The **eastern tiger swallowtail** *(Papilio glaucus)* is yellow, with black stripes on its body and wings and a blue border along its bottom wings (the female has more blue). Some females are all black, mimicking the foul-tasting pipevine swallowtail. The caterpillar has large fake eyespots. *Max. wingspan:* 6 inches. *Caterpillar food:* tulip, poplar, wild cherry, magnolia, sassafras and other trees.

The black, white, orange and yellow **monarch butterfly** *(Danaus plexippus)* migrates from the U.S. to Mexico every fall. The trip takes several generations of butterflies to accomplish. The monarch has been nominated as the national insect. *Max. wingspan:* 4.9 inches. *Caterpillar food:* milkweed.

The **queen butterfly** *(Danaus gilippus)* lives in Florida year-round. Like its cousin the monarch, it is distasteful to predators. The underside looks similar to a monarch, but the top is more solid orange, with fewer spots and no yellow. *Max. wingspan:* 4 inches. *Caterpillar food:* milkweed.

The wings of the **Virginia lady** *(Vanessa*

*virginiensis)* are mostly orange on top, with black and white spots and stripes. Underneath an elaborate webbed pattern has pink, gold, rust and black colors. The Virginia lady is sometimes called the American painted lady. *Max. wingspan:* 2 inches. *Caterpillar food:* cudweeds.

Florida's state butterfly, the **zebra longwing** *(Heliconius charitonius)* has a different life than most other species. It eats pollen, instead of just nectar. The extra nutrition helps it live much longer: 5 or 6 months instead of several weeks. This social butterfly roosts with others at night, sleeping so soundly you can pick one up and return it without disturbing the rest. The caterpillar is white, with long black (harmless) spines and a pale yellow head. It molts five times before it pupates. The chrysalis turns transparent just before it splits open. As the name suggests, the zebra longwing's wings are long and narrow, black with yellow stripes and spots. *Max. wingspan:* 4 inches. *Caterpillar food:* passion flower vine.

## OTHER INSECTS

**Fire ants** *(Solenopsis invicta)* attack you. Step on a mound — a pile of sand about 6 to 12 inches high, often at the side of a road — and these red monsters will attack your foot and leg with a vengeance. The bites hurt, and will swell and itch for days. Slightly larger than black ants, fire ants are about ⅛-inch long. They were brought into the United States by accident, when a boat from Brazil docked in Alabama in the 1920s. They spread to southern Florida in the early 1970s.

Sanibel is No. 1 in mosquitos. It holds the world's record for the most mosquitos caught in a light trap in a single night: 365,000. Fortunately that was in 1953, before helicopters and DC-3s began routinely spraying the island with repellent. Today's situation is much better, but **saltwater mosquitos** *(Aedes australis)* still breed profusely here. To help avoid them, don't wear perfume or cologne.

The bite of a **sand fly** *(Ceretopogonidae leptoconops)* hurts worse than a mosquito bite.

**Monarch butterfly**

**Virginia lady butterfly**

**Queen butterfly**

**Zebra longwing butterfly**

**"It's a panther!"** Each year about a dozen people call the refuge to report seeing a rare Florida panther roaming the islands. But they're seeing bobcats. The panther is a much bigger animal — up to 6 feet long, weighing up to 200 pounds. Its tail alone can be longer than a bobcat. One reason for the confusion: some island bobcats have longer than usual tails. Only 60 to 70 Florida panthers exist in the wild, though most do live in southern Florida.

**Playing possum.** When attacked, an opossum will go into a state of shock. Its body will become stiff, its breathing will slow down, and drool will trickle from its mouth. Sometimes this makes the predator give up its attack, as it thinks the opossum is already dead.

**Armadillos are related to anteaters and sloths.** They developed in South America about 50 million years ago. Many wander Sanibel today.

JOHN AND KAREN HOLLINGSWORTH/USFWS

It cuts your skin and laps up your blood. The irritating wound can leave a scar. Also called a "no-see-um," the tiny sand fly is almost invisible, small enough to get through the mesh of a screened porch.

The sting from a **brown scorpion** *(Centruroides gracilis)* can make you sick, but it won't kill you; it's not as poisonous as other varieties. Ammonia will help ease the pain. Scorpions mostly stay hidden, under boards, branches or old towels. They live on dead palm fronds. Island scorpions are 1 to 6 inches long.

# Land animals

## Mammals

The **nine-banded armadillo** *(Dasypus novemcinctus)* looks like a giant mouse in a suit of armor. It can curl into a ball to protect itself. It squeaks when frightened. This shy creature is tough to see, but many live on the islands.

The **bobcat** *(Felis rufus)* is the islands' most dangerous mammal. This secretive creature hunts at night, stalking rats, rabbits, birds, reptiles — just about anything it can catch. It pounces on its prey, often killing it with a single bite. It can climb trees, and swim.

At 2 to 3 feet long, a Florida bobcat is skinnier, with less fur, than its mountain cousin. It has a spotted coat, though the spots are often covered up by sand or other debris. It differs from a domestic cat by its larger size, pointed teeth and bigger ears. Most bobcats have a short ("bobbed"), black-tipped tail. We've spotted bobcats near Gulfside City Park, on the bike path alongside Sanibel-Captiva Road, and, once, in our own front yard. Your best chance to see one is right at dusk or dawn.

An **opossum** *(Didelphis virginiana)* is the only marsupial in North America. It carries its young in a pouch, and eventually on its back. The opossum has two claims to fame in the animal kingdom: it has more teeth than any other land mammal (50) and the shortest gestation of any mammal, just 8 to 13 days (newborns are the size of a bumble bee). But it's none too bright. An opossum takes forever to hide from a predator or get out of the way of a car. A mother often doesn't notice when a baby falls off her back. It rarely lives beyond two years.

Many opossums wander alongside Sanibel-Captiva Road at night.

The **river otter** *(Lutra canadensis)* is playful. It swims on its back and slides down pilings. A pair will play with each other like

dogs. Though its hind feet are webbed, a river otter can run and slide along on the ground up to 15 mph. It can stay under the water for more than four minutes. The animal was nearly hunted to extinction for its pelt in the 19th and 20th centuries, and is still a rare species in North America. Look for it along the docks of Captiva's Green Flash Restaurant and at Captiva marinas.

A **marsh rabbit** *(Sylvilagus palustris)* isn't your typical Peter Cottontail. It doesn't even have a "cotton"tail (i.e., fluffy and white), but rather a small brown one. And it doesn't hop, it walks. A marsh rabbit has five or six litters each year. It has a 5-week gestation period, and produces three to five young. It's the only rabbit on the islands. Sanibel's Rabbit Road was named for the many marsh rabbits there.

It's almost impossible not to see a **raccoon** *(Procyon lotor)* on the islands. They wander Sanibel and Captiva day and night, often in families. They cross Sanibel-Captiva Road at night. Every restaurant has some around its dumpster (take a look behind the Lazy Flamingo on Periwinkle Way). Island raccoons love the berries of cabbage palms, and often rest in the top fronds. Despite the legend, these masked rodents don't really wash their food. It just looks that way, as they often eat at the water's edge. *Don't leave food in an open car, especially at night. Raccoons will climb in and eat it while you're away.*

**Young river otters** relax on a Sanibel dock. The animals have great senses of smell and hearing.

**Awaiting the return** of its parents, a baby raccoon hides out in the top of a cabbage palm

**An American alligator** at Alligator Curve, near the end of Wildlife Drive

**Most alligators weigh** about 250 pounds, and are 6 to 10 feet long. The largest ever seen on Sanibel was 14 feet long.

**An alligator can have 3,000 teeth** over its lifetime. It has about 80 teeth in its mouth. But sharp, new replacements are always coming in, about one a week.

**Pores in a gator's head** can sense even slight movements, alerting it to nearby prey or danger

**Leapin' lizard!** A gator can jump up to five feet out of the water to snatch a bird as it flies by.

# Reptiles

### ALLIGATOR

An **American alligator** *(Alligator mississippiensis)* looks like something from a 1950s monster movie. Its back has rows of embedded bony plates. Its feet are webbed, like those of a duck. Its thick, wrinkled skin is lined with rows of horny scales.

In fact, alligators are true prehistoric beasts, having hardly changed for more than 100 million years. They are among the last surviving members of the Archosauria, the Super Order which included most dinosaurs.

An alligator eats only once or twice a week, hunting at night for fish, birds, snakes and turtles. It usually drowns its prey, then swallows it whole (a gator's teeth are mainly for catching, not chewing). If it has to, an alligator can eat larger animals such as raccoons and bobcats, but only after it lets them decompose for a few days.

Sanibel alligators breed in April and May. The female builds a nest out of sticks, mud and vegetation, and lays 30 to 50 eggs. A newborn is about 6 inches long and has yellow stripes. It grows about a foot a year for eight years, then about 6 inches a year after that. It can get up to 19 feet long. (Gators grow faster in warmer weather, so Florida alligators are usually larger than those in other states.)

Most baby alligators don't live long: the adults eat them! Adult males snack on young gators as a routine. And, though a mother alligator cares for her infants for nearly a year, *she will eat her own offspring* if they compete with her for food. If it can survive its parents, an alligator can live 40 or 50 years.

This cold-blooded reptile needs the sun to survive. Its internal temperature, and activity level, varies with the amount of heat it absorbs through its body. In fact, it needs sunlight to even digest its food. If the weather turns cold and cloudy after a gator has eaten a large meal, it can die as the food rots in its stomach. To stay warm, an alligator will routinely bask in the sun, laying on a bank or stretch of sand for hours.

The American alligator is the only animal on the islands that has actually killed someone. Walking his small dog, an older man was attacked and killed by an alligator behind Rabbit Road a few years ago.

The tragedy didn't change the islands' acceptance of this remarkable creature. Most residents are happy to have alligators here. About 250 roam Sanibel; there are few, if any on Captiva. In its natural state, a gator will remain still when it sees a person, or even crawl or swim away.

But, yes, a gator can attack you. If you provoke one, or threaten a female near its nest, you're asking for trouble.

Most alligator problems, however, come from people doing what may seem like an innocent, even friendly activity: tossing one some food. Once it associates humans with food, a gator then comes up to people expecting to be fed. Unfortunately, it doesn't distinguish between the piece of bread someone tossed at it a few hours ago and the small pet, or child, it now sees with you.

There's a reason New World explorers named the creature "el lagarto," the lizard. Though it looks slow and clumsy when it lies still, an alligator moves just like a lizard, able to dart forward or sideways, or spin around, instantly. If you're in front of it, an alligator can leap from 0 to 20 mph within three seconds, much faster than you can. If you're standing to its side, it can snap its tail and knock you over before you can blink. Even a tiny gator can cause a serious wound. More than 200 alligator attacks have occurred in the U.S. since 1948, causing 11 deaths (including five children).

We're not trying to scare you, but we do want you to appreciate the powers of this reptile. Truth is, nearly all alligators are harmless if you keep your distance and don't feed them. To be safe, stay alert, stay respectful, and stay back at least 15 feet. Don't leave kids or pets alone near any inland water on Sanibel, including swimming pools.

The American alligator is no longer an endangered species, but still protected. The U.S. classifies it as a threatened species, because of its similarity to the nearly extinct American crocodile. *A Florida Species of Special Concern.*

**An alligator can control** how long it can stay underwater by recycling the oxygen in its blood. It can stay submerged for 20 minutes when active; for hours when at rest.

**An alligator's tail** is a weapon, a propeller, and a warehouse, where the alligator stores fat to get through the winter.

**The sex of incubating alligators** is determined by the air temperature around them: less than 86 degrees makes females, above 90 makes males, in between makes both

**Sanibel alligators** don't stay in one spot; they wander the island as they please. In fact, if it's fresh water, there's an alligator in there somewhere. (They can swim in salt water, too.)

**Don't feed an alligator.** The fine is $500 and up to 60 days in jail for you. And the gator has to be killed.

**Even if you just see its head in the water,** it's easy to figure out how long an alligator is. Guess the number of inches from its eyes to its nose, then convert this number to feet. Ten inches from the nose to the eyes means a 10-foot gator.

**Crocodile mating rituals**
start with the female. She lifts her head to expose her throat, a sign of nonaggression. Then she'll nuzzle the sides of a male's head and neck until he begins to caress her.

**American crocodiles** have been seen far out at sea and have traveled hundreds of miles across the ocean to reach some isolated volcanic islands

**The brain of the American crocodile** is the most advanced of any reptile

**The word "crocodile"** comes from the Greek word "krokodeilos," which translates as "pebble worm"

**Tempting?** The American crocodile attracts fish by vomiting a small amount of food into the water.

**An American crocodile poses no real danger** to humans unless it is provoked or fed. But, like an alligator, it should only be observed from at least 15 feet away.

**Previous pages:**
Nicknamed "Wilma" or "Clementine" by island residents, the Sanibel croc smiles for the camera

# CROCODILE

Steve Irwin would have an easy time with the **American crocodile** (*Crocodylus acutus*). This species is much less aggressive than its Nile and Australian cousins who often appear on Irwin's "Crocodile Hunter" television program. American croc attacks on humans are virtually nonexistent. Most people will never even see this reclusive reptile, even if it's nearby.

But you might see one on Sanibel. We have one — only one — a 12-foot female around 40 years old. At 400 pounds, she goes where she pleases, but you'll usually find her in the refuge. Hunting at night, she eats fish, crabs, turtles, waterfowl and small mammals found around the water. She should live another 10 to 20 years.

This crocodile originally swam to Sanibel from nearby Pine Island back in the 1980s. The state of Florida captured her and relocated her to swamps near Naples, about 30 miles south. But a year later she swam back to Sanibel. This time, officials decided to just let her be.

Every year she builds a nest and lays eggs. But since she has no mate, the eggs aren't fertilized and don't hatch. Female crocodiles (and alligators) can store sperm for up to 10 years, but this girl's been without a guy for decades. In 1995, she forcibly took over a nest of newborn alligators from their mother. She guarded the baby gators for about a week, responding to their cries. When she left the nest a week later — standard croc mom behavior — the alligator mother returned.

The crocodile is quite welcome on the island. Having her spend time in your yard is a reason to find the camera and call the neighbors. The National Park Service has designated Sanibel as an official Crocodile Sanctuary. If another croc comes here, it can stay.

Sanibel residents once tried to start a crocodile breeding program on the island, but the state of Florida vetoed the idea, as Sanibel is at the extreme northern edge of where American crocodiles can survive.

The American crocodile is becoming extinct, due to early hunting of its hides, poaching and recent loss of habitat, particularly as development has grown in the Florida Keys and from Miami into the Everglades. Only about 500 American crocodiles are left in the U.S., all in Florida. Another 5,000 or so live in Central and South America.

You can tell an American crocodile from an alligator by looking at its head. The croc has a skinnier, longer snout, and its fourth tooth on either side of its lower jaw shows when its mouth is shut.

*A U.S. and Florida Endangered Species.*

## SNAKES

The **eastern indigo snake** *(Drymarchon corais)* is the largest nonpoisonous snake in North America. It can grow more than 8½ feet long. The dark blue, almost black snake eats palm rats, frogs, toads and other snakes. It eats its prey live, head first. Much of its habitat has been lost. It lives in palm hammocks, near ponds and in gopher tortoise burrows and stump holes. Once common on the islands, indigos are now rare here outside of conservation land. *A U.S. and Florida Threatened Species.*

The nonpoisonous **southern black racer** *(Coluber constrictor priapis)* is often confused with the indigo. But it's true black, much smaller, and much more common.

Four poisonous varieties of snakes roam through Sanibel and Captiva. The rarely seen **eastern coral snake** *(Micrurus fulvius)* is the most deadly. Island preschoolers learn the phrase "Red touches yellow, a dangerous fellow," to remember its unique red, black and yellow color scheme. The **eastern diamondback rattlesnake** *(Crotalus adamanteus)*, the **cottonmouth** *(Agkistrodon piscivorus)* and the **dusky pygmy rattlesnake** *(Sistrurus miliarius)* are also on the islands. But your chances of being bitten by one are almost nil. Still, watch all snakes from a distance, and leave them alone. All species are protected, either by island, state or federal laws.

## TORTOISE

The **gopher tortoise** *(Gopherus polyphemus)* lives underground. It digs burrows in the ground, usually 20 or 30 feet long and up to 8 feet deep. Its territory consists of groups of burrows, covering a few acres, that it shares with other tortoises, snakes, armadillos, lizards, frogs and toads. Tortoise burrows are common on the drier areas of Sanibel, especially in the refuge and other conservation land.

A tortoise leaves its burrows during the day, crawling out to munch on grasses, cactus and other plants. Shaped like a dome, it looks like an old military helmet with four rugged legs sticking out of the sides. It averages 10 inches long, and weighs about 10 pounds. It can live up to 60 years in the wild. Occasionally you'll see a gopher tortoise walking along the side of Sanibel-Captiva Road. You can help one cross a road (place it on the side it was headed to, pointed the same way), but it's against the law to touch one unless it's in danger. *A U.S. Threatened Species, a Florida Species of Special Concern.*

**Tortoise crossings** are a common sight on Sanibel

**What's the difference** between a tortoise and a turtle? In the U.S., the word "tortoise" refers to a land reptile, with stumpy back feet similar to those of an elephant, while a "turtle" is found in and around water, and has webbed back feet.

**When you see a gopher tortoise** or a turtle crossing a road, pick it up and help it across. Place it off the road, facing the direction it was going. Don't put a gopher tortoise in water. It belongs on the ground.

**Gopher tortoise**

**A dolphin is never completely asleep.** It always keeps half its brain conscious and one eye open. When it rests, it floats vertically just under the surface, with its tail pointed down. It turns around in a slow circle, coming up to breathe twice a minute.

**Nice S!** A male dolphin courts a female by dancing around her, twisting his body into an "S." The female then decides if she wants the guy. Mates show affection by caressing and rubbing their snouts together.

**Pre-causeway.** Some area dolphins may have been alive when the Sanibel Causeway was built in 1963. Bottlenose dolphins live up to 50 years.

**As a dolphin swims just a few feet away,** a lucky beachcomber at the Sanibel lighthouse gets a memorable photograph

# Sea life

## Crabs

The **blue crab** *(Callinectes sapidus)* is actually greenish blue. An average adult is 6 inches wide and 3 inches long. Blue crabs live in brackish areas, such as around the culverts on Wildlife Drive in the refuge.

A male **fiddler crab** *(Uca minax)* has one giant claw and one small claw. It looks like he's carrying a fiddle. He uses it to attract females and protect his territory. Fiddler crabs live among the roots of mangrove trees, in small holes they dig in the sand. When one crawls out, it uses its claws to push the sand out in front of it.

A **hermit crab** *(Pagurus sp.)* has no armor on its tail, so it protects itself by living in an abandoned snail shell. As it grows, it finds bigger and bigger shells to call home. If it needs to, a hermit crab will pull a live snail out of its shell, eat it, then move in. Look for hermit crabs at the beach.

As its name suggests, the **mangrove tree crab** *(Aratus pisoni)* lives in trees, eating red mangrove leaves and debris. About 3 inches long, this shy, brown crab looks like a knot on the tree. Look closely to see the sharp tips on its legs, which allow it to climb trunks and roots. It's common along the walkway of the Red Mangrove Overlook.

At first glance, a **sand flea** *(Emerita talpoida)* looks like the head of a shrimp. Also called a mole crab, this 1-inch-long beach creature creates burrows with its back legs, backing into a hole as it digs. Its antennae stick together to form feeding tubes, which you can often see sticking out of the sand.

## Dolphin

The **bottlenose dolphin** *(Tursiops truncatus)* is one of the smartest animals on earth. It has a bigger brain than a person does. In fact, only humans have a larger brain in proportion to the size of their body.

A dolphin can find an object underwater even if it can't see it, a technique called "echolocation." The dolphin makes noises, listens for their echo, then determines how far away, and exactly where, a particular object is.

It can even figure out *what* the object is — a fish, a crab, a rock, a shark, a shell, or another dolphin — and even find and identify an object *obscured behind another object,* such as a fish hiding behind a manatee.

In tests, dolphins have used this ability to be able to swim around a pool blindfolded — always a few inches from the wall, but never touching it.

Dolphins can be cunning planners. At Marine World Africa USA in Sacramento, Calif., one had been taught to retrieve trash from the bottom of a pool, in exchange for fish. But even after the pool was clean, the dolphin continued to bring up trash and get rewarded. Eventually, the trainers caught on: the dolphin had tricked them into feeding it extra fish! It had hidden trash in a corner of the pool, and was tearing it into small pieces, bringing up a bit at a time. Some researchers believe dolphins have a developed sense of humor.

A dolphin breathes air — it's a mammal, not a fish. It takes in air through the blowhole on top of its head, which is like a nose with only one nostril. It "holds its nose" underwater by shutting a valve near the blowhole's opening. A dolphin usually comes up to breathe every 30 seconds, but it can stay submerged for up to 15 minutes.

Its diet is mainly fish and squid, though it will grab a bird now and then. A dolphin eats about 15 pounds of food a day. It feeds at the water's surface, sometimes using its tail to injure or stun its prey before swallowing it whole.

Dolphins live in family groups, called pods, of up to a dozen. They swim, hunt, and care for each other as a group. When one gets sick, others guide it to the surface to breathe, and take turns towing it.

Females give birth to one baby every two or three years after a pregnancy of 12 months. As the baby, or pup, is born, the pod gathers around the mother to protect her. Then the group pushes the newborn to the surface for its first breath. Later, other females will pitch in as nannies and babysitters.

Newborns are about 3 feet long, and weigh about 25 pounds. They can hear, see and swim immediately. Pups nurse every 15 minutes — the nipples pop out of slits in the mother's belly — and begin to eat fish in about six months. Around Sanibel and Captiva most dolphin births are in February and May. Young stay with their mothers for a year. A full-grown dolphin averages 9 feet long, and weighs up to 650 pounds.

Sharks are the natural enemy of dolphins, but don't catch that many. A dolphin can outswim a shark, and, if caught, can get away by whacking the shark with its snout.

Dolphins are easy to spot around the islands. If you keep your eyes peeled you can see one almost any time you go to the beach. Boaters see dolphins without even trying, as pods roam throughout the bay and Gulf waters. Often dolphins will follow and play in a wake, sometimes just a foot or two behind the boat. (Dolphins are one of the few wild animals that will come up to humans on their own, even when they're not looking for food.)

**Dolphin or shark?** It's easy to tell the difference; just watch how the fin moves. A dolphin's fin arcs up, out, and down (it's coming to the surface to take a breath). A shark's fin stays up for a long period, parallel to the surface (it's swimming, looking for fish).

**Tale of the tail.** A fish has a vertical tail, and swims by wiggling it sideways, left and right. A dolphin has a horizontal tail (called a "fluke"), and swims by flapping it up and down.

**A nasal voice.** A dolphin doesn't use its mouth to make noise. All of its sounds come out of its blowhole, the "nose" on top of its head.

**The best time to see a dolphin** is at dawn or dusk. But since they have to come up to breathe, those dark arcing fins are out there all day.

**If you're on a boat** a dolphin may race your bow or swim in your wake. But watch closely. They often swim silently, without a ripple, at speeds up to 22 mph.

**Overleaf:** Moments after taking a breath, a dolphin dives back under the sea

**A horseshoe crab** was once called a "horsefoot crab" because its shell resembles a horse hoof

**In Imperial Japan,** a warrior who honorably died in battle was said to be reborn as a horseshoe crab. His helmet became the shell, eternally patrolling the sea.

**You can be stung** by a moon jellyfish while swimming or by picking one up off the beach. The pain's about the same as a bee sting. It can produce an itchy rash. Use meat tenderizer and ammonia to relieve the pain.

# Horseshoe crab

A **horseshoe crab** *(Limulus polyphemus)* looks basically the same as it did 500 million years ago. Sort of a mix between a crab and a spider, it has two pincers and five pairs of legs, covered by a hard top shell. Two menacing eyes seem to peer out from the top, but they're fakes, simply bulges in the shell. The tail looks like a dangerous spike, but it's really just a rudder.

Close to shore you'll often see one horseshoe crab on top of another. They're not mating, though that is the male on top. He's attached himself to the female because she's about the crawl up on the beach to lay her eggs. He wants to make sure he's the male that fertilizes them.

A horseshoe crab feeds at night, eating worms and mollusks. In deep water it swims on the surface, sometimes upside down, paddling with its legs.

A full-grown adult can be up to 2 feet long and weigh up to 10 pounds. But it grows slowly: a 1-year-old is only the size of a nickel. The animal sheds its shell as it grows. It can create, and discard, up to two shells per year.

Look for horseshoe crabs throughout the wildlife refuge, especially along the Cross Dike. You'll find old shells along the Red Mangrove Overlook.

# Jellyfish

The **moon jellyfish** *(Aurelia aurita)* has a mild sting, like that of a bee. Its round body, up to 18 inches wide, has a fringe of tentacles. It swims gently through the water, and often washes up on beaches after a storm. Not a true fish, a jellyfish doesn't have a brain, heart, blood or gills. It's 95 percent water.

# Manatee

The **Florida manatee** *(Trichechus manatus latirostris)* is the largest mammal in Florida waters. It lives in shallow areas around the state's peninsula. A sub-species of the West Indian manatee, it's a member of the order Sirenia (as are the dugong and extinct Steller sea cow), the only sea mammals which eat plants.

Sailors once mistook manatees for mermaids. In fact, the name "Sirenia" refers to those sensuous, dangerous females. Call a woman a siren, you're calling her a manatee.

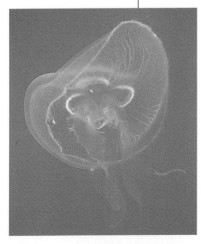

Siren status aside, a manatee has an odd look for a sea creature. Descended from land-based ancestors, it has the shape of a cow and the skin of an elephant, its closest relative. Its rear legs have evolved into a beaver-like tail; its front legs have become flippers. A manatee's skin is covered with one- to two-inch hairs. Its face has thick whiskers on the upper lip and small (though developed) eyes. Ear slits, almost impossible to see, are behind the eyes.

A manatee averages 12 feet long, about 1,200 pounds. The large oval shape makes it look fat. Actually it's built like a balloon: large lungs take up most of its middle body.

Not territorial or aggressive, a manatee spends its days playing and swimming. It moves gracefully, like a slow-motion ballerina, at 3 to 5 mph. It can roll, somersault and swim upside down. It moves its tail to go forward, and uses its flippers to move left or right.

Manatees appear to sense impending cold weather. Right before a cold front, the manatees around the islands swim over to Fort Myers to the warm waters of the Caloosahatchee River power plant.

During mating season, a female lives up to her siren reputation. She breeds at random with a group of up to a dozen males who follow her around. A single calf is born about 13 months later. It averages 3 to 4 feet long, and weighs about 65 pounds.

The mother and calf have a close relationship. They spend up to two years together, often swimming side by side (a baby holds onto its mom with one of its tiny flippers). The two touch often, and even make cooing sounds

**A baby manatee nurses** for up to two years. The mom's teats are under her side flippers. Calves eat plants, too, just a few weeks after birth.

**Manatees make sounds** to communicate with each other. A mother and calf "talk" often. Other chirps, whistles and squeaks express fear or anger.

**Manatees show affection** by rubbing their bodies together and smooching their noses and mouths together.

**Manatee brains have a higher gray-matter** to white-matter ratio than any other mammal, including a human. The gray matter of the brain is where thinking occurs.

# A Fishy Femme Fatale

Are mermaids real? Half of them are.

Specifically, the bottom half. The top — the beautiful, nude girl — is a fictitious creation of men who had been at sea too long. But the giant fishlike tail is real. It's the stylized back end of a manatee.

In fact, that's what a mermaid really is: a manatee, viewed through the eyes of a lonely sailor. The lore of mermaids is simply the lives of manatees, retold a few times over a few bottles of gin.

According to legend, a mermaid was a sign of trouble. Her haunting songs and lovely appearance lured men to sail up to her. When they got close, she captured them, taking them underwater to her deadly prison. In truth, seeing a manatee *was* a sign of trouble — shallow water. Sailing up to it almost always meant running aground. And wrecking a ship during a storm, or in unfriendly territory, sometimes did lead to death. (While manatees don't sing, they do make sounds — blowing air when they come to the surface, and softly grunting when they, well, want to make out.)

Tales of fish-people have been around for thousands of years. The first was Atargatis, a Syrian moon-goddess. She eventually transformed herself completely into a fish, after she gave birth to a normal human and was so ashamed of her "deformed" son. A painting in the Louvre depicts Oannes, a Babylonian sea-god with the body of a man and the tail of a fish. And the Greeks gave us Aphrodite, the goddess of love, beauty and sexual allure. She was born in the ocean, and arose out of the sea foam in a scallop shell.

The iconic image of a mermaid with a comb and mirror in hand comes from the Middle Ages. Promoted by the Christian church, these mermaids symbolized the evils of vanity, as well as how pretty females could lure young men to sin.

Literature and films have embraced the myth, too. Hans Christian Anderson's 1836 story "The Little Mermaid" told the tale of a young mermaid who gave up her identity (her tail) to be with a man, and, having failed, "threw herself from the ship into the sea." Glynis Johns (left) tempted men as "Miranda" in 1948, reprising the role in 1954's "Mad About Men" (she later played Mrs. Banks in "Mary Poppins"). 1984's "Splash" turned Anderson's story inside-out — the man, Tom Hanks, gave up *his* world to be with the mermaid, in this case Daryl Hannah. Disney's 1989 version returned to Anderson's order of things, as feisty teenager Ariel declares herself one of the "bright young women, sick o' swimmin'" and again yearns for wedded bliss with a prince (in this case, of course, she lives happily ever after).

The mermaid was accepted as a real creature, even by scientists, until the late 1800s. Roman historian Pliny the Elder recorded her in detail in his exhaustive "Historia Naturalis." Spanish explorers reported many sightings. "A crewman saw three mermaids," reads a Christopher Columbus log entry, "who rose very high from the sea, but they are not so beautiful as they are painted, though to some extent they have a human appearance about the face." P.T. Barnum got in on the act in 1842, when he displayed what he claimed was a mermaid corpse in New York (newspaper ads showed a topless woman with a tail; the display case held a shriveled monkey head stitched to a fish).

In the early 1980s, natives of New Ireland, north of New Guinea, reported seeing unknown sea mammals. They said the creatures, which they called pishmeri ("fish-women") had fishlike lower bodies, human heads and torsos, and noticeable breasts. Anthropologists came to the area in 1985, and discovered that the pishmeri were none other than the Indo-Pacific dugong, that region's version of, yes, a manatee.

**Facing page:** A manatee breathes every few minutes, sticking its face out of the water and making a loud snort. It sleeps underwater, but still floats up every 10 to 15 minutes and takes an unconscious breath.

**A strict vegetarian,** a manatee can eat up to 15 percent of its body weight a day. Sometimes it eats floating seaweed, or even shore grass, using a flipper to guide it to its face.

**A manatee can't turn its head.** It doesn't have enough bones in its neck.

**Struck and killed by a boat,** this pregnant female sustained 15 prop cuts, broken ribs and shattered vertebrae

together. Females give birth to one calf every 2 to 5 years.

In theory, a manatee can live up to 60 years. Snooty, a manatee born in captivity and now living at the South Florida Museum in Bradenton, Fla., is over 50.

Manatees have no natural predators. They're too big for alligators, or the small sharks that share their waters. Still, they've become an endangered species.

High-powered, shallow-draft boats have allowed man to share the manatee's habitat, and enjoy the efficiency of getting to these areas quickly to catch fish. Unfortunately, this makes collisions with manatees inevitable, as the slow-moving, poor-hearing creatures are nearly impossible to see from a distance. The impact kills the animal, as the hard fiberglass slams through the manatee's skin and breaks its ribs. More manatees die from boating accidents in Lee County than anywhere else in the state.

Scientists believe that in order to maintain a stable population, only 2 percent of manatees can die each year of unnatural causes. In Lee County, boats alone are killing 4 percent. There are only 400 or so manatees left in the area, and an average of 15 to 20 boating deaths a year (based on the years 2000-2002). For manatees to survive, local boating accidents need to drop by 50 percent. For the animals to recover and flourish as they once did, these collisions have to be, essentially, eliminated. Wildlife officials are trying to establish more protection areas, but often meet with stiff resistence from the public.

The best place on the islands to see a manatee is at the South Seas Resort, in the lagoon to the south of the

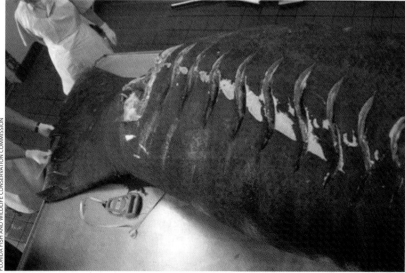

FLORIDA FISH AND WILDLIFE CONSERVATION COMMISSION

**Sandbar sharks** swim near the islands. They come close to shore at dusk to feed.

**To avoid getting stung** by a stingray, do the Stingray Shuffle: As you walk in the water, scoot your feet in the sand, instead of taking high, deliberate steps. This will scare off any rays buried in front of you, and give you a safe path.

The stings are painful. You can get fixed up at Sanibel's HealthPark clinic *(395-1414)* or the San-Cap Medical Center *(472-0700)*. Most of the pain goes away in a few hours.

To care for the wound yourself, flush it out with water and Epsom salts. Make sure no part of the ray's spine is in your foot. Soak the wound in hot water for an hour, or until the intense pain stops.

You must see a doctor if the cut is big enough for stitches, if you need a tetanus shot, or if you are stung in the stomach or chest (these stings require immediate medical attention).

Captiva Cruises dock. You may see one at Jensen's Marina or in the refuge, on the right side of Wildlife Drive. Look for a disturbance in the water, then a big gray nose.

*A U.S. and Florida Endangered Species.*

## Shark

**Sharks** *(Carcharhinus sp.)* are rarely seen from the islands. But eleven species, including bull, hammerhead, sandbar, nurse and tiger, swim in the waters here. Bulls and hammerheads will fight fishermen in Boca Grande Pass for tarpon, sometimes taking the fish right off the anglers' hooks.

A shark has no bones; its skeleton is cartilage, like a person's nose or ear. Its mouth has up to 3,000 teeth, in up to 15 rows. And it's been around forever. Some fossils are 100 million years older than dinosaur bones.

In today's world of bubbleheaded journalism, shark attacks make a lot of news. The whole story? Bees, wasps, snakes, even coconuts kill more people. In a typical year, 300 people die from lightning strikes, 150 people die of being hit on the head by a coconut; 10 die by sharks.

When an 8-year-old boy was attacked by a shark on a Florida beach during the summer of 2001, even Time magazine labeled it "The summer of the shark." (The Weekly World News ran this headline: "Castro trained killer sharks to attack U.S.") No one mentioned that there were actually 13 *fewer* shark attacks in 2001 than the year before, or that deaths from sharks, worldwide, dropped from 13 to 4. "The public's fearful fascination with sharks," wrote Miami Herald columnist Carl Hiaasen, "is matched only by the media's google-eyed gullibility."

Bull sharks are the most likely to attack people, as they can swim in shallow water. To stay safe, don't swim in the Gulf or bay late in the day, especially at dusk.

## Stingray

Related to sharks, **stingrays** *(Dasyatidae sp.)* roam around the islands in the summer. Schools of **southern stingrays** *(Dasyatis americana)* swim a few feet off the beach. American-, cow-nose, yellow and spotted-eagle rays are also here.

Flapping its wing-like side fins, this nonaggressive creature appears to fly through the water. Its mouth is underneath; sucking up small fish and other sea life.

When it rests, it buries itself in the sand. That's when it's dangerous. When you walk in the water you can step on a stingray's back. That scares it. So it responds by flipping up its tail and jabbing you with the poisonous barb

at the tail's base. Ironically, the weight of your foot holds the ray still, letting it get a good shot at you.

## Turtle

Huge **loggerhead turtles** *(Caretta caretta)* nest on Sanibel and Captiva. Hundreds migrate here to lay their eggs, though they spend most of their lives far out at sea.

Loggerheads usually nest at night. A female crawls far onto the beach, digs a hole with her back flippers, deposits her eggs and buries them. Then she pulls herself back into the surf. The whole process can take three hours.

The eggs hatch about two months later. The 2-inch hatchlings make a risky dash for the Gulf — they dehydrate if they don't reach the water within a few minutes, and birds and crabs grab many for food. In the sea the hatchlings become prey for other animals. About one in a hundred will become an adult turtle, which takes 16 years.

Females lay eggs only after they're 16 years old, and only every two or three years. A nest contains up to 100 eggs, each about the size of a ping-pong ball. The shells are rugged but pliable, like leather.

Island nests are easy to spot, since most are roped off, marked and identified by volunteers. Look for these folks on the beach early each morning, April through October. They'll be happy to answer your questions.

Loggerheads are protected under state and federal law. The number of nesting females

**Southern stingrays** hide in the sand as a southern and cow-nose ray glide by

**Adopt a sea turtle nest** through SCCF *(472-2329)*. Volunteers monitor it and tell you how many eggs hatched. You get a T-shirt and newsletter, too.

**Overleaf:** A loggerhead nests on Sanibel

**Most loggerhead turtles** weigh 200 to 350 pounds. They can weigh 400.

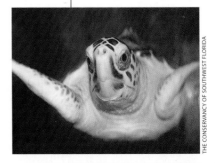

THE CONSERVANCY OF SOUTHWEST FLORIDA

OVERLEAF: SCCF SEA TURTLE MONITORING PROGRAM

**Bird watchers** find plenty to see on Wildlife Drive

**Caged animals.** Sanibel offers two spots to see wildlife from other areas:

■ Exotic birds, miniature deer, lemurs and monkeys are at the Periwinkle Park Campground *(1119 Periwinkle Way, Sanibel; 472-1433).* Camping is for paid guests only, but the attendant will let you in to look at the animals (below) free of charge if you ask nicely. Children love it here.

■ The campground has some of its birds in the courtyard outside Jerry's Foods *(1700 Periwinkle Way, Sanibel; 472-9300).* Cages hold macaws, cockatoos and parrots. These birds actually talk — when they feel like it.

continues to decline. A third of all nests, worldwide, are in Florida. There were 536 on Sanibel and Captiva in the 2000 season. *A U.S. and Florida Threatened Species.*

# Where to see wildlife

## Natural areas

Sanibel's **J.N. "Ding" Darling National Wildlife Refuge** *(entrance off Sanibel-Captiva Rd., 2½ miles west of Tarpon Bay Rd.; One Wildlife Dr., Sanibel; 472-1100)* is one of the best birding spots in the U.S. Over 230 species have been seen here. During the winter whole flocks of migrating birds make this area a birder's dream. Other animals are here too, including many alligators, manatees and raccoons.

Paved, four-mile-long Wildlife Drive gives you access to several great birding spots. Walk along the shores of the Cross Dike Trail to find herons, anhingas and fiddler crabs. Stop at the Red Mangrove Overlook to see mangrove tree crabs and angulate periwinkles. You also may see osprey, green herons and horseshoe crabs. Look for pileated wood-peckers and raccoons on the Shell Mound Trail.

Hike down the two-mile Indigo Trail to experience more remote areas. On the left ibis roost and feed, on the right look for spoonbills. Alligators routinely cross this path; at the sandy western end of the trail look for their tail-and-claw prints crossing from one side to the other.

Volunteers often set up along Wildlife Drive and the Cross Dike, ready to answer questions or let you view an animal through a spotting scope. Look for their golf carts.

Guided tours include the relaxing tram ride as well as many walking excursions. Contact the visitors center for a current schedule.

The Bailey Tract, a separate piece of land off Tarpon Bay Road, has two miles of trails through freshwater habitat. Look for birds, raccoons, bobcats, alligators and snakes.

Four miles of trails lead through pristine habitat at the **Sanibel-Captiva Conservation Foundation** *(3333 Sanibel-Captiva Rd., Sanibel; 472-2329).* Alligators, wading birds and other wildlife feed here. You can roam around by yourself, take a guided tour or join in on a birding trip. A butterfly house is also outside. The visitors center has a knee-level touch tank with live sea creatures, perfect for kids, as well as taxidermy animals. Admission is $3 for adults, free for children under 17. In the winter SCCF has guided tours of Sanibel's beaches and marinas on Thursday mornings, giving you the chance to spot dolphins, manatees and shore birds.

**Tarpon Bay Explorers** *(900 Tarpon Bay Rd., Sanibel; 472-8900)* has a new pontoon-boat ride, as well as a new 20,000-gallon aquarium and touch tank full of local fish, crabs, whelks, conchs, tulips, sea stars, sea urchins and sand dollars. A marine biologist can answer your questions and help you handle the sea life.

For migrating birds also try the lighthouse area from mid-April to mid-May. The Sanibel Causeway is a great spot for pelicans and dolphins in the early evening. Rent a boat to search for dolphins in the bay (idle into Dinkin's Bayou to watch them feed).

Clam Bayou is a once and future Gulfside estuary, at the west end of Sanibel. It's currently under review for restoration. Silver Key, an island within the bayou a mile north of Bowman's Beach park, has a small trail and a bald eagle nest. Launch your canoe or kayak at the small dock off the park's spillover-parking lot.

**Bird guide Bev Postmus** chats with guests at the Sanibel-Captiva Conservation Foundation

## Guided tours

You'll join the former mayor of Sanibel at **Canoe Adventures and Wilderness Tours** *(472-5218)*. Mark "Bird" Westall will take you on a canoe trip through the remote areas of the refuge, down the Sanibel River or through Buck Key, a small island off Captiva. River trips can be at night. A true wildlife expert, Bird shares his wisdom as well as his opinions on man's environmental responsibilities. He limits his trips to just a few people at a time. He has two 17-foot canoes that hold three people and one 20-footer that fits five. He'll take you out any day but Friday.

Birding tours aren't just for Jane Hathaway types. Beginners and neophytes are welcome, too. Local trips are arranged by the **Sanibel-Captiva Conservation Foundation** *(3333 Sanibel-Captiva Rd., Sanibel; 472-2329)*, often on Friday mornings.

The Sealife Encounter excursion at **Adventures in Paradise** *(departing from Port Sanibel Marina, on the mainland 1 mile east of the Sanibel Causeway on Summerlin Road; 472-8443 or 437-1660)* gives you a hands-on

**Bird Westall** of Canoe Adventures and Wilderness Tours prepares a guest for a winter morning trip in the refuge

**Exam complete,** Micaela Neal, 8, releases a burrfish during a Sealife Encounter trip. Facing page: checking net finds off a small island.

**A secret spot to see butterflies** is the small garden adjacent to The Bean on Periwinkle Way

**Learn more about island wildlife** at the Sanibel Public Library *(770 Dunlop Rd.; 472-2483)*. You'll find nature books, magazines and local newsletters.

sealife experience. Cruising Pine Island Sound, you'll use a net to catch some creatures yourself and examine others your guide (a licensed marine biologist) will bring up with a trawl net. Children on board help release the live animals before returning to the dock. The trip is 2½ hours long, from 12:30 to 3 p.m. It costs $35 for adults, $25 for kids. Children under 3 are free.

Fans of Animal Planet's "Wildlife Emergency" will recognize the **Clinic for the Rehabilitation of Wildlife** *(3883 Sanibel-Captiva Rd., Sanibel; 472-3644).* It was featured in 11 episodes. CROW presents a short lecture, video presentation and small tour of its outdoor cages most weekdays at 11 a.m. and most Sundays at 1 p.m. (call to confirm days). The cost is $5 for adults, free for children.

The wildlife hospital and rehabilitation center cares for animals from throughout Southwest Florida. Over 2,000 patients are treated annually. Ninety percent have been injured by humans, usually by being hit by a car or caught up in fishing line or hooks.

The clinic is open 8 a.m. to 5 p.m. You can drop off animals until 8 p.m., seven days a week After hours leave them under the building for safety from predators.

Funded by donations and private groups, CROW gets no government money. Volunteers make up most of the staff. The two Sanibel supermarkets, Bailey's General Store and Jerry's Foods, contribute food.

*One final note: please help our wildlife by not littering. Food, wrappers and soda cans tossed out of a car attract animals to the side of the road, often with fatal results.*

# Would 'Flipper' Bite a Human?

## By Mark 'Bird' Westall

A few years back, the Duchess of York was on national network television promoting ecotourism. Great! We need celebrities championing the concept of coexisting with our natural environment. The problem is, the way she did this was by participating in a scuba "ecotour" in the Bahamas, where they gave her chain-mail to put over her wetsuit so she could go down and hand-feed the sharks!

Now first of all, this tells me how bored we all are in our society, that we have to get our jollies by hand-feeding sharks. But there may be more serious consequences to this type of behavior. Scientists in Florida can't understand why shark attacks are on the increase along the east coast of the state. Well, duh. I don't think that it takes a genius to suggest that we have a lot of very tame sharks swimming along the Gulf Stream between the Bahamas and Florida that used to basically ignore swimmers (along the Florida coastline), but now are approaching more of them, looking for handouts.

The same thing is happening with dolphins throughout coastal Florida. I had a fishing guide here on Sanibel tell me that he makes bigger tips if he feeds the dolphins on his trips and brings them in close to his boat. But guess what? The dolphins also are becoming more aggressive and biting more and more swimmers in the areas where these dolphin hand-feeding tours are occurring.

And I love the reaction of people when I tell them about the dangerous dolphins just after I've told the story about the increased shark attacks. They can easily accept the idea that a shark would want to attack us, but when they hear about the dolphins, their usual response is, "What? Flipper bite a human? Flipper wouldn't do that! Flipper's our friend!"

Flipper isn't biting those people to eat them — he's biting them to get their attention. And when a large animal like a dolphin or a shark bites someone, they bleed. The problem is, we tend to blame the animal and not the people who created the problem.

As a matter of fact, I firmly agree with much of the new research that tends to show that most shark attacks are accidents. Sharks are nearsighted and think they are hitting prey other than humans. That's why so many people survive shark attacks and only receive one initial bite. Basically, we may not taste good to a shark. However, once any large carnivore — such as a shark, dolphin, grizzly or an alligator — gets put on animal welfare, it begins to approach people looking for free handouts; and it literally doesn't know the difference between the hand (or leg) and the handout.

So how come hand-feeding is such a bad idea, if it makes so many people feel closer to nature? The answer is simple, really. Food is the most powerful stimulus to all living creatures, including people. An animal which has been hand-fed by someone naturally becomes more aggressive towards people because its own selfish genes alter its natural fear, or at least respect, of humans and it begins to act as though the reason that ALL humans exist is to give them food for free. Why go out and hunt for a living, if you can just hang out around humans and get a free lunch?

Understanding these basic concepts, in 1976 Sanibel was the first community in the state of Florida to make it against the law to feed alligators. Naturalists living on the island, along with the refuge staff, recognized the increasing conflicts which were surfacing in Yellowstone National Park with grizzlies being fed by the tourists. They postulated that this was analogous to our alligator situation here on Sanibel. Eventually, the state followed Sanibel's lead and it is now against state law to feed alligators. But even though it is against the law to feed alligators everywhere in Florida, it is amazing to me how many people have found the urge to feed these potentially dangerous animals irresistible.

When I used to live near the exit of Wildlife Drive, the alligators would sun themselves along the bank which paralleled the Drive and my backyard. I could sit inside my house when the windows were open and hear people say, "Oh, look dear. He's eaten the cracker already!" At first, I would run out and yell for them to stop feeding the alligator because it was against the law. The response I got was, "So what? Everybody breaks the law." The next time it happened, I ran out and said, "Don't feed the 'gator because it will become more aggressive towards people and we'll have to have the animal destroyed." The reply I got back was, "So what? You have lots of alligators on Sanibel."

Years later, shortly after a little girl was killed by a tame alligator up in Englewood, Fla., I put up a sign in the backyard which stated, "*Please help protect our children!* Don't feed or throw *anything* at the 'gators. Your actions make them more dangerous towards humans and that threatens our children!" Isn't it amazing what psychological games have to be played to get our "intelligent" species to understand the consequences of our actions?

Concurrently with the death of the Englewood child and the placement of my sign, the refuge staff did a little study of their own trying to determine if people were negatively interacting with the alligators along the Alligator Curve of the Wildlife Drive. During a two-week study, volunteers observed six people feeding the alligators and 20 people throwing rocks or shells in the direction of the alligators to get them to move.

The throwing of the rocks and shells is an example of random reinforcement. If you want an animal to do a trick, don't reward him with food every time he does what you want him to. That way, he will do the asked-for behavior whether he gets a reward or not.

To an alligator, the rock or shell hitting the water imitates the sound of food hitting the water, and the gator just assumes that he missed the food that time. Eventually, all a person has to do is approach the edge of the bank and the alligator moves toward the person in anticipation of the handout. The scary part is: what if the person is only a small child? It is a tragedy waiting to happen.

But what really scared the refuge staff during the study is that six people walked over to the alligators sunning along the edge of the road and actually *touched* the alligators. Now, I think we should live in a free society. If people want to do risky things like climb sheer cliffs or bungee jump, they should be allowed to (as long as I don't have to pay their hospital or funeral bills). So if a person wants to touch an alligator… hey, it's a free country. But if that alligator grabs hold of that person and pulls him down into the water and drowns him… well to me that is natural selection at work! That human was not a very bright creature and, hopefully, hasn't bred yet, so he won't be passing on any genes that say it is OK to go over and touch alligators. The problem is, we live in a society that says, "No, that person has a *right* to be stupid. And if he's going to be that stupid, well then, we need to remove the alligator from the area so that individual can continue his dimwitted ways."

One incident observed during the study was a father who actually took his toddling child over to the side of a sunning gator and had his child *pet the back* of that lounging reptile. How do we protect our children from the actions of irresponsible adults? Do we destroy the alligators to remove the risks?

The feeding of wildlife, particularly of alligators, is a constant concern of the refuge staff. The next time you drive through Alligator Curve, notice that there are no longer any basking areas within reach of people. Vegetation buffers have been planted to limit the risk, but the feeding problems still persist.

We as a species seem to have an irresistible urge to feed animals.

— *A former mayor of Sanibel, Westall today runs Canoe Adventures and Wilderness Tours. He lives on the Sanibel River.*

# Conservation Land

*M*ost of Sanibel is preserved in an undeveloped state. The island's wildlife refuge takes up most of the northern half, while private conservation groups have purchased most center wetlands. Much of this land is open to the public, creating some great opportunities to get out and explore. *Circled numbers refer to trail locations on the Sanibel and Captiva maps on pages 8 through 10.*

## J.N. 'Ding' Darling National Wildlife Refuge

The pleasures of Sanibel's 6,400-acre federal wildlife refuge *(Refuge office: One Wildlife Dr., Sanibel; 472-1100)* are subtle. This is a natural home for wild animals, a combination of hammocks, marshes and bays. The wildlife, including large birds and even larger reptiles, comes and goes as it pleases, and isn't fed.

This is one of the Top 10 birding spots in the United States. Two hundred and thirty species of birds can be found here. The prime season is the winter, when migratory birds fill the estuaries. The refuge also has 50 species of reptiles and amphibians and 32 species of mammals.

The animals are often easy to see. The four-mile Wildlife Drive meanders through many idyllic habitats, letting you drive, bike or walk within a few feet of exotic native creatures. Miles of hiking and biking trails take you through remote feeding and nesting grounds. There are water trails, too, and kayaks to explore them *(at Tarpon Bay Explorers, 900 Tarpon Bay Rd., Sanibel; 472-8900).*

"Ding" Darling is one of the most visited federal refuges in the country. Hundreds of thousands of visitors come here each year. In the 1980s, motorcycles and giant tour buses held up traffic on Wildlife Drive, sightseeing airplanes landed on Tarpon Bay and Jet Skis buzzed in the bays. "At times there was nothing but wall-to-wall cars and buses and mopeds," says former Refuge Manager Lou Hinds. Most land is still open to the public, but motorcycles, outside buses and airplanes are banned, while power boating is heavily restricted. Forty-four percent of the refuge — 2,800 acres — is federally designated Wilderness Area, with limited human use. Rangers actively maintain the area, removing nonnative plants and trees, restoring native species, and holding prescribed burns to eliminate underbrush and enhance growth (the burns mimic natural fire cycles).

### Darling Tract

The Darling Tract *(entrance off Sanibel-Captiva Rd., 2½ miles west of Tarpon Bay Rd.)* is 4,900 acres of wetlands and mud flats on the bay side of Sanibel. Flocks of migratory and wading birds feed here, especially in two brackish impoundments totaling 850 acres.

---

**Facing page:** Roseate spoonbills feed around the mangroves in the Darling Tract

White pelicans paddle along Wildlife Drive

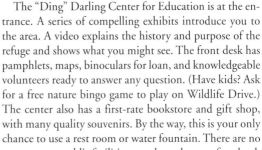

**Facing page:** Measuring water at the Bailey Tract

**Refuge docent** Carolyn Johns waits to share her binoculars with visitors

The "Ding" Darling Center for Education is at the entrance. A series of compelling exhibits introduce you to the area. A video explains the history and purpose of the refuge and shows what you might see. The front desk has pamphlets, maps, binoculars for loan, and knowledgeable volunteers ready to answer any question. (Have kids? Ask for a free nature bingo game to play on Wildlife Drive.) The center also has a first-rate bookstore and gift shop, with many quality souvenirs. By the way, this is your only chance to use a rest room or water fountain. There are no public facilities anywhere else on refuge land.

Some recent improvements are making the Darling Tract even more visitor friendly. A new observation tower features permanently mounted spotting scopes. Three new, 30-foot fishing piers let you get closer to the animals. Back at the visitors center, a live video feed from the tower is displayed on a high-resolution, plasma television.

## HOURS AND FEES

The refuge visitors center *(no charge)* is open 9 a.m. daily. It closes at 5 p.m. from November through April; 4 p.m. from May through October. **The Darling Tract is closed on Friday,** but open every other day from one hour after sunrise to 30 minutes before sunset (*$5 per car, $1 per hiking or biking group, exact change only*).

## WILDLIFE DRIVE

Most visitors first travel the paved Wildlife Drive *(open daily except Friday from one hour after sunrise to 30 minutes before sunset, $5 per car, $1 per hiking or biking group, exact change only).* This man-made dike runs through estuaries, giving you many views of wildlife from your car.

But don't stay in your car. Walk the shore, wander the adjacent trails, climb the observation tower. You'll see much more, at closer range. Volunteers (in golf carts with "Info" signs on the side) often point out sightings.

Come at low tide to see wading birds feeding on the mud flats. The reddish, shallow water may have crown conchs moving on the mud. You may see thousands of tiny fish. At higher tide look for birds roosting in the trees.

Get an up-close view of the mangrove ecosystem at the Red Mangrove Overlook. Look closely to see the change from white to black to red mangroves. Watch the trees for mangrove tree crabs. Look in the mud to spot fiddler crabs. A viewing platform overlooks a bay estuary.

A 90-minute **tram tour** *(run by Tarpon Bay Explorers, 472-8900, $10 for adults, $7 for children under 12, reservations required, daily except Friday)* offers an informative, relaxing introduction to the area. A naturalist calls your attention to habitats and foliage, identifies wildlife, and sometimes offers his own take on the battle between man and nature. During the winter the tram leaves every hour, 8 a.m. to 5 p.m. It makes several trips a day in the summer (call for a schedule). Boarding is at the visitors center or at Tarpon Bay Explorers.

**Tram tourers** listen to their guide at the Red Mangrove Overlook

**Wildlife Drive** was built in 1965. Culverts, added in 1972, close in the summer to keep mosquitos from laying eggs on mud flats. In the winter, the culverts stay open; the natural tides give migrating birds a large foraging area. The road was paved in 2002 to stop dust from coating the mangroves and polluting the water.

**The Perry Tract** is three acres of beachfront property adjacent to Gulfside City Park, filled only with native plants

**Facing page:** Visiting from St. Louis, Dan Terpstra takes photos of birds alongside Wildlife Drive

**Jay Darling** as a Sioux City Journal cartoonist in 1904. Later working for the Des Moines Register, he won two Pulitzer prizes for his conservation-themed cartoons (which he signed "Ding," a contraction of his last name). A winter resident of Captiva, he also became the first head of the U.S. Biological Survey, today's U.S. Fish and Wildlife Service. He arranged for the federal government to lease much of Sanibel's north shore from the state of Florida in the 1940s, creating the Sanibel National Wildlife Refuge. When federal officials purchased the land outright in 1967, it was renamed in his honor.

**The Bailey Tract** was purchased from the Bailey family in 1952 for $5,000

## DARLING TRACT HIKING TRAILS

**Indigo Trail** ❶ runs two miles from the visitors center to just past the Cross Dike. It starts as a boardwalk winding under mangrove, white stopper and buttonwood trees. At Wildlife Drive the trail turns to crushed shell as it tops a long dike through remote land, and then ends as a short sand path. There's a bench on your left at the halfway point. Give yourself two to three hours for the round trip. The boardwalk is a great place to see songbirds. The dike has wading birds on both sides, including roseate spoonbills and ibis, and wild coffee trees tucked in under taller foliage. On the final sand trail, hundreds of wading and shore birds often feed where the trees thin out on your right and the water turns into marsh. Indigo Trail is the only part of the Darling Tract open on Fridays.

The ¼-mile **Cross Dike Trail** ❷ rejoins Wildlife Drive, and again has wetlands on both sides. A covered viewing pavilion, built where the refuge's lone crocodile often basks in the sun, has benches and a viewing scope.

For a good hike, start at the visitors center, take Indigo Trail to the Cross Dike Trail, and return via Wildlife Drive. You'll pass a dense mangrove swamp, filled with snails, raccoons and coon oysters. As you walk the final mile, you'll pass many wading bird habitats.

Give yourself 20 minutes to take in the **Shell Mound Trail** ❸, a ⅓-mile boardwalk that winds through a rich tropical hardwood hammock, unique in southern Florida, near the end of Wildlife Drive. Shady palms and trees arch over you. Look closely to find a small stand of key lime trees, left over from the island's farming past. Interpretive signs identify the different vegetation. The trail encircles a Calusa Indian shell mound.

## Bailey Tract

Head over to the freshwater **Bailey Tract** ❹ *(on Tarpon Bay Rd., between Periwinkle Way and West Gulf Dr.)* to explore an inland marsh. Several peaceful but sunny trails crisscross the hundred acres here; it's a great spot for hiking and biking. The freshwater marsh is home to alligators, turtles, snakes, gopher tortoises and many birds. Most trails connect with each other in giant rectangles; their total length is 1.75 miles. Allow at least an hour here.

The Bailey Tract is open sunrise to sunset daily. Parking and admission are free.

# The Inside Story
### *Sanibel's unique freshwater wetlands*

Natural fresh water is a rare feature for an island, but Sanibel has it. In fact, today Sanibel is the only island in Florida with fresh water (Palm Beach and Miami Beach had it before development). The water is simply accumulated rain, 1,200 acres of standing water and small swamps in the lower, central areas of the island.

The wetlands have played a vital role in Sanibel's history. They attracted wildlife, which attracted early conservationists. Fresh water also allowed a small, permanent community to form, which provided manpower to fight development pressures.

The U.S. Army Corps of Engineers connected these areas with a nine-mile canal, the Sanibel River, in the 1950s, so mosquito-larva-eating fish could thrive and spread.

Much of the land was damaged in the 1950s and 1960s. Australian pines and other exotics took over hundreds of acres. Developers filled in other areas to build homes.

The Sanibel-Captiva Conservation Foundation (SCCF) preserves and restores these special areas. The private group raises money to buy wetlands. Then it restores them by eliminating exotic plants, replanting native vegetation and redigging ponds.

SCCF also uses the areas to educate the public. Island kids get hands-on environmental lessons at the 26-acre Pick Preserve, across from the Sanibel School. Kindergartners plant pond apples. Middle schoolers make and maintain the trails and signs, and tag monarch butterflies (right). Third graders plant seedlings from historically famous trees, including one at the Alamo, the Seven Sisters tree in Louisiana, and the Ray Charles tree at the School for the Deaf and Blind in St. Augustine.

**Silver Key.** This 64-acre Gulfside island is within Clam Bayou and Old Blind Pass at the west end of Sanibel. A 1,200-foot path ⑨ leads to a small dock, but the real hike is getting here. It's a good mile up Bowman's Beach from the parking lot. Give yourself two hours.

Unfortunately, Silver Key is infested with Australian pines, which have killed off nearly every palm and other native plant. Most wildlife is gone too. Silver Key and Clam Bayou were once a thriving Gulfside estuary. They could be again, after a serious restoration effort.

To get to Silver Key from Bowman's Beach, walk west, through some fallen pines and across the closed eastern Clam Bayou inlet. From Turner Beach walk east, across a wide sandbar that blocks the other inlet. A large sign, set back in the trees, marks the start of the trail.

**SCCF trails** wander through 207 acres of island wilderness

**The small Sanibel Cemetery** contains graves dating back to 1889. You can make pencil rubbings of headstones.

**Facing page:** Cabbage palms line the Gulfside Park Preserve trail

# SCCF

Don't miss the four miles of shady trails through interior wetlands at the Sanibel-Captiva Conservation Foundation *(3333 Sanibel-Captiva Rd., Sanibel; 472-2329)*. We recommend two round-trip trails: the 1.1-mile **East River Trail** ⑤ takes you to a primitive observation tower then runs along the Sanibel River; the 1.3-mile **Sabal Palm Trail** ⑥ winds through a palm forest to Alligator Hole. You can walk the trails on your own or go on a group trip with an SCCF guide at no extra charge. Our choice: take the guided tour — learning about the wild vegetation here is fascinating, and you won't get so nervous when you hear the gators croaking in the distance. Also on the grounds are an education center (with a touch tank for kids), a butterfly house and a native-plant nursery.

# Gulfside City Park

Located off a little-known bike path that cuts through Gulfside City Park, the 22-acre **Gulfside Park Preserve** ⑦ is open to the public free of charge. The trail is ¾ of a mile long and takes about 45 minutes to explore.

A footbridge crosses a wetland covered in saw grass and leads you to the circular trail, which winds past a pond, through palm groves, and under strangler figs and sea grape trees. Butterflies and dragonflies dart about, attracted to the lantanas. Interpretive signs identify various plants and trees. There's a picnic table, then a bench halfway around, in beautiful, shady spots. A little farther up you'll walk past booted and even scorched cabbage palms.

Sanibel purchased the land in 1996, through a grant from the Florida Communities Trust. Workers cleared it of Brazilian pepper and Australian pines, built bird houses and restored the area to its natural state. The trail is made from crushed coconut husks and cabbage palm boots.

Located between Casa Ybel Road and Middle Gulf Drive, the Preserve is visible from neither. It's near the east end of the bike path that cuts between Middle Gulf and Algiers Drive, by the tiny Sanibel Cemetery. Park at the Gulfside City Park lot on Algiers Drive.

The Preserve is next to **Gulfside City Park** ⑧, 47 acres of palm forest and wetlands. Give yourself another 45 minutes or so here. Most visitors only see the few acres of the park next to the beach, but hidden along the bike path is a natural paradise. Tortoise burrows are easy to see. Primitive trails wander off the path. One follows a stream; another is the old Middle Gulf Drive, once the route for mule wagons to bring vacationers to Casa Ybel.

# Trees & Plants

S anibel and Captiva have some strange trees and plants. We have trees that are not trees. Trees that strangle each other. Trees that live up in the air. One even does impressions — maybe of you. We even have a cactus. It climbs in the tree that's not a tree, that's being strangled by the tree that lives up in the air!

## Palms

Though most people think of it as a tree, a palm is actually a type of grass. It has no bark, no branches, no leaves and no wood. Instead, it's a single fibrous stalk, with green grassy blades, called fronds, shooting out of the top.

### Cabbage (sabal) palm

The most common palm on the islands, a **cabbage palm** *(Sabal palmetto)* looks like an upside-down dust mop. Like other palms, a cabbage discards its old brown fronds as new ones sprout out of its top. But on some cabbage palms the frond bases, called boots, stay on, becoming spikes up to three or four feet long. (Commercial landscapers often cut off the brown fronds for a neater appearance and to control insects.)

The palm's berries are a staple of birds and raccoons. Lizards and insects live on the trunk and boots. Cacti and vines, including poison ivy, grow on the trunk.

This hearty palm can survive almost anything. Most fires don't bother it; the dense fiber trunk protects the moisture inside even if the surface burns (charred cabbage palms are alongside San-Cap Road and on the SCCF hiking trails). Storms are no problem either. When Hurricane Andrew hit Miami, 92 percent of the cabbage palms escaped unharmed.

The cabbage palm is Florida's official state tree. Its "cabbage" name comes from the fact that its terminal bud looks like a cabbage. It's also called a sabal palm.

### Coconut palm

A **coconut palm** *(Cocos nucifera)* is easy to identify by its nut clusters, each of which has up to 20 nuts. The nuts ripen in nine to 10 months. They hang at the base of the fronds, which average 15 feet long.

Naturally, the trunk grows out of the side of the nut, curving up toward the sun. But landscapers often

**Coconut palm**

**Facing page:** A cabbage palm grows in Sanibel's Bailey Tract

# Mangroves
## *The trees that built the islands*

Mangroves created Sanibel and Captiva. Thousands of years ago, when the islands were just sandbars, mangroves held the sand in place, letting it accumulate to the mile-wide land we know today. In the U.S., mangroves only grow on the shores of southern Florida.

Growing in the water, the **red mangrove** *(Rhizophora mangle)* (above) keeps the bay side of the islands from washing away. Its above-ground roots trap leaves, twigs, grasses and silt, which, in turn, trap sand. The roots also give fish and wildlife a safe and nourishing environment to grow and raise young. Crabs and shrimp eat fallen mangrove leaves. And they get plenty of food — each year one acre of trees will produce eight tons of leaves. Red mangroves also keep the water clean, filtering out waste and pollution. A pigment in the bark makes the surrounding water red, but it's some of the cleanest water in nature.

Each red mangrove produces about 300 seeds a year. The seed sprouts into a 6-inch seedling, complete with a root and stem, *before* it falls from the tree. Some seedlings drift for miles before they reach land. Local mangroves are descendants of trees in Africa.

The red mangrove is called the "walking tree" because the exposed portions of its roots look like legs (the complete root extends a foot or more in the sand).

The **black mangrove** *(Avicennia germinans)* grows at the water's edge, behind the red. You can identify it by its hundreds of short, pencil-like roots that stick up out of the mud. Connected to roots underneath, these "breathing tubes" provide oxygen and help keep the tree stable in the sand. It also has a black trunk and, often, crystals of salt on its leaves. During the summer, its small flowers attract swarms of bees. The white honey produced is sold in stores under the name "mangrove honey."

**White mangroves** *(Laguncularia racemosa)* and their cousins, **buttonwood trees** *(Conocarpus erectus),* grow in the dense sand reds and blacks have created. A white mangrove is a conventional tree, with its roots in the ground except for a tube or two. Like a black mangrove, it excretes salt through its leaves. Its greenish-white flowers grow on spikes. Many buttonwoods fall over, and then grow new trunks out of their sides. The tree gets its name from its fruit: small berries that resemble vintage shoe buttons.

plant nuts straight up and down. The short trunk of a young palm looks like it's wrapped in burlap.

Most coconut palms on the islands have been planted. Years ago, the favorite variety was the Jamaica Tall, which grows up to a hundred feet high. But lethal-yellowing disease destroyed most of these in the late 1960s (some remain on the Sanibel Causeway). Today the most popular is the Malayan Dwarf. Resistant to lethal yellowing, it grows 30 feet high, and starts producing nuts when its trunk is just 3 feet tall.

A coconut palm needs 40 to 50 inches of rain a year and temperatures that stay above freezing. Not originally native to Florida, it was naturalized here before Columbus.

The palm is invaluable to man. People shred the meat (which has as much protein as beef) to add taste to cookies, pies and other treats. It's also used to make cooking oil, margarine, soaps and candles. Fiber from the husk (coir) is used to make rugs, rope, brushes, doormats and mattresses. The sap is a popular drink in some areas, either straight or fermented as wine. Local weavers make baskets and hats from the fronds; Seminole Indians use fronds for thatch huts. Hawaiians make drums from the trunks. Some people chew the roots for their narcotic properties.

In other words, we're cuckoo for coconuts.

**Gumbo limbo**

# Other trees and plants

The **gumbo limbo** *(Bursera simaruba)* has paper-thin, reddish-brown bark that constantly peels; it's said to be doing an impression of a sunburned vacationer (earning it the nickname "tourist tree"). The leaves are clustered at the end of its branches, which spread out in all directions. A gumbo limbo can grow up to 50 feet tall; the trunk can be 3 feet thick. It is one of the few local trees that sheds its leaves.

**Horrible thistle**

Unique to coastal southern Florida in the U.S., the tree also grows in Central America and the West Indies. The soft wood was once used for carousel horses. Its sap has been used for incense and as a varnish, glue and salve. "Gumbo limbo" comes from a Spanish name for gummy sap, "gumma elemba." There's a large gumbo limbo at the refuge on the Shell Mound Trail, close to the boardwalk.

The squat, prickly **horrible thistle** *(Cirsium horridulum)* has dangerous-looking spines and thorns. The fluffy flowers can be purple, cream or yellow. A member of the aster family, the plant grows in the

**Moon morning glory**

**Prickly pear cactus**

**Sea grape**

**Saw grass**

**Facing page:** Foliage at the Shell Mound trail

Bailey Tract and other conservation lands near, appropriately, Casa Ybel's Thistle Lodge.

Also called the moonflower or white tropical morning glory, the fragrant **moon morning glory** *(Ipomoea alba)* blooms at night. It's related to the sweet potato. Many grow in the Bailey Tract by a middle trail footbridge.

**Prickly pear cactus** *(Opuntia compressa)* grows in open sandy areas and especially in the sand dunes next to beaches. Easily recognizable by its large pads covered with spines, the plant is usually about 2 feet tall. Yellow flowers bloom from spring to fall, followed by a plump, reddish-purple fruit that some islanders use to make jelly (see page 252). The whole plant is edible; gopher tortoises love to munch on it. You'll see good specimens on the trails at SCCF and along the walkway to Bowman's Beach.

Before the post office tightened its rules, islanders would use the leaves of the **sea grape** *(Coccoloba uvifera)* tree for postcards. The sturdy, leathery leaves make a decent, and certainly unique, writing surface. Though it can grow to 45 feet tall, a typical sea grape is less than half that size. It has a contorted trunk, and round, red-veined leaves that are up to 11 inches wide. The berries — another source of islander jelly — look like small grapes and grow in late summer and early fall. Only female sea grapes bear fruit.

Each blade of **saw grass** *(Cladium jamaicensis)* has a serrated, saw-like edge so sharp it can cut into your skin. From a distance saw grass looks deceptively soft and fluffy. Common on the islands, it grows in the wetlands in thick clusters, providing cover and nesting sites for birds. Migrating ducks eat the seeds to restore their energy. Saw grass is easy to identify in late spring and early summer, when its swaying, reddish-brown seed heads bloom. It's common in the Bailey Tract of the refuge. Not a grass at all (it's a sedge), saw grass has triangle-shaped, instead of round, stems. The leaves sprout tiny flowers.

True amber waves of grain, **sea oats** *(Uniola paniculata)* serve a vital purpose: they bind the sand to the shore, preventing erosion. The most common plant along the dunes, sea oats grow in dense clumps, with stalks up to 7 feet high, topped with flowers and seeds. Strong underground stems anchor them to the sand. Because of their importance to the beaches, sea oats in Florida cannot be picked or removed.

The **strangler fig** *(Ficus aurea)* is well named: it wraps itself around a cabbage palm and strangles it to death! It

gets its start from wildlife. Birds and raccoons love the fruit — they pick it off an existing fig, then climb up a nearby cabbage palm to eat. When a seed leaves the animal's digestive tract it gets stuck on the palm's ragged trunk. The fig "takes root" right there, sometimes 15 feet up in the air. Roots head toward the ground, many wrapping themselves around the palm's trunk, preventing it from expanding. Meanwhile, the fig's branches and leaves grow up and above the poor palm, blocking it from the sun. The palm dies in about 20 years, then the fig's roots grow together to form a trunk. The fig then becomes a free-standing tree, and the process starts over again.

Ironically, the deadly tree sustains the life of many animals. Nooks and crannies in its hollow trunk become home to bats, birds, reptiles and amphibians.

Many strangler figs line Sanibel's Periwinkle Way. You can examine one up close on the boardwalk at the Lazy Flamingo restaurant.

The **white stopper** *(Eugenia sp.)* tree will stop you in your tracks. It smells like a skunk, especially after a rain. This small, stubby tree flowers late in the summer. Actually, the name "stopper" refers to its use as a remedy for diarrhea. Eating its fruit or making tea from its leaves are both said to stop the problem. A white stopper's smell is strongest about 25 feet away. Look, or sniff, for one on the trails at SCCF.

**Sea oats**

**Facing page:** Claudia Mayer weaves baskets and hats from single coconut fronds. The technique dates to the 1800s.

**A strangler fig** grips a palm at the Village Shops

# Alien Invaders
## Nonnative trees and plants destroy paradise

A pop quiz: What destroyed the most wildlife habitat on Sanibel and Captiva in the 20th century? a) Greedy developers. b) Hurricanes. c) Imported trees and plants.

The answer is C. Imported trees and plants have wiped out more natural habitat on the islands than anything else — even those greedy developers! Some exotics, like melaleuca, have already been eliminated. But others, particularly the aggressive **Australian pine** *(Casuarina equisetifolia)* and **Brazilian pepper** *(Schinus terebinthifolius)* trees, are still here.

The Australian pine has killed off hundreds of acres of native vegetation. By creating dense shade and covering the ground with its needlelike leaves, it prevents native plants from growing. This has destroyed much of the island's ecosystem and taken away food and shelter from thousands of animals, dramatically reducing the amount of wildlife here.

At the beach, it wipes out the vegetation that keeps the sand in place. Then the pine falls over, too — its flat, shallow roots are not made for sand — and the beach washes away. At the west end of Bowman's Beach, fallen trees stop many sea turtles from coming onshore to lay their eggs, and confuse hatchlings trying to find their way to the water.

The tree flourishes here because it makes its own fertilizer — nodules on the roots add nitrogen to the sandy soil. But the roots can't handle strong winds, an ominous sign for the islands' pine-lined hurricane evacuation routes. When Hurricane Andrew hit Homestead in 1992, every Australian pine in the area was leveled. (By comparison, most coconut palms lost only some fronds; nearly every cabbage palm survived intact.)

One hundred and fifty types of trees and plants naturally grow on Sanibel and Captiva. Australian pines kill off 145. Strict laws protect wildlife and natural vegetation, but, ironically, there is no law prohibiting this menace that destroys them.

**Forty feet high** in the air, a worker cuts down an Australian pine piece-by-piece, restoring a gopher tortoise habitat

The tree has been removed from most conservation lands. The city of Sanibel recently cleared the pines from 300 acres of land in the middle of the island, just west of Tarpon Bay Road. The area is being restored to become a public wildlife preserve with winding hiking trails. Similar work has been done near the causeway, alongside Bailey Road.

But the trees thrive nearly everywhere else. In fact, they have spread over so much of the island that many people are unaware of how Sanibel looks in its natural state.

Some residents refuse to see the tree's problems. They think the tree is pretty and like the shade, and have persuaded island officials to keep the trees legal. Meanwhile, the seeds continue to spread, and hundreds of new seedlings are taking root.

The Australian pine is misnamed — it's not really a pine tree. But it looks like one. A tall, fluffy evergreen, it has needlelike leaves. Australian pines were brought to Florida

**After Australian pines kill off** the sea oats and other plants that hold a beach in place, they fall over into the sea as the beach erodes. With no dunes left, this section of Bowman's Beach, a mile north of the public park, is completely washing away.

in the early 1900s. Farmers and inn owners brought them to Sanibel and Captiva in the 1920s. ("I detest the Australian pines," wrote "Ding" Darling in 1941. "To me they are about as unsuitable as red flannel underwear on a Tahiti native.") The trees spread throughout the islands after Hurricane Donna in 1960, which blew the seeds everywhere.

Islanders brought Brazilian pepper here in the 1950s as a landscape plant, and, ironically, to provide food for wildlife. But like the Australian pine, it wipes out wildlife by taking over habitat. The berries are toxic to many animals. But not to many birds, who pass the berries through their systems intact, spreading the seeds to new areas.

Now illegal to plant, Brazilian pepper has to be removed from a property before the owner can get a development permit. Sanibel removes pepper from its public land. The all-volunteer Pepper Busters chops it down in other areas.

Also called the Florida holly, Brazilian pepper is a dense, bushy green tree, usually about 12 feet high. It has beautiful red berries for part of the year. As you drive up San-Cap toward Captiva it lines the left side for nearly the entire route.

*Chain of fool. When workers were clearing a small section of Australian pines from Bowman's Beach a few years ago, a misguided "environmentalist" chained himself to a tree and threw away the key, "rescuing" the tree by refusing to let the workers break his chain. Then, as dusk settled and the workers began to pack up for the night, he was attacked by mosquitoes, and demanded that workers break his chain. They left him there. (This area, along the walkway, has since been restored with palms.)*

**Deadly beauty.** Brazilian pepper berries.

# Biking

*T*he best way to see Sanibel is on a bike. You'll feel the sun on your back, smell the tropical scents, and hear the wildlife. Since the island is almost perfectly flat, even a child can ride for miles with ease. Twenty-three miles of paved bike paths run alongside every major road. Everywhere you want to go — beaches, restaurants, theaters, shops, groceries, museums, even the refuge — is on a bike path.

## Where to go biking

You can go anywhere on Sanibel on a bike. But here are seven itineraries to help get you started. They include trips to major sites, attractions and beaches, and into hidden areas. *Circled numbers refer to locations on the bike path map on page 205.*

**❶ Periwinkle Way commercial area.** *(Along the west end of Periwinkle Way. 5.4 miles round trip. Allow 90 minutes for bikes, 30 minutes for scooters, two or three hours for surreys.)* It's Sanibel's main drag, but Periwinkle Way has a rural feel. The bike path often ambles away from the road; the middle section is lined with tropical foliage. The Periwinkle Place Shopping Center is a good resting spot, with a small playground for kids. *Diversion:* Stop at the Periwinkle Park campground and see its collection of exotic animals kept in a small walk-around mini-zoo. Ask permission from the gate attendant before you ride in.

**❷ Sanibel lighthouse area.** *(Periwinkle Way from Causeway Blvd. (Lindgren Blvd.) to the lighthouse. 2.6 miles round trip. Allow two hours for bikes, one for scooters, three hours for surreys; more time if you stay awhile at the beach.)* This trip takes you over canals and to the lighthouse and its beach. There's a drinking fountain at the beach parking lot; restrooms by the lighthouse. *Diversion:* At the four-way stop of Periwinkle and Lindgren, go south on Lindgren to ride through Shell Harbor, a 1960s subdivision. Head left (east) down any side street to see vintage concrete-block homes, some with their original rock yards. *Beach access points:* At the lighthouse and the south ends of Buttonwood and Seagrape Lanes.

**❸ Gulf Drives tour.** *(East Gulf Dr. to Middle Gulf Dr. to Casa Ybel Rd., out to West Gulf Dr. and Rabbit Rd., then return via Sanibel-Captiva Rd. 13.1 miles round trip, plus side trips. Allow at least four hours for bikes, one hour for scooters. Add more time if you stop at the beaches or attractions.)* This calm ride takes you along the front of Sanibel's Gulf-front resorts and past many beach access points. The Rabbit Road leg is off the road, running along a canal, past two large ponds and over the Sanibel River. Public restrooms are at Gulfside City Park and the Tarpon Bay Road Beach. Attractions along the return route (Sanibel-Captiva Road) include the Sanibel-Captiva Conservation Foundation (SCCF) and the Bailey-Matthews Shell Museum. *Diversions:* As you ride west on Middle Gulf Drive, just after the bike path crosses the road, watch for a second bike path veering off to the left. This path goes through a remote area of Gulfside City Park, past the Gulfside

---

**Facing page:** A bike path leads through Sanibel's Gulfside City Park

**Ready to leave Billy's Rentals,** Illinois' Kara Clark has 4-year-old daugher Ashley on a trail-a-bike

**Public restrooms** along the Sanibel bike paths:

■ Chamber of Commerce, on Causeway Blvd.

■ At the lighthouse

■ The Tahitian Gardens and Periwinkle Place shopping centers, on Periwinkle Way

■ Gulfside City Park, just off Casa Ybel Road

■ Tarpon Bay Road Beach, at West Gulf Drive

■ The visitors center at the J.N. "Ding" Darling National Wildlife Refuge

■ The Sanibel Recreational Complex, next to the pool

■ Bowman's Beach

■ Turner Beach, at the west end of the island

Park Preserve hiking trail and the little-known historic Sanibel Cemetery. At Algiers Drive, turn left to go to the beach, or right to leave the park and return to the main bike path on Casa Ybel Road. *Beach access points:* (1) At the first curve on East Gulf Drive; (2) at Beach Road; (3) at the end of Nerita Street; (4) at Donax Street; (5) at the 90-degree turn of Middle Gulf Drive (near Par View Drive); (6) at Gulfside City Park; (7) at the Tarpon Bay Road Beach. There are also seven little-known beach-access points along West Gulf Drive, past Rabbit Road. Watch for a series of paths, most with a tiny parking lot, every tenth of a mile or so. Only island residents can park vehicles here, but it's fine to prop up a bike (not a scooter) along the fences. The beaches are open to the public.

❹ **Dunes subdivision tour.** *(From Periwinkle Way: Bailey Rd. to Sandcastle Rd., and return. 3.2 miles round trip. Allow one hour for bikes, 25 minutes for scooters.)* This tour of Sanibel's main subdivision takes you down Sandcastle Road, a relatively calm loop street (not a bike path) that surrounds a golf course. Note the odd island architecture of the newer homes: elevated first floors, tin roofs and the abundance of vinyl siding (a must in this salty environment). During the winter, the south side of Sandcastle gets heavy traffic between 3 and 6 p.m. *Diversion:* As you leave the Dunes turn left at Bailey Road to go to either San Carlos Bay (no real beach, but a nice spot to take a break) or Bay Road (a shady 1.3-mile trip to a little-known Sanibel bayside subdivision). *Beach access points:* At the end of Bailey Road and at the end of Bay Road.

❺ **Dixie Beach Road.** *(Off Periwinkle Way. Three miles round trip. Allow 45 minutes for bikes, 15 minutes for scooters, not counting diversions.)* This straight line leads to tiny bayfront Peace Park. The bike path falls apart after a few hundred yards, but road traffic is light. *Diversions:* Stop at the culvert halfway down for a close-up view of a mangrove jungle. At the bay, turn right to see unique waterfront homes; go left for a taste of rural island life.

❻ **Refuge tour.** *(From Sanibel-Captiva Rd.: Through the refuge on Wildlife Dr. and return. 8.3 miles round trip. Allow three to four hours for bikes. Scooters cannot enter the refuge. $1 per bike-family group, cash only. Open sunrise to sunset.)* The wildlife refuge is the best place to bike on the islands. Wildlife Drive and the Cross Dike Trail are paved. All but the west end of Indigo Trail is small, crushed shell.

## SANIBEL BIKING

**RECOMMENDED ROUTES**

1 Periwinkle Way Commercial Area
2 Sanibel Lighthouse Area
3 Gulf Drives Tour
4 Dunes Subdivision Tour
5 Dixie Beach Road
6 Refuge Tour
7 Bowman's Beach Trip

Other Bike Path

Other Road

**B** Bench
**G** Gazebo
Water Fountain
Picnic Tables
Public Beach Access
Bike Rental
Point of Interest
Public Pool
First Aid

J.N. "Ding" Darling
National Wildlife Refuge

N

1 mi
1 km

Pine Island Sound

Gulf of Mexico

Tarpon Bay

SANTIVA
TO CAPTIVA
TURNER BEACH
BOWMAN'S BEACH
SANIBEL-CAPTIVA ROAD
WILDLIFE DRIVE
Cross Dike Trail
Indigo Trail
WILDLIFE REFUGE VISITORS CNTR
RECREATIONAL COMPLEX
CROW
SCCF NATURE CNTR
SHELL MUSEUM
RABBIT ROAD
WEST GULF DRIVE
TARPON BAY ROAD BEACH
TARPON BAY RD
GULFSIDE PARK PRESERVE
PERIWINKLE PLACE
MIDDLE GULF DRIVE
SANIBEL CEMETERY
CASA YBEL ROAD
GULFSIDE CITY PARK
DONAX
PERIWINKLE PARK
PERIWINKLE WAY
DIXIE BEACH ROAD
BAY ROAD
MANGROVE JUNGLE VIEW
LINDGREN BLVD
SHELL HARBOR SUBDIVISION
EAST GULF DRIVE
SANIBEL LIGHTHOUSE
LIGHTHOUSE BEACH

The air-conditioned visitors center has drinking fountains and restrooms. *Diversions:* East of the refuge entrance is the Shell Museum and SCCF. Just west is the Sanibel Recreational Complex, with soda machines and a public pool.

⑦ **Bowman's Beach trip.** *(From Tarpon Bay Rd.: Sanibel-Captiva Rd. to Bowman's Beach Rd. and to the beach. 11 miles round trip. Allow one hour for bikes, plus time at the beach and diversions, up to a full day.)* You'll ride past miles of refuge land on the way to Bowman's, which has two shady picnic areas, restrooms, outdoor showers and a water fountain. *Diversions:* On your way you'll pass the air-conditioned Shell Museum and SCCF, as well as the Recreational Complex. Continue past Bowman's on San-Cap 1.5 miles to reach Santiva and Turner Beach.

# Rental shops

Sanibel bike shops rent bikes and accessories to fit any need. Choose from mountain, hybrid and pro-series bikes, as well as tandems ("bicycles built for two"), surreys, motor scooters, in-line skates and adult trikes. There are complete rental lines for kids (bikes, in-line skates and foot scooters) as well as infants and toddlers (bike trailers, single and double baby joggers and single or double trail-a-bikes — bicycles with everything but the front wheel that attach to adult machines).

Founded in 1975, **Billy's Rentals** *(1470 Periwinkle Way, Sanibel; 472-5248)* is the granddaddy of island renters. Billy Kirkland's shop is the only place to rent a surrey, and the only spot on Sanibel to rent a scooter. Billy's also rents bikes at Casa Ybel and the West Wind Inn. Tucked in behind Winds beach shop, **Finnimore's Cycle Shop** *(2353 Periwinkle Way, Sanibel; 472-5577)* has 100 bikes to rent, is the only place on Sanibel renting in-line skates, and sells skateboards. Rentals of three days or more include free delivery and pickup. **Bike Route** *(2330 Palm Ridge Rd., Sanibel; 472-1955)* targets serious bikers. There's no pickup or delivery, but owner Bill Wallstedt will loan you a car rack for an hour or two. **Tarpon Bay Explorers** *(900 Tarpon Bay Rd., Sanibel; 472-8900)* is the closest rental spot to the refuge.

**Jim's Rentals** *(11534 Andy Rosse Ln., Captiva; 472-1296)* rents bikes, motor scooters and skates on Captiva. Scooter rentals require a competency test. Many hotels and resorts rent bikes, too.

**Visiting from Michigan,** Jessica Rohrs, 16, and Marissa Heyblom, 14, tour Sanibel in a surrey

**The Sanibel bike paths** were created in the early 1970s. Island kids loved to ride, but a development frenzy was bringing in dangerous traffic. Families organized and arranged for bike paths to be built throughout the island.

**The Bailey Tract** is a hidden gem for bikers. A network of short, connecting trails roams through freshwater wetlands and alongside the Sanibel River.

**Riding after a rain** is a special treat. Frogs, snakes and tadpoles are out and about; the aroma of the tropical foliage is strong and sweet. In the summer, some islanders even ride *during* a shower. The raindrops are warm.

**Facing page:** Indiana's Durell Freeze is ready to ride on a retriculated bike

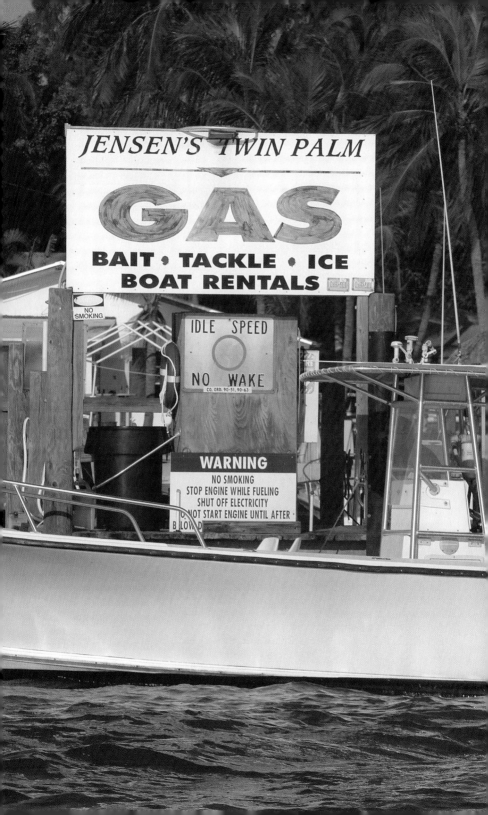

# Boating

*P*ine Island Sound is a picturesque haven. There are more dolphins here than any other spot in the Western Hemisphere. Osprey nests top channel markers and abandoned fishing shacks sit in the distance. And a handful of remote out islands make fascinating rest stops or destinations.

Closer to shore, Canoe and Kayak magazine has named Sanibel's Tarpon Bay and adjoining Commodore Creek Water Trail one of the top 10 places to paddle in the U.S. Back at the beach you can rent a Waverunner, learn to windsurf or try parasailing, an effortless way to soar above the landscape.

## Charters

Sailing from the 'Tween Waters Marina, **Mike Fuery's Tours** *(466-3649)* offers 3-hour nature tours and party boats; **Capt. Jim's Charters** *(472-1779)* has 2- to 4-hour nature tours and lunch cruises, with longer trips available; and **Capt. Randy's Fishy Business Charters** *(472-2628)* has 2- to 8-hour kid-friendly dolphin watches and snorkeling trips, plus breakfast and lunch trips to North Captiva, Cabbage Key, Useppa and Boca Grande.

**Adventure Sailing Charters** *(472-5300)* is based at the South Seas Resort. The 30-foot Adventure has room for six; a second boat comes for larger groups. The captain will urge you to take the controls. Bring food; the boat has a refrigerator and head. The rate is $95 an hour with a two-hour minimum. Sails of more than 7 hours are discounted 20 percent.

Sanibel charters (most from the Sanibel Marina) include Capt. Brian Holaway's **Around the Sound Tours** *(849-8687)* through tidal creeks, bayous, keys and islands; **Sanibel Island Adventures'** *(826-7566)* 47-ft. Adventure Cat catamaran, which can sail throughout Southwest Florida (catering and crew optional); Capt. John Gaffney's **Sanibel Island Cruise Line** *(472-5799)*, which offers sightseeing, snorkeling and shelling trips with coolers, ice, beach chairs, beach umbrellas, towels, snorkeling gear, shell nets and shell bags provided free of charge; and **Viking Voyages'** *(472-6946, no credit cards)* 33-foot pontoon boat with a private upper deck for cruising, shelling, nature photography and light fishing. Sanibel's Castaways Marina is the home base of **Capt. Joe's Charters** *(472-8658)*, which offers 2-hour to all-day nature tours and lunch or dinner cruises.

## Kayaks and canoes

Brian Houston's **Adventure Sea Kayak Wildlife Tours** *(departing from 'Tween Waters Marina, 15951 Captiva Dr., Captiva; 472-5161 ext. 2 or 432-0956 after 6 p.m.)* offers eco-tours and classes. **Canoe Adventures** *(Sanibel; 472-5218)* offers canoe tours with former Sanibel mayor Mark "Bird" Westall: Head down the Sanibel River, through the

---

**Rental boat**

**Watch for a group of yellow runabouts** in Pine Island Sound. These are Mercury Marine factory boats, evaluating outboards and sterndrives for saltwater durability. Though it may be leaving the area soon, Mercury has tested motors here since the 1980s.

**Dolphins love to surf a wake,** even from a kayak. Look behind you!

**To keep dolphins from leaving** when you approach, come up beside them going the same direction

**Previous pages:** Kayaking on Tarpon Bay

refuge or to Buck Key, an undeveloped bay island a stone's throw from Captiva. **Captiva Kayak & Wildside Adventures** *(11401 Andy Rosse Ln., Captiva; 395-2925 or 877-EZ-KAYAK)* rents kayaks and canoes by the hour, half-day, day and week. It offers guided kayak and canoe trips at sunrise, sunset, even at night. Try it during a full moon. **Tarpon Bay Explorers** *(900 Tarpon Bay Rd., Sanibel; 472-8900)* rents kayaks and canoes for exploring the bay and Commodore Creek mangrove areas of the refuge. Rates are $20 for two hours; $5 each additional hour.

If it's under 14 feet, you can launch your own canoe, kayak or motorized boat off Wildlife Drive. A non-motorized site is near the refuge entrance (motor boats have to pole or paddle out). A site for motorized boats is just past the observation tower.

## Power boats

Anyone can rent a power boat: the boat hand will show you how to work the controls and read markers and charts (water maps). Most are outboard-powered center consoles, 16 to 21 feet long. Many boats have coolers, so bring drinks and snacks.

Captiva has the pricier rentals, but you start off much closer to the out islands. The nicest boats are at **Sweetwater Boat Rentals** *(at the 'Tween Waters Marina, 15951 Captiva Dr.; 472-6336)*. Half-day rentals are $160; full days are $275. **Jensen's Twin Palm Marina** *(15107 Captiva Dr.; 472-5800)* rents a 14-foot skiff, 18-foot center consoles and bowriders and a 24-foot pontoon that seats 12. Half days are $80–$170, full days $115–$260. **Seawave Boat Rental** *(at the South Seas Resort Bayside Marina, 5400 Plantation Rd.; 472-1744)* offers boats for two to 10 people.

The **Sanibel Marina** *(634 N. Yachtsman Dr., Sanibel; 472-2531)* has nice boats for $90–$125 for a half day, $165–$200 for a full day. And there are a few rental boats at the **Castaways Marina** *(6460 Sanibel-Captiva Rd., Sanibel; 472-1112 or 800-375-0152)*.

### POWER BOATING TIPS

■ **'Red right return.'** When you return to shore, keep the red buoys on your right, the green on your left. This keeps you in the deep water channel.

■ **Read your chart.** Pine Island Sound is incredibly shallow; even near-shore Gulf waters are unpredictable.

■ **Wear polarized sunglasses.** They cut the glare and let you see into the water.

■ **Store water-sensitive items** in waterproof bags and baggies. Your boat's interior is likely to get splashed with saltwater.

■ **Rental rates do not include tax, gas or oil.** These will add $50 to $75 to your bill.

## Sailboats

Rent your own sailboat at **Captiva Kayak & Wildside Adventures** *(11401 Andy Rosse Ln., Captiva; 395-2925 or 877-EZ-KAYAK).* The rate for a single-person sailboat is $25 an hour. A 3-person Windrider trimaran goes for $35 for one hour, $100 for four hours, $175 for 8 hours. The larger Gulf-front resorts rent boats, too. Learn to sail at the **Offshore Sailing School** *(454-1700 or 888-454-8002).* Operating from the South Seas Resort, it offers one- to seven-day courses for any skill level.

**Lady Chadwick** tour boat captain Bob Rando

**Overleaf:** Offshore Sailing School, South Seas Resort

**Captiva Cruises** sails the 84-foot Island Lady

## Tour boats

**Captiva Cruises** *(11401 Andy Rosse Ln., Captiva; 472-5300)* has popular wildlife, natural history and sunset cruises, as well as trips to Cabbage Key, Useppa Island, Cayo Costa and Boca Grande. A new weekly cruise to Pine Island includes a tour of one of the largest Calusa Indian sites. Prices are $17.50 to $35 for adults, $10 to

INTERSTATE HOTELS & RESORTS

$17.50 for kids. Reservations are required. Lunch and dinner cruises, party boats, nature tours and sailing excursions are also available. On a smaller scale, the **Sanibel Marina** *(634 N. Yachtsman Dr., Sanibel; 472-2723)* hosts the intimate Stars and Stripes excursion boat; 1½ hour tours are $15 for adults, $9.50 for children 3 to 12. **Tarpon Bay Explorers** *(900 Tarpon Bay Rd., Sanibel; 472-8900)* takes pontoon-boat tours onto tranquil, wildlife-rich Tarpon Bay. The one-hour cruise costs $20 for adults, $12 for children. You can also take a guided kayak tour through the water trail, or a Sunset Paddle out to rookery islands to watch hundreds of birds come in for the night.

## Watersports

Take a Waverunner out in the Gulf at **YOLO Watersports** *(11534 Andy Rosse Ln., Captiva, 472-YOLO)* for $60 for a half-hour; an hour is $85. Guided one-hour tours are $120. Prices are per Waverunner, with no charge for additional riders. Renters have to be at least 18 years old, but drivers need to be only 16. Passengers must be at least 44 inches tall. Per-person parasailing prices start at $45; you can fly single, double or triple. Non-flyers can ride in the boat ($10) if there's space. Trips start at 9 a.m.; each is on the water an hour to 90 minutes.

**Above:** Parasailing flights feature dry takeoffs and landings from the boat.
**Facing page:** Using an ATV to pull a Waverunner out of the water, Brett Borchers works at the South Seas Resort. **Below:** Learning to windsurf off the Sanibel Causeway.

**Holiday Water Sports** *(in the South Seas Resort but open to the public, Captiva; 472-5111, ext. 3433)* has Waverunners starting at $35 for a half-hour on a single-rider machine; three-person units are available. Guided "Waverunner Safaris" start at $100 per person. Parasailing prices start at $60 for a single rider on a 600-foot line (teenagers get a break on Wednesdays, when their rate is cut to $45). Observers can ride in the boat ($10), but may be bumped for flyers. Holiday Water Sports also rents hydrobikes, sailboats, windsurfers, kayaks and canoes. Other organized activities include water skiing, banana boat rides and sailboat and windsurfing lessons.

You can learn to windsurf on the Sanibel Causeway. New wide boards make learning easy. Look for the white delivery truck of **Ace Performer** *(16842 McGregor Blvd., Fort Myers; 489-3513)* near the drawbridge. You'll get instruction, then take off on your own.

# Adventures at Sea

We had a terrific time on Holiday Water Sports' Waverunner Safari, a two-hour trip around the out islands. Afterward we jotted down our experience:

*We meet at the beach. Our group has seven people, three riding on their own Waverunners and four people doubling up on two machines. As we put on our life jackets, our guide shows us how to operate the machine, tells us what to look for on our trip, and teaches us some basic hand signals so we can communicate with each other while we travel.*

*Like a motorcycle gang, we climb on our "bikes" and head out. Once we're out in the Gulf our guide gives us 10 minutes to zip around to get used to the machines. We learn to speed up to turn (a Waverunner steers by propelling water through its nozzle jets) and to crouch when the water gets rough.*

*Then we're off. As we cruise down the Gulf side of North Captiva we spot a pod of dolphins. Our guide slows us down, and we each roam through the herd. There are about six or seven dolphins in the group, including some youngsters that jump all the way out of the water. We are so close — sometimes just a few feet away — we can hear the sound of their blowholes when they surface. It takes your breath away.*

*We cruise around the Gulf, then head over to Pine Island Sound. We stop for a rest (above) and our guide tells us the history of the area, complete with some wild pirate tales. We watch a manatee surface, then ride over to a deserted fish camp — an old shack out in the water, on stilts. On the way back to South Seas the water is so smooth our guide leads us through a series of tight "S" turns. We carve up the sea with abandon.*

Parasailing is another unforgettable experience. We've gone with YOLO quite a few times. You meet your guides at the beach (the guides look like they live in the sun, with bleached hair and bronzed skin), then wade out to the boat and climb in.

The driver zooms out to deeper water, and then comes those exhilarating words: "Your turn!" You're fitted with a harness around your waist and thighs; it feels like a swing. A large parachute is secured to its top, the front is clipped on to a long rope (wound, for the moment, down inside the boat), and you waddle onto the large carpeted launch pad. The driver slowly accelerates, the parachute fills with air, and instantly you lift off.

As the line spools out you soar higher and higher, eventually 500 feet or more above the water. It's quiet up there, and calm.

And the view is spectacular — not just of the islands, but into the water. We saw some huge rays swimming under the surface. Eventually the boat reels you back in, dipping you into the water once if you ask for it ahead of time.

*Note: Young kids can go parasailing, too. They ride with a parent, strapped in front.*

# The Out Islands

We probably overuse the word "paradise" in this book, but it's deserved for Cabbage Key and Cayo Costa. These islands, accessible only by boat, are where to go when Sanibel starts to seem like a big city. Tour boats visit daily. But if you can rent a boat and come just with your family don't pass it up; you'll remember your trip forever.

The 85-acre **Cabbage Key** *(12 miles north of Captiva's Roosevelt Channel, adjacent to Intercoastal Waterway marker No. 61)* is home to the Cabbage Key Restaurant and Inn *(breakfast, lunch and dinner daily; 283-2278)*. Built in 1938 by playwright Mary Roberts Rinehart, the buildings are still in their original state, as the weathered wood floors attest. Previous diners have pasted thousands of dollar bills to the walls and ceilings of the restaurant; each has a personal message scrawled across the face. The tradition began in 1941, when a fisherman signed and taped his last dollar to the wall to assure he'd still have money for beer when he came back. Money that falls off is donated to children's charities and marine research. For food, get the thick cheeseburger and the huge piece of frozen key lime pie. (No wonder it's said Jimmy Buffett wrote "Cheeseburger in Paradise" about this place.) After lunch, climb the short water tower then hike down the

**Signed dollar bills** cover the walls of the Cabbage Key restaurant. Famous contributors include Julia Roberts and "Simpsons" creator Matt Groening.

**Big smile:** Kimberly Rintz tends bar at Cabbage Key

**Cabbage Key** patio diners enjoy lunch (below); the main dock (bottom)

winding nature trail. The island is named for its many cabbage palms, but it's also dense with bougainvillea and citrus, mango and royal poinciana trees. The center is a Calusa shell mound 38 feet above sea level, one of the highest spots in this part of Florida. Plan plenty of time here; you won't want to leave.

Captiva Cruises *(472-5300)* takes a daily lunch trip to Cabbage Key, and offers dinner cruises twice a week. Jensen's Marina *(472-5800)* has a round-trip water taxi, $130 for up to 6 people. If you're taking your own boat (see Power Boats in this chapter), get here before Captiva Cruises does and you won't wait for a table.

One of Florida's largest undeveloped islands, **Cayo Costa** *(southern tip west of Intercoastal Waterway marker No. 48; state park dock west of marker No. 72, 14 miles north of Captiva's Roosevelt Channel; park office: 964-0375)* looks much like it did 500 years ago. Ninety percent of Cayo Costa is owned by the state or public agencies. It has 9 miles of nearly deserted beaches, with an interior of palm hammocks, mangrove swamps, lots of wildlife, a few basic trails and a couple of sand "roads." Best of all, most of it is a state park — the least visited in the Sunshine State. There's a nice park dock in the tranquil Pelican Bay, toward the northern end of the island. Park admission is $1. Rangers run a free tractor-pulled trailer across to the Gulf.

Waiting for the tractor saves energy, but

walking this ½-mile gives you that back-to-nature feeling you simply can't get too many places today. The island has a variety of wildlife, including feral pigs descended from those brought over by 16th-century Spanish explorers. Many hiking trails beckon you; one leads to a 100-year-old cemetery, dating from the island's past ties to a booming phosphate industry on Boca Grande.

The Gulf side of the park includes picnic tables, grills and two pavilions, as well as 12 tiny cabins *(for reservations call 964-0375 or 800-326-3521).* This area has bathrooms, showers and drinking water (not the best), but no electricity, food or other supplies. Bring what you need, including bug spray.

Many boaters pull up at the south tip of Cayo Costa and walk around to the beach. Anglers catch tarpon, flounder, snook, redfish, trout, snapper and sheepshead at the northern end, a mile north of the campground. Pets, intoxicants and firearms are not allowed on Cayo Costa.

By the way, "Cayo Costa" is Spanish for "island by the coast." Pretty creative, huh?

**Main road,** Cayo Costa

Though the 100-acre **Useppa Island** *(directly east of Cabbage Key)* is a private resort, day visitors are allowed through a Captiva Cruises lunch tour. Otherwise, visitors are not welcome. The restaurant is in the former vacation home of Barron Collier, who bought the island in 1912 and made it a haven for wealthy tarpon fishermen. The CIA trained Cuban nationals on Useppa in 1961 for the Bay of Pigs invasion. If you do stop, don't miss the small museum; it has Calusa Indian and Bay of Pigs displays.

**Rental cabin,** Cayo Costa

Part of Captiva until a 1920s hurricane, **North Captiva** *(southern tip across Redfish Pass from Captiva, Safety Harbor west of Intercoastal Waterway marker No. 48; also called Upper Captiva)* today is a reclusive haven for an eclectic group of homeowners, some of whom live here year-round. The small Safety Harbor restaurant Barnacle Phil's promotes its black-bean soup, but our experiences here always send us back to Cabbage Key.

**Resident club,** N. Captiva

# Fishing

*T*he waters around Sanibel and Captiva are a haven for anglers. Pine Island Sound has more species of fish than any other spot in Florida. Snapper and grouper hang out in droves just three miles offshore, on a series of rocky underwater ledges. Just to the north, Boca Grande Pass is the tarpon fishing capital of the world. Many people fish right on the beach. Bait casting, spin casting, fly fishing — the islands offer nearly everything a fisherman — or woman — loves.

## Fishing charters

Many fishing guides operate from the islands. Using a guide can be expensive, but convenient — the bait and equipment are provided, you don't need a license, and most guides will clean your catch. And, of course, guides know where to fish, making it easy to have a great day. If you have a good trip, you should tip your guide. Local guides include:

**Back Country Fishing Charters** *(433-1007).* Capt. Paul Hobby is a lifetime Southwest Florida resident, specializing in fly fishing and light-tackle fishing for snook, redfish, tarpon and others in calm, shallow waters. Half-day and full-day trips are available.

**Bait Box Guide Service** *(1041 Periwinkle Way, Sanibel; 472-1618 or 472-3035)* offers over 100 years of local experience. The Bait Box is run by the Woodring family, who have been guides here since the late 1800s. Today they offer charters for tarpon, snook, redfish, grouper, trout, snapper, cobia, shark and mackerel.

**Bayside Charters** *(454-4270)* with Capt. Kelly Kaminski offers 4-, 6- and 8-hour backwater trips for trout, redfish, tarpon and snook, specializing in fly and light-tackle fishing.

**Capt. Joe Burnsed's Charters** *(at Castaways Marina, Sanibel; 472-8658)* provides back bay, deep-sea and fly-fishing. Half- and full-day trips are available, as are split trips.

**Capt. Dave Godfrey** *(at Jensen's Marina, Captiva; 565-4471)* offers back-country light-tackle fishing. Natural history and ecology tours are also available.

**Fintastic Charters** *(850-0716)* with Capt. Randy Eastvold provides half-day, ¾-day and full-day trips trips into Pine Island Sound and the Gulf of Mexico for snook, redfish, tarpon, trout and shark. Shelling and sightseeing trips are also available.

**Flying Fish & Co.** *(590-6428)* with Capt. Sean Middleton offers half-day, ¾-day and full-day bay trips or 6- to 8-hour tarpon adventures. Night trips are available, as are shelling and sightseeing tours. Sean's 20-foot flats boat is great for up-close-and-personal fishing. He can take up to three people fishing for snook, trout, redfish or tarpon.

**Makin' Waves Charter Services** *(Captiva; 395-7696 or 560-6300)* and Capt. Tim Hickey provide your choice of an 18-foot flats boat or a 26-foot Dusky, on half- or full-day trips for tarpon, snook, redfish, snapper and shark.

---

**Left:** Sanibel resident Brenda Tate holds a snook she caught on a Flying Fish & Co. charter

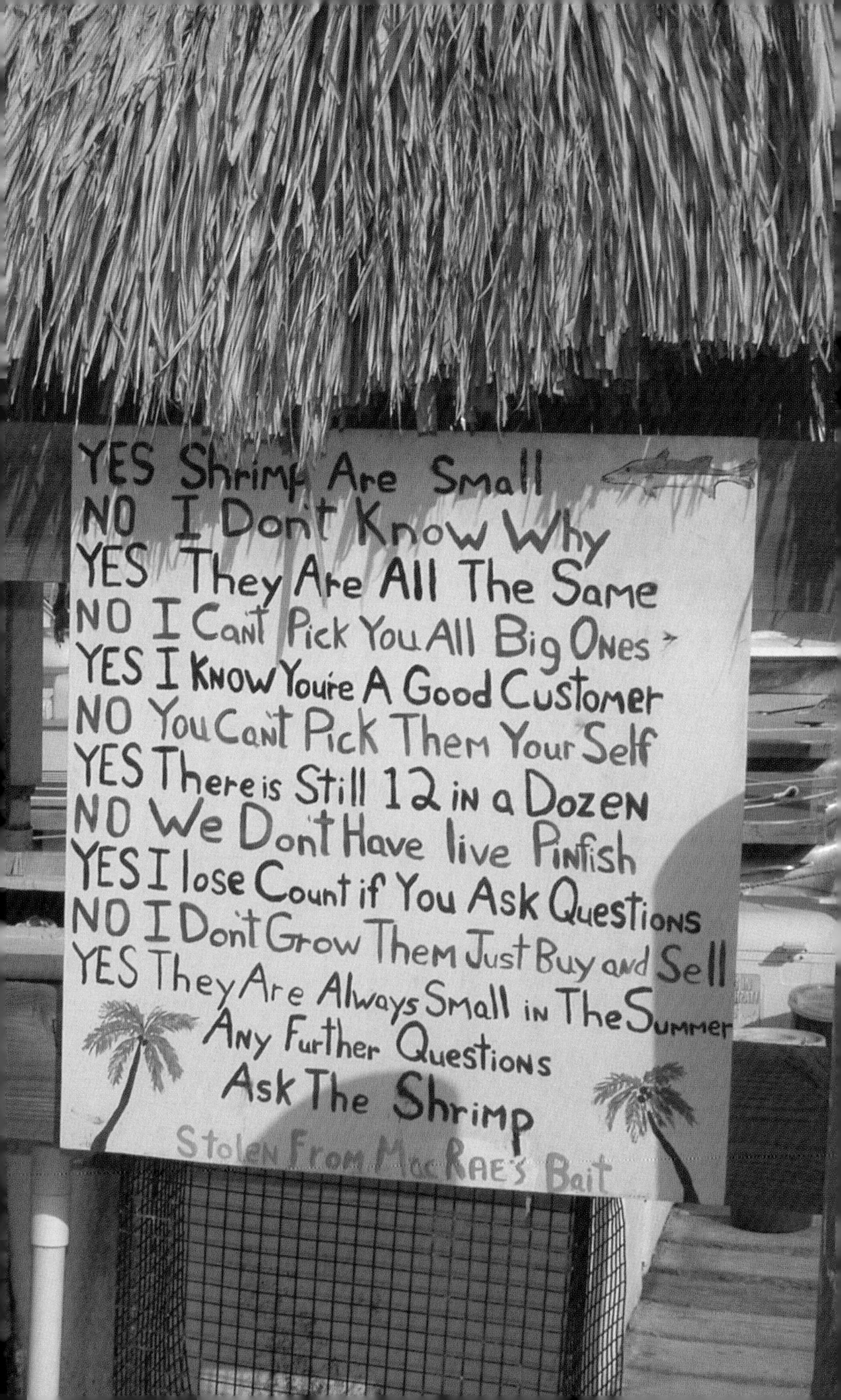

YES Shrimp Are Small
NO I Don't Know Why
YES They Are All The Same
NO I Can't Pick You All Big Ones
YES I Know You're A Good Customer
NO You Can't Pick Them Your Self
YES There is Still 12 in a Dozen
NO We Don't Have live Pinfish
YES I lose Count if You Ask Questions
NO I Don't Grow Them Just Buy and Sell
YES They Are Always Small in The Summer
Any Further Questions
Ask The Shrimp
Stolen From Mac Rae's Bait

**Captiva's Island Store** doesn't sell bait, but this sign is still part of its decor

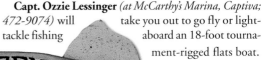

**Island fishing secrets**

■ **Keep your hands clean** when you handle bait. Fish won't bite if gas, oil, sunscreen or cigarette odors are on bait. If your hands get dirty, use lime juice or fish slime to clean off these scents. Spitting on the bait helps, too.

■ **Find the birds.** Wading birds indicate the presence of bait fish and, therefore, the fish that eat them such as snook, redfish and trout. Offshore, noisy terns often fly above mackerel and other migratory fish.

■ **Fish the waters that are slightly murky.** Most fish need some sand and silt in the water to strike. Ideal visibility: 5 or 6 feet.

■ **Wear polarized sunglasses.** They reduce surface glare, helping you see into the water and avoid manatees and grass.

■ **Read your charts.** Most of Pine Island Sound is only a few feet deep, even at high tide. Pay attention so you don't run aground.

**Previous pages:** Have questions about shrimp? The answers are waiting at Jensen's Marina.

**Capt. Ozzie Lessinger** *(at McCarthy's Marina, Captiva; 472-9074)* will take you out to go fly or light-tackle fishing aboard an 18-foot tournament-rigged flats boat.

**Capt. Pat Lovetro** *(at Sanibel Marina; 472-2723 or 826-3156)* has been fishing locally for 20 years. Join him on his 25-foot Parker for 4-hour, 6-hour or full-day trips to search for tarpon, shark, trout, snook and more.

**Capt. Randy's Fishy Business Charters** *(at 'Tween Waters Marina, Captiva; 472-2628)* features back bay or offshore fishing. Trips can also include shell collecting, dolphin watches, snorkeling, and breakfast or lunch trips on North Captiva, Cabbage Key, Useppa and Boca Grande. Child friendly.

**Joyce Rehr's Fly Fishing & Light Tackle Guide Service** *(1155 Buttonwood Ln., Sanibel; 472-3308)* will take you in the flats, back bay and offshore. Novice to advanced anglers will enjoy fly and light-tackle fishing for half-day, ¾-day and full-day trips.

**Capt. Bob Sabatino** *(at Jensen's Marina, Captiva; 472-1451 or 851-0330)* has been a guide on the islands since 1960, and he's known for his knowledge and dependability. Sabatino uses a 25-foot center console boat. He has been featured on "Fishing with Orlando Wilson."

**Santiva Saltwater Fishing Team** *(at 'Tween Waters Marina, Captiva; 472-1779)* offers back bay fishing with native guides Capts. Jim and Jimmy Burnsed. Private 2-, 3- and 4-hour trips are available. Children are welcome.

**Tarpon Bay Explorers** *(in the J.N. "Ding" Darling National Wildlife Refuge, 900 Tarpon Bay Rd., Sanibel; 472-8900)* offers guided canoe fishing tours. It also rents broad-beam and square-stern fishing canoes, with electric trolling motors. Bait and tackle are available in the rental store.

**Ultimate Charters** *(542-9315)* with Capt. Gary Clark provides half-day or full-day trips for snook, tarpon, cobia, trout and others. Gary has a new 23-foot Bay Ranger bay boat, a 20-foot back-country flats boats and state-of-the-art light tackle. Fly tackle is also available, or you can bring your own.

# Catch and release tips

Today most Florida anglers don't keep their catch. They release many, if not most, of their fish back in the water so they can continue to reproduce. Some folks release everything they catch. Regulated species, such as redfish, should be released if they are outside their slot limit, either too small or too large.

Taking an exhausted fish out of the water is like placing a plastic bag over the head of a marathon runner. It needs oxygen! Fish in good shape should be released immediately by removing the hook, or cutting the leader as close to the hook as possible.

Large gamefish such as billfish, tuna, shark and tarpon should be brought alongside the boat as quickly as possible. Don't boat these big guys — they're dangerous to both themselves and you. Many times large gamefish evert their stomachs when hooked. Don't attempt to replace it; the fish will swallow it after release. Other tips:

**1. Don't wear it out.** Playing the fish to exhaustion depletes its energy reserves, which puts it at risk of death by predation or metabolic imbalances.

**2. Avoid gut hooking.** Set the hook on the strike, before the fish swallows the bait. If you do gut-hook a fish, cut the line and leave the hook in place. Don't lift the fish by the leader; this increases tissue damage.

**3. Use barbless hooks.** Using circle hooks with natural baits reduces gut hooking and increases your hookup ratio. Don't use hooks coated with cadmium, which is toxic to fish.

**4. Use artificial lures when possible.** Fishing with artificial bait, with single hooks, decreases the likelihood of gut-hooking.

**5. Wet your hands.** If you can't leave the fish in the water during a release, gently cradle it under the rib cage using wet hands. Nets, dry hands, towels and gloves remove too much of the fish's protective slime and put it at risk of infection.

**6. Handle the fish as little as possible.** Never lift a fish by the gills or eyes if it is to be released. A fish can be calmed during release-handling by turning it on its back or by covering its eyes with a wet towel. Use needle-nose pliers or a dehooker to remove the hook. Keep these tools in a convenient place so you can release fish quickly.

**7. Revive the fish.** Hold the fish head-first into the current until it swims away. Don't throw the fish into the water, or drop it sideways. If the fish is exhausted, revive it by making sure the head is totally submerged and towing it gently forward. When releasing a fish from a bridge, pier or boat, gently drop it into the water head-first to reduce the impact and force water through its gills.

**Preparing for a morning** of beach fishing

**Getting ready.** Light tackle, using a line weight of 6 to 20 pounds, is fine for almost anything but large tarpon and offshore fishing. Many anglers catch their own bait, using a cast net.

You'll need a Florida fishing license unless you're with a licensed charter captain. Even so, you'll still need to bring a good pair of sunglasses, a cap or hat and something to eat and drink.

The Bait Box *(1041 Periwinkle Way, Sanibel; 472-1618)* is a good bet for tackle, bait and current regulations. Bailey's General Store *(2477 Periwinkle Way, Sanibel; 472-1516)* has a good fishing department, too, with a smart staff.

## GUIDE TO LOCAL FISH

Also called the striped bass, the **black sea bass** *(Roccus saxatilis)* has a jutting lower jaw and a heavy belly. It's dark brown or black, with darker stripes running the length of the body. The dorsal fin has white stripes. *Avg. size:* 1 to 2 lbs. *Max. size:* 5 lbs. *Season:* Warm weather. *Where found:* Structures offshore. *Bait:* Mullet, crabs, spoons, jigs. *Edibility:* Excellent. Fine for baking.

The dorsal spine of the **gafftopsail catfish** *(Bagre marinus)* looks like a sail when extended. Long barbels ("whiskers") extend under the mouth. A mucous film covers the skin. The pectoral and dorsal fins are barbed and emit a painful poison. When hungry the catfish can drive other fish out of its territory. Also called a sailcat. *Avg. size:* 1 to 5 lbs. *Max. size:* 8 lbs. *Season:* Year-round. *Where found:* Saltwater, will enter brackish waters. Often near docks and bridges. *Bait:* Minnows or worms. *Edibility:* Good. Pink, sweet meat. Nip spines before cleaning to avoid injury. Skin before cooking.

It's possible to mistake the bullet-shaped **cobia** *(Rachycentron canadus)* for a small shark or a snook. Like a shark, the front of its dorsal fin can stick out of the water when it cruises at the surface. Like a snook,

a cobia has a stripe from its snout to the tail (but, unlike the snook, it's surrounded with two paler stripes). The cobia has a broad head and snout, with a protruding lower jaw. The back and fins are dark brown, sometimes nearly black. It's one of the strongest fish in the flats. *Avg. size:* 15 to 20 lbs. *Max. size:* 70 lbs. *Season:* Most of the year, whenever waters are at least 68 degrees. *Where found:* Submerged structures (i.e., channel buoys, bridge supports), floating objects and floating grasses. Sometimes swims alongside rays. *Bait:* Live or cut bait; lures. *Edibility:* Fish under 20 lbs. are excellent. Meat is white with fine grain, like grouper. Skin before cooking: a second layer of small scales is embedded in a layer of skin beneath the surface scales.

**Drum** get their name from the "bub-bub-bub" sound they make underwater as they contract their muscles over their swim bladders, organs which give them buoyancy. There are two drum around the islands:

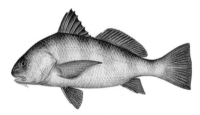

The short, solid **black drum** *(Pogonias cromis)* has a body similar to a sheepshead, and a small "beard" of barbels. Scales have a dark, metallic sheen. Older fish are blackish; young are more silvery and have vertical bars. *Avg. size:* 3 to 5 lbs. *Max. size:* 50 lbs. or more. *Season:* December through March. *Where found:* Bay, rivers, offshore. *Bait:* Crabs, cut bait. *Edibility:* Coarse, almost tasteless meat, best used for chowder. Worms and parasites are common, though harmless.

The **redfish** *(Sciaenops ocellatus)*, or red drum, has a copper, reddish or gray body.

The head is blunt. Most have a large black spot on either side near the tail fin. Some have no spot; others many. The elongated body resembles the black drum, but redfish lack chin barbels. Younger reds ("red rats") feed on crabs and other invertebrates around oyster bars and mangroves. Larger bull reds are often in the passes and offshore. Redfish are also known as "red bass" or "channel bass." But they're drum, not bass. *Avg. size:* 3 to 8 lbs. *Max. size:* 30 lbs. *Season:* Best mid-April through July. Year-round for smaller fish. Larger bull reds common in spring and fall. *Where found:* Inshore, bay, grass flats, the pier at the lighthouse, along Wildlife Drive, at the mouth of the Caloosahatchee River. *Bait:* Shrimp, lures, minnows, crabs. *Edibility:* Small fish up to 12 lbs. are excellent. Large reds have coarse meat, only fair flavor. Most fishermen fillet their catch. Also good stuffed and baked whole.

### Grouper

The **black grouper** *(Mycteroperca bonaci)* has dark blotches on its sides. Many anglers mistake it for a gag. Like all grouper, it has a large head and a broad, down-slanted mouth. The chameleon-like fish can lighten or darken its color to suit its environment. You can see this change when you put the fish in a white-sided live well. *Avg. size:* 3 to 15 lbs. *Max. size:* 50 lbs. or more. *Season:* Year-round. *Where found:* Offshore for large fish; inshore for small. *Bait:* Live or cut bait, jigs, chum. *Edibility:* Excellent.

Formerly known as the jewfish, the **goliath grouper** *(Epinephelus itajara)* can weigh up to 700 lbs., and be four to five feet long. Unlike other grouper, it has a curved tail. Young fish have bright spots and side mottling. These details fade on larger, older fish, which have a patchy, blackish-brown color. The goliath grouper is protected from harvest in Florida waters. If you catch one you must release it. *Avg. size:* 20 to 100 lbs. *Max. size:* 700 lbs. or more. *Season:* Year-round. *Where found:* Nearshore around docks, in deep holes and on ledges. *Bait:* Spanish mackerel, bonito, jack cravalle.

The **red grouper** *(Epinephelus morio)* is the grouper most often served in restaurants. It's reddish brown and splotchy over its entire body. The open mouth has a brilliant scarlet color. *Avg. size:* 2 to 5 lbs. *Max. size:* 20 lbs. *Season:* Year-round. *Where found:* Offshore. *Bait:* Live or cut bait; jigs. *Edibility:* Excellent. Firm, white, tasty meat. Widely used for chowder if not steaked. Should always be skinned, as the skin is tough and strong-flavored. Note: Some red grouper have worms. Watch for them when cleaning.

### Mackerel

The long, streamlined **king mackerel** *(Scomberomorus cavalla),* or kingfish, flashes an overall green and silver iridescence. It has tarnished silver sides with no spots, except when very young, when it has yellowish spots like that of the Spanish mackerel. The tail fin is deeply forked. Far larger than either the related Spanish mackerel or cero, it also should not be confused with the yellow dotted and spotted cero. *Avg. size:* 3 to 8 lbs. *Max. size:* 40 lbs. *Season:*

Spring and fall migrators. *Where found:* Offshore, inshore near submerged structures (i.e., channel buoys, bridge supports). *Bait:* Live bait, jigs, spoons, chum. *Edibility:* Excellent filleted or steaked. Oily. Spoils quickly. Keep well-iced from the moment caught.

The handsome **Spanish mackerel** *(Scomberomorus maculatus)* has silver sides with brilliant large bronze dots and a silver belly. The back is iridescent greenish-blue, the mouth fairly large with small needle-sharp teeth. *Avg. size:* 2 to 4 lbs. *Max. size:* 20 lbs. *Season:* Spring and fall, some during the summer. *Where found:* Gulf and bay, the pier at the lighthouse. *Bait:* Live bait, small jigs, spoons. *Edibility:* Good table fish. Easy to fillet, but spoils quickly. Ice as soon as caught on all-day trips in high temperatures.

Up to 18 inches long, the slender **black** (or striped) **mullet** *(Mugil cephalus)* has a rounded head, small mouth, and large scales with dark centers. The fish leaps out of the water, apparently to clean its gills or rid its body of parasites. (Or perhaps it's trying to fly. See below). Mullet is the most widely used bait in Florida, as all game fish seek it. Juveniles, often used as bait for tarpon, stay in Pine Island Sound and other area estuaries until at least six months old. Mullet roe is exported to Japan, where it sells for up to $100 a pound. *Avg. size:* Fingerlings to 5 lbs. *Max. size:* 5 lbs. *Season:* Year-round. *Where found:* Inshore. *Bait:* Mostly vegetarian, mullet are hard to catch by hook and line. Cast nets and gill nets work best. Some anglers use cornmeal balls. *Edibility:* Smoked mullet is popular with Floridians. It's also good broiled or fried.

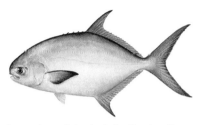

A member of the Jack family, the silvery **Florida pompano** *(Trachinotus carolinus)* has a gray-blue back and dark upper fins. The underside and deeply-forked tail have a yellow tint. A blue patch appears just above the eye. The head is rounded, with a small mouth. Pompano often leap out of the water and slap the tops of the waves. *Avg. size:* 1 to 3 lbs. *Max. size:* 5 lbs. *Season:* Year-round; most common in cooler weather. *Where found:* Bay and inshore, the Gulf side of the causeway islands. *Bait:* Shrimp, sand fleas, small jigs. *Edibility:* Gourmet-quality, fine-textured meat. Florida pompano brings the highest commercial price of any fish in Florida.

## Fishy lawyer, fowl play

Is a mullet a bird? A Florida court once said yes! In 1919, several teenagers were charged with catching fish, in particular mullet, out-of-season. It appeared to be an open-and-shut case, as the boys were caught red-handed. In court, however, their attorney made an incredible defense. First, he said that a mullet has a gizzard,* and supported this with science. Then he presented scientific evidence that only birds have gizzards. Therefore, he concluded, a mullet must be a bird, and the boys must be innocent. The judge threw out the case. (It helped that the judge was related to the defendants.) Afterward, the state of Florida rewrote its fish conservation law to include mullet by name. *Primarily a vegetarian, a mullet has a gizzard-like organ in its stomach to help grind up plant material.*

Florida's most caught game fish, the **spotted seatrout** *(Cynoscion nebulosus)* will take any kind of lure and forgive a bad cast. It will hit your line decisively and fight all the way to the boat. Black dots pepper its upper sides, back, tail and second dorsal fin. The underside has a sky-blue tint. The mouth is soft and tears easily. There are usually two distinct canine teeth at the tip of the upper jaw. The sides are silvery, the back grayish to dark. Variations occur depending on the waters from which the fish is taken — darker from mud flats and back bays, lighter from inlets and channels. *Avg. size:* 2 to 3 lbs. *Max. size:* 10 lbs. *Season:* Year-round, peak activity is spring and fall. *Where found:* Grass flats, the lighthouse pier, either side of the causeway islands, Wildlife Drive, edges of oyster bars, other grassy bottom areas near sandy depressions. *Bait:* Jigs, live bait, lures. *Edibility:* Good to excellent, best during cooler months. Meat softens and deteriorates with long icing.

A **sheepshead** *(Archosargus probatocephalus)* is easy to recognize by its chunky body and dark vertical stripes. In younger fish the stripes look like prison clothes. The mouth and incisor-like teeth — which can cut fishing line — resemble those of a sheep. Sheepshead are expert bait-stealers: with shrimp, they will hover near the bait then quickly suck the meat out of the shell. Difficult to clean, sheepshead have a heavy set of ribs in their "shoulders" that make filleting tough. Some say the only way to clean one is with a chain saw! *Avg. size:* 1 to 2 lbs. *Max. size:* 11 lbs. *Season:* Winter. A few

stay all year. *Where found:* Gulf, bay, the lighthouse pier, the bay beach and causeway islands. *Bait:* Shrimp, fiddler crabs, sand fleas. *Edibility:* Good baked or filleted. Skin first.

Reddish bands mark the sides of the **mangrove** (gray) **snapper** *(Lutjanus griseus).* The sides are gray offshore, reddish in the bay. Dorsal and tail fins are dark; pectoral and anal fins slightly pink. Red eye. In young fish, a dark streak runs from the nose to the dorsal fin. The fish feeds with an inhaling, snapping action. Once landed it will snap at your finger. *Avg. size:* 1 to 2 lbs. inshore, larger offshore. *Max. size:* 10 lbs. *Season:* Year-round. *Where found:* Bay, Wildlife Dr. *Bait:* Lures, shrimp, minnows. *Edibility:* Great filleted.

The **snook** *(Centropomus undecimalis)* is the most pursued, but least caught, game fish in Florida. It behaves like a fast, powerful largemouth bass. Called "linesides" by some, "robalo" by others, the fish has an ob-

## Sneaky snook

Snook are wary, shy, tricky, finicky, and some of the smartest fish around. Experts in the art of escape, they learn their environment quickly and will use oyster-covered mangrove roots, pilings, oyster bars, and even their own razor-sharp gill plates to cut your line and free themselves. Their abrasive mouths can quickly wear through the toughest of leader materials. Snook will leap in the air, and are masters at throwing the hook during a jump.

## Tarpon tips

No other fish in Florida is as thrilling to catch as a tarpon. No fish jumps as high, is as hard to set a hook in, or starts hearts pumping as fast. Once hooked, this fighter immediately takes to the air, its huge gills extended and rattling, smashing off across the surface in leap after leap. This battle is easy to see, as a tarpon will often strike within 40 feet of your boat. It can jump high enough to clear a small boat and cover a distance of up to 20 feet. It will jump up to a dozen times during a catch.

And you don't have to have a million-dollar boat or solid-gold reels to catch one. With light- to medium-weight tackle, a 14- to 25-foot boat and reasonable weather, tarpon can be caught by most anglers. Most use a flats boat, with a guide poling while the guide and the caster watch for fish. You can also catch one straight off the beach.

Hire a professional guide for the best results. Novice anglers can end up so frustrated they give up fishing. A tarpon's bony mouth makes it tough to set a hook. When it senses danger, a tarpon can become so violent that keeping it on the line can seem impossible. Some other tips:

■ **Fish over a light bottom** to spot tarpon easily. Their dark bodies will look like silhouettes.

■ **During the day,** fish during the first two hours of an incoming tide or the end of an outgoing tide.

■ **You can catch tarpon at night, too,** in calm water with a light wind.

Success is measured in the number of fish jumped, not caught. If you jump half a dozen tarpon in a morning, you've had a great day. A typical angler will be lucky to land one or two fish out of 10 hookups. An experienced fisherman, with good tackle, can reel in a 150-pounder in 25 to 30 minutes.

vious black stripe on each side of its body. The back is yellow-brown, the sides and belly are yellowish with gold-tipped fins. Pointed snout, protruding lower jaw. *Avg. size:* 8 to 12 lbs. *Max. size:* 40 lbs. *Season:* All year. Summer is closed season for keeping snook (it's spawning season), but the best time for catch-and-release. *Where found:* Pine Island Sound offers some of the best snook fishing anywhere. Good spots include pockets of deep water surrounded by shallow water, or bottlenecks between small mangrove islands. *Bait:* Shrimp, lures, cut bait, minnows. *Edibility:* Excellent filleted up to 10 lbs. Skin first: the skin adds a soapy flavor (snook used to be called "soapfish"). Fresh baked snook is delicious.

Up to seven feet long, **tarpon** *(Megalops atlanticus)* migrate here from the Keys in mid-April, feeding in the shallows and flats until mid-summer. They swim right past the islands, sometimes just five feet offshore. Unlike any other fish, tarpon can gulp air. They rise to the surface, roll, and breathe. On a still morning at sunrise, you can hear them coming. Boca Grande Pass, just north of Captiva, is the acknowledged tarpon capital of the world. The heavy-bodied fish has a protruding lower jaw and a huge mouth. A feather-like filament streams from the back of the dorsal fin. Tarpon grow slowly: a fish over 100 lbs. is at least 15 years old. *Avg. size:* 50 to 200 lbs. *Max. size:* 250 lbs. *Season:* Spring through summer. Peak activity in June and July. *Where found:* Bay, Gulf, the mouth of the Caloosahatchee River, Boca Grande Pass. *Bait:* Live or cut bait, chum, lures. *Edibility:* Not eaten in the U.S. Meat is dark, soft, lacking in flavor. Catch-and-release with a release gaff. Get a trophy of your catch by taking its picture at the side of the boat, then gently pulling a scale from the middle of the fish. The scale can be dried and "mounted" on a plaque.

# Morning on the Flats

**By Julie Neal**

My nine-year-old daughter Micaela and I spent a December morning fishing with Capt. Sean Middleton of Flying Fish & Co. It was fascinating, and worth the trip.

I hadn't been fishing since I was seven.

Sean meets us at the Sanibel boat ramp promptly at 9, pulling up to the dock in his small flats boat. Micaela and I hop in, then off we go.

As the boat picks up speed, I feel like a dog with his head hanging out a car window. The clear cold air is full of smells; green, salty, alive. My hair whips back. My eyes narrow and leak tears in the wind. I clutch my baseball cap in my hands; no hat will stay on when the boat is moving.

It was smart to bring a jacket. The temperature is 55 degrees, and the moving boat makes it feel about 10 degrees cooler.

I glance over at Micaela. She gives me a huge grin, blonde ponytail flying straight back. She urges Sean to go faster, faster.

As we get to the first fishing spot, Sean tells us that he goes out early in the morning to catch bait, then picks up his customers. A live well in the front of the boat has shrimp and little bait fish called shiners. As soon as Micaela learns this, she positions herself by the live well and pretty much stays there for the next hour, using a net to catch the live bait and examine it close up.

When we stop to fish, Sean explains what to do. Micaela nets a shrimp for bait, and Sean baits the hook and casts. There is no bobber on the line — you have to watch the line move to see if a fish has taken the bait.

It takes a while for a fish to bite. We move to a couple of different spots. I can tell Sean is getting nervous about the lack of nibbles; he is used to catching something right away.

As for me, I'm completely relaxed, enjoying the silence and the calm bay waters.

Micaela is making one of the shiners sing "Jingle Bells," opening and closing its tiny mouth, before slipping it back in the live well.

Soon the fishing line jerks, and Sean hands the pole to Micaela. She starts reeling the fish in, and it comes up alongside the low edges of the boat. Then it flips its tail and falls off the hook. Sean says it was a spotted sea trout, about 22 inches long. A three-pounder.

We hook three trout before one stays on the line long enough for us to look at. Sean uses a special gentle tool called a Boga grip to hold the fish by the lip before release. He holds the fish there by the boat while it twists and looks at us with its big staring eye.

The beauty of the fish surprises me. This trout is all pink iridescence and shiny, flashing color. As it flexes on the grip, it looks strong, evolved to just pure muscle.

After that we catch lots of fish, first trout then redfish. Each one is just under the size limit, or not in season, but we aren't interested in keeping them anyway. We just want to catch them. We hook seven trout, including a 26-incher, and about a dozen redfish.

It takes muscles to do this. You feel the animal struggling against you. Sometimes the fish splashes out of the water as you are bringing it in, and you can see a flash of silver.

When you find a good spot, you can catch fish one after another, bang bang bang. Late in the morning Micaela and I each have a line in the water, and both are getting bites nonstop. We simply cast our lines, wait about 10 seconds, then reel in our fish.

We keep this up for an hour, then head back to Sanibel.

As Sean drops us off at the dock, I feel intimately connected with the water. Because, now, I've seen what's underneath.

# Diversions

What do you do when you've had your fill of beaches and birds, loafing and sun? First, consider the Bailey-Matthews Shell Museum and the Sanibel Historical Village and Museum. The islands offer a variety of other activities, too, including live theater, golf and a first-class library. More unique diversions are just a short drive away on the Florida mainland.

## Museums

The **Bailey-Matthews Shell Museum** *(3075 Sanibel-Captiva Rd., Sanibel; (888) 679-6450, 395-2233)* introduces you to the world of mollusks, their shells, and their role in human history. A series of exhibits holds hundreds of bizarre and beautiful shells from around the world. Dry aquariums and dioramas recreate a mangrove jungle, the Florida Everglades and other mollusk habitats. The displays also illustrate the role mollusks and shells have played in design, food, literature, medicine and religion. Special attention is paid to scallops, tree snails, fossil shells and micromollusks (shells as small as half a millimeter). A separate area is devoted to squid, octopus and other cephalopods.

Don't miss the collection of sailor's valentines. These elaborate shell boxes — created by Caribbean women for New England whalers to take home to their loved ones — are a marvel of planning and patience. One valentine, from Barbados, is from the mid-1800s.

A new exhibit, "Calusa: The Original Shell People," explains the rise and fall of Sanibel's native inhabitants, and their use of shells as tools and art. Nearly three dozen artifacts are on display, on permanent loan from the Florida Museum of History. Some were found on Sanibel, near Wulfert Road. Mannequins illustrate Calusa hairstyles and dress.

Even young children can have a good time at the Shell Museum. The Children's Learning Lab has hands-on displays, a live-shell tank, shell games and a video. Kids love to see the giant clam in the Great Hall of Shells, as well as the 13-foot model of a giant squid hanging from the ceiling.

Spend at least an hour here, as there is much to take in. The detailed exhibits take time to appreciate, and there's a fascinating presentation every hour in the auditorium.

The museum store has a quality selection of shell-themed items, without the kitsch that dominates less serious shops. Here you'll find china, hand-painted silk scarves and jackets, jewelry, wind chimes, garden supplies, as well as stationery, posters, picture frames and postcards. There's also a nice selection of shell books and guides. The children's selection includes books, puzzles, games, stuffed animals, jewelry and clothing.

Director Dr. José H. Leal was a post-doctoral fellow at the Smithsonian and a scientist at the Muséum National d'Histoire Naturelle in Paris. Key benefactors have included the late actor Raymond Burr and television personality Willard Scott. Comedian Kevin Nealon

---

**Facing page:** Detail from a sailor's valentine at the Bailey-Matthews Shell Museum

**Probably the smallest movie theater** you'll ever be in, the two-screen Island Cinema *(next to Bailey's General Store, Sanibel; 472-1701)* is newly renovated. It shows the latest releases.

**Facing page:** an early lighthouse lens on display at the Sanibel Historical Village and Museum

**The museum's Bailey's General Store** is filled with historic food boxes, including those of Kellogg's Shredded Krumbles and Coffeola. An old Western Union office sits in the corner.

**A furnished home from the 1920s,** the Morning Glories cottage is the museum's latest addition

helps out, too. About 50,000 people a year visit the museum, which is named for two pioneer island families.

Museum admission is $5 for adults, $3 for youth 8 to 16. Children 7 and under are free. Special group programs and tours are available. The museum is open every day but Monday, from 10 a.m. to 4 p.m.

The **Sanibel Historical Village and Museum** *(850 Dunlop Rd., Sanibel; 472-4648)* is a collection of six restored island buildings. Included are two homes, Sanibel's tiny first post office and the 1935 Bailey's General Store. Bailey's 1926 Model-T delivery truck is viewable through the windows of the garage in back. Another building stores a 1900-era surrey. The oldest building is the 1898 Burnap cottage, which houses an early lighthouse lens. Our favorite spot is Morning Glories, a 1925 Sears Roebuck mail-order kit home packed with architectural detail (notice the built-in cabinets and plate racks). Furnishings and exhibits add to your immersion in this bygone era. A garden has castor beans and key lime trees. Best of all, nothing is roped off. You can walk around as you please.

Ask one of the guides to let you play the Rutland House piano, work the General Store scale, ring an old ship's bell or pull weeds in the garden. During the holidays children can leave letters to Santa at the post office.

Maintained by passionate volunteers, the museum is open Wednesday through Saturday, 10 a.m. to 4 p.m. Nov. 1 through Aug. 15, to 1 p.m. from June 1 to Aug. 15. It's closed Aug. 15 through Nov. 1 and on holidays. A small donation is requested.

**Facing page:** The charming exterior complements the lighthearted musicals inside at Sanibel's Old Schoolhouse Theater

**Pay attention when you play golf** on the islands. Don't be surprised if you see an alligator sharing the course with you.

**Every seat's a good one** at the Old Schoolhouse Theater; it holds just 93 people. The farthest seat from the stage is only seven rows back. The front row is inches from the stage.

**ABC Nightline anchor Ted Koppel** takes questions from the audience during an appearance at BIG Arts

# Live theater

The casual **Old Schoolhouse Theater** *(1905 Periwinkle Way, Sanibel; 472-6862)* is a great bet for a fun evening out. The building was Sanibel's 1896 one-room schoolhouse until broadway veteran Ruth Hunter transformed it into a tiny nonprofit theater in 1964. For the past 12 years it has been home to artist-in-residence J.T. Smith and his high-energy, original musicals. Shows get a little randy at times, but are generally appropriate for children. The "Ho Ho Ho" show is a holiday tradition (be ready to sing "The Twelve Days of Christmas").

The theater recently installed new padded seats. Volunteers offer beer, soft drinks and snacks at intermission on a pay-what-you-feel basis. Some actors who perform here go on to Broadway and network television roles.

Showtime is 8 p.m. Monday through Saturday. Occasional matinees are Wednesdays at 2 p.m. and Saturdays at 4 p.m. Tickets are $25.

The **SCA Periwinkle Playhouse** *(2200 Periwinkle Way, Sanibel; 472-2155)* is the latest incarnation of Sanibel's serious theater. A victim of bad management and nasty infighting, this first-class facility was formerly the Wood Theatre and, before that, the Pirate Playhouse.

# BIG Arts

The **Barrier Island Group for the Arts** *(between Sanibel City Hall and the Sanibel Historical Village, 900 Dunlop Rd., Sanibel; 395-0900)* has a performance hall, two art galleries and five classrooms. About two dozen jazz, classical and pop concerts are held each year in the 414-seat Schein Performance Hall, with artists from throughout the U.S. and Europe.

The Phillips Gallery has different exhibits and juried shows monthly, with all art for sale (hours are generally 1 to 4 p.m. weekdays). Over 160 workshops teach painting, pottery, weaving, dance, photography and other skills. Most are available on a per-session basis so island visitors can attend.

Discussion group members share their thoughts on books, current events, music and art. The BIG Arts Film Society brings residents and visitors together to view and discuss selected movies, with a focus on independent and foreign films not widely seen in commercial theaters. Other activities include

lectures, language workshops, civic events, a Thanksgiving juried Fine Arts and Contemporary Craft Fair, fitness classes such as Pilates body conditioning, yoga and dance, and many children's programs.

# Golf and tennis

Golfers of every level can have a good time on the islands. Most fairways and greens have been built with the leisurely duffer in mind. All island courses use Bermuda grass.

The par-70, 5,600-yard course at the semiprivate **Dunes Golf & Tennis Club** *(949 Sandcastle Rd., Sanibel; 472-2535)* has water on all 18 holes. Most greens have forced carries over water; one has an island fairway. You'll need to hit your mid-to-low irons consistently well. Touring pro Mark McCumber redesigned the course in 1995. The new layout has an emphasis on chipping. The Dunes also has a water range, the only one on the islands. The clubhouse includes a dining room, grill and bar. Club rental, repair, fitting and PGA instruction are available. Pro shop hours are 7 a.m. to 5:30 p.m. daily. The pro is Kevin McCune. Make reservations at least four days in advance (six days for South Seas Resorts guests). For tennis, the Dunes has seven soft clay Har-Tru courts. There's a summer tennis camp for kids. The tennis pro is Terry See.

The semiprivate course at the **Beachview Golf & Tennis Club** *(1100 Parview Dr., Sanibel; 472-2626)* has numerous waterways. Older players and duffers who play once or twice a year will feel at home on this 6,320-yard, par-71 course: the fairways are open; the greens generous. Coconut and cabbage palms, as well as macadamia, grapefruit and lime trees, are common throughout the course. The clubhouse includes a snack bar, restaurant and lounge. Club rental, repair and fitting are available. Pro shop hours are 7 a.m. to 5:30 p.m. daily. Pro Robby Wilson has been here since 1974. Call at least two days in advance for reservations, earlier during season. Club members have priority. The Beachview tennis center features five HydroGrid clay courts. Watered from underneath, they're rarely closed and stay in good shape. The surrounding facility has an elevated deck with 270 degrees of courtside viewing. Daily packages are available. The tennis pro shop is open 8 a.m. to 5:30 p.m. daily. Private lessons are available from pro Russ Crutchfield.

# Libraries

Open to residents and visitors, the **Sanibel Public Library** *(770 Dunlop Rd., Sanibel; 472-2483)* has over

## USPGA course ratings

| Dunes | COURSE | SLOPE |
|---|---|---|
| Back | 68.4 | 124 |
| Middle | 67.0 | 121 |
| Ladies | 64.9 | 113 |

| Beachview | COURSE | SLOPE |
|---|---|---|
| Blue | 70.8 | 127 |
| White | 67.8 | 118 |
| Gold | 63.5 | 105 |
| Red | 67.6 | 114 |

**The back nine** of the Dunes course is a wildlife preserve sanctioned by the Audubon Cooperative Society

**Private courses.** The South Seas Resort on Captiva has a 9-hole course for its guests and members, with fairways along the beach. Sanibel is home to the ultra-exclusive Sanctuary Golf Club. Its course winds through palm hammocks and along the bay.

**The Sanibel library** began in a closet-sized room in the Community House in the 1960s. Volunteers collected books left in hotel rooms, and donated others from their homes. Today's building was built with private donations. Another expansion broke ground in 2003.

**Facing page:** The sea cow jumps over the moon at the Sanibel Public Library

**Attend an NPR concert.**
The Sanibel Music Festival (336-7999) offers a series of performances each spring at the Sanibel Congregational Church, some broadcast on National Public Radio. A true delight, the festival includes piano and chamber music, two operas and a children's concert. Artists have included the Julliard String Quartet. Ticket prices are low for shows of this quality: $22 to $30.

**Got some time?** Check out the longer historical or botanical tour at the Edison-Ford Winter Estates, or the super trip that includes a ride through the Fort Myers historic district and a boat ride on the Caloosahatchee River. Reservations are required for the longer tours.

**The National Audubon Society** manages the 11,000-acre Corkscrew Swamp Sanctuary (375 Sanctuary Rd., Naples; 348-9151) an hour or so southeast of Sanibel off I-75. The preserve features the country's largest stand of virgin bald cypress trees. Take the boardwalk tour of pinelands, wet prairies, hammocks and cypress ponds. Many imaginative adult, family and kids programs are available.

50,000 books. They include multiple copies of current best-sellers, a local-history collection and numerous videos, CDs and books on tape, as well as a great children's section. The impressive 19,000-square-foot building has many clean, comfortable spots to read and relax. Unexpected touches include a reading porch and murals in the children's library that depict island-style Mother Goose rhymes. The lobby has collections of local shells and fossils, including a tooth of a prehistoric North American camel. The library offers free high-speed Internet access, available to everyone (even those without a library card). Programs include book discussion groups, lectures and book signings. Children's activities include "Small Wonders – Lapsit" for infants, "Pre-School Bookworms," "Family Story Night" and "Craft Time." Nonresidents can get a library card for $10, good for one year. The library is closed on Sundays, but open late (til 8 p.m.) on Mondays and Thursdays.

The tiny **Captiva Memorial Library** (11560 Chapin Lane, Captiva; 472-2133) emphasizes local information and nature sources. Hours are Tuesday, Thursday, Friday and Saturday 9 a.m. to 5 p.m.; Wednesdays noon to 8 p.m. Visitor cards are $5.

# Fitness centers

Most visitors assume the **Sanibel Recreational Complex** (3840 Sanibel-Captiva Rd., Sanibel; 472-0345) is only for locals. But everyone is welcome here. The free facility is run by the city of Sanibel, and features a large pool with swimming lanes; a gym with basketball courts and a weight room; and baseball, tennis and volleyball courts. Some amenities may be closed during the expansion of the adjacent Sanibel School, scheduled to be completed in 2005.

The exercise classes at the **Sanibel Fitness Center** (975 Rabbit Rd., Sanibel; 395-BODY) include aerobics, body-shaping and indoor cycling. Other classes feature yoga, karate and weight-loss, and exercise and dance for kids. Certified personal trainers are available.

The historic **Sanibel Community House** (2173 Periwinkle Way, Sanibel; 472-2155) has programs sponsored by the Sanibel Community Association, including Kripalu Hatha Yoga, Pilates mat classes and no-impact workouts.

Administered by the city of Sanibel, the **Island Seniors Program** at the Sanibel Civic Center (2401 Library Way, Sanibel; 472-5743) is designed for people over 50. Activities include low-impact aerobics, line dancing, bowling, hiking and swimming. You have to be a member to participate here, but the yearly fee is only $15.

# Day trips

The **Edison-Ford Winter Estates** preserve 1920s-era seasonal homes of legendary inventor Thomas Edison and next-door neighbor Henry Ford *(2350 McGregor Blvd., Fort Myers; 334-7419, 888-377-9475)*, nestled on the banks of the Caloosahatchee River. Daily 90-minute tours combine both estates. The main tour includes Edison's gardens, the world's largest collection of his inventions and memorabilia, a stop at his winter laboratory, and a few of Ford's early automobiles. Don't miss the unusual swimming pool. Open daily except Thanksgiving and Christmas.

**Edison home**

Get an up-close look at Florida's citrus industry at **Sun Harvest Citrus.** It offers free tours of its 24,000-square-foot packinghouse *(14810 Metro Pkwy., Fort Myers; 768-2686 or 800-743-1480)*. The market has gourmet foods and free juice samples, as well as delicious fruit smoothies and orange and lime ice cream. Groups of more than 10 require reservations, otherwise you can just drop in.

**Sun Harvest Citrus**

**Have a beer** and watch the Red Sox and Twins during spring training

The **Koreshan State Historic Site** *(U.S. 41 at Corkscrew Rd., Estero; 992-0311)* recognizes a religious community from the late 1800s that believed the earth is a hollow sphere and that the planets, moon and sun exist at the core. Envisioned for 10 million residents, the group's planned Utopian city, preserved here, never got above 250. The last four members donated the land to the state of Florida in 1961. You can tour the grounds, or rent a canoe.

**Spring training** has been a tradition in Fort Myers since the 1920s. The home teams are the Boston Red Sox and Minnesota Twins, who each play about a half-dozen games here each March. The Red Sox hold their spring training games at the 6,900-seat City of Palms Park *(downtown at 2201 Edison Ave., Ft. Myers; 334-4799)*. The Twins play at the 7,500-seat Lee County Sports Complex *(near the airport at 14100 Ben C. Pratt/Six Mile Cypress Pkwy., Ft. Myers; 768-4225)*. The small stadiums give you a unique, up-close-and-personal experience. It's a great way to spend an afternoon, especially when major stars are playing. Tickets average $10.

# Starry Starry Nights
## Island stargazing

In a typical U.S. suburb you can see about 200 stars in the night sky. But on Sanibel and Captiva you can see 3,000. The skies are ideal for stargazing here; clear, smog-free, and pitch black. Much of the land, including all the beaches, is restricted from development, so there are no lights. Even commercial areas stay dark. Street lights have been banned, as have those mercury-vapor and high-pressure sodium lights so common elsewhere.

And the night air is usually calm, giving you a clear view of indistinct objects.

You can see plenty even without a telescope; just pull out your binoculars and look up. You'll have a terrific view of the moon's surface, the phases of Venus, the four large moons of Jupiter, even the polar caps of Mars.

Pick a clear night and head outside to the beach or other dark spot. Wait 10 minutes for your eyes to adapt, then start looking at the sky. To see a faint object more clearly look slightly to the side of it, letting its light fall on the more sensitive, outer part of your eye. Try to avoid pitch-black skies (the profusion of stars makes identification more difficult) and nights with a full moon (too few stars will be visible, and the direct sunlight minimizes shadows on the moon).

Many features on the **moon's** surface are easy to see on Sanibel and Captiva. With a good pair of binoculars you can spot dozens of craters, mountain peaks and even subtle ripples on the plains. The moon is highest in the sky here in December, when it passes directly overhead. In the summer it rises only about 40 degrees.

The **Milky Way galaxy** appears as a misty band arcing over Sanibel and Captiva during the summer. In winter it's dimmer and less structured. Our neighborhood in the universe, the Milky Way has several hundred billion stars, though you can see only 5 percent of them with the naked eye. Our sun is about two-thirds of the way out from the center.

Once you've spotted one of the **planets** it's easy to see the rest: they're always in a straight line! Called the ecliptic, this line includes the sun, moon and all the eight other planets. Mercury, Venus, Mars, Jupiter and Saturn are visible from the islands with the naked eye.

Mercury is rarely seen; its tight orbit keeps it close to the sun. It hugs the morning or evening horizon. The darkest planet, it reflects only 6 percent of the sunlight it receives.

Venus, the brightest planet, alternates between being our "morning star" and "evening star," depending on its orbit. It's visible either for four hours after sunset or for four hours before sunrise. Look for Venus near the horizon in the twilight.

Called the red planet because sunlight reflects off its reddish deserts, Mars often looks like a pale red dot. It changes brightness more than any other planet, as its distance to Earth varies greatly as it circles the sun. With a small telescope you can see the planet's polar caps. With a large telescope you can see its two moons.

Jupiter glows a steady, creamy white. The second brightest planet, its four largest moons can often be seen on the islands with binoculars. Also look for the shadow cast by a Jovian moon, looking like a bullet hole in Jupiter's surface. You may be able to see the Great Red Spot, a cloud system three times wider than the Earth.

You can see the rings of Saturn with even the smallest telescope, sometimes even a pair of binoculars. Also look for the shadows the rings cast on the planet's surface. Saturn itself is a pale yellow orb.

You can see Uranus (pronounced "YER-an-us," not "your-AY-nus") with binoculars, appearing as a small blue-green disk, as well as Neptune, though it's tough to identify. Pluto is impossible to see without at least a 6-inch telescope. (Junior-high trivia: The blue-green color of Uranus is from a covering of methane gas.)

How do you tell a planet from a star? Planets don't twinkle like stars do. Twinkling occurs due to atmospheric turbulence. Planets are close enough to Earth to look like tiny disks instead of pinpoints of wavering light.

All major **constellations,** including the Southern Cross, are relatively easy to see in the dark island skies. The seven stars of the Big Dipper look like a ladle. But they're actually part of a larger constellation, Ursa Major, the large bear in mythology that guards the polar regions. The Big Dipper is always above the horizon, never rising or setting. Its stars include "The Pointers" — the two stars on the far side of the bowl from the handle.

Orion ("oh-RYE-un") is the second most prominent constellation. It represents the great hunter who bragged that he could kill any creature on earth, but met his match when a scorpion stung him on his heel and killed him. The constellation has a glittering three-star belt framed by four prominent stars, set in an hourglass, marking the hunter's shoulders and legs.

Sanibel and Captiva are the northernmost areas to see the Southern Cross, the constellation Crux. In the spring look for it due south, just above the horizon. The best month to see it is April. The Southern Cross actually looks more like the "Southern Kite," as there is no bright central star. The smallest constellation, its vertical bar points to true south.

Each **star** is a sun, just like our own. But the stars vary greatly in size and luminosity. And, from our vantage point, everything depends upon the star's distance from Earth. The closer stars look brighter, the most distant stars are invisible. Marking true north, Polaris ("poh-LAIR-iss") is the Night Star, one of the brightest stars in the sky. Find it by looking at the Big Dipper's "Pointers," and extending an imaginary line upward. Sirius ("SEAR-ee-us," which means "scorching" in Greek) is the brightest star in the sky, even brighter than most planets. Only Jupiter, Venus and Mars are brighter. Locate Sirius by first finding Orion's belt, then following the imaginary line of the belt to the left. When the air is turbulent, Sirius appears to twinkle violently, changing colors from white to blue to yellow, glittering like a diamond. When the air is still, the star has a bluish-white tinge.

Each night you can see many **satellites** in the island sky, including the International Space Station, the Hubble Space Telescope, the Tropical Rainfall Monitoring Mission and many spent Cosmos, Milstar, Delta, Progress and Meteor rockets. These satellites take just two or three minutes to cross the sky. The best time to look is during the first hour of darkness in the spring and summer, or the last hour before sunrise, as most satellites are only high enough to catch and reflect sunlight during these times. A careful observer on the islands should see at least 10 satellites in the first hour after nightfall.

How do you tell a satellite from an airplane? Satellites fade quickly from view in a clear sky; a high-flying plane doesn't. Also, satellites appear white, like stars without the twinkles. Most airplanes have flashing lights. For up-to-date, local information on satellite viewing times visit www.heavens-above.com. (Don't have your PC with you? Surf online for free at the Sanibel Public Library.)

You can even watch the **Space Shuttle** take off from the islands. The best viewing spot is the Sanibel fishing pier or the Sanibel Causeway. Look to the northeast to see the smoke trail arc up left to right across the sky.

*Sanibel was the first Florida community to adopt a Dark Skies ordinance, forcing all lights on the island to point down. The only exceptions are Christmas lights and the lighthouse beacon. The law is being phased in over 15 years to give businesses time to retrofit commercial signs.*

# Island Living

**By Mike Neal**

*M*y family and I moved here from Atlanta. We lived on the north side, in the middle of a large business and commercial area called Perimeter Center. Our apartment complex held 1,500 people, but no one knew each other. The place was vacant during the day. And though it was in one of the nicest parts of the city, most people were afraid to go for a walk outside at night.

It was hard to meet people at work, too. Though our office was in a huge complex — a three-tower mini-city that housed 3,000 workers — most everyone worked behind security-keyed doors. We knew our two secretaries, but we only saw them at work. They lived 15 or 20 miles away, in different directions.

That life went away when we moved to Sanibel. My first day here was a shock.

It started fine. I had taken our daughter to the Sanibel pool, and Micaela and I were playing in the water. But then a woman swam up next to me. Right next to me. Then she looked at me. I thought I must have violated some pool rule.

"Hi, I'm Lisa Williams," she said. Beat. Oh, my turn? "Mike Neal, and this is Micaela." It was the first time a stranger had come up and talked with me, just right out in the open, for no official reason, in years. Later I drove up to the Hess station to buy gas. "Hi Mike." It was that same woman again, pumping gas right next to me! Now what do I say? What was her name? "Hi..... Lisa."

Then I drove over to the post office. "Hi Mike." There she was again! What is going on? Why is she following me? How many different ways can you say "Hi Lisa?"

Never, ever had I lived anywhere where you see people you know over and over again, the same people in the same day. I went home and had a beer.

I had the same experience over and over again. Kevin and Cindy Pierce introduced themselves to me at the preschool. They invited Julie, Micaela and me to their home for Halloween. There we met a dozen more families, *four* of which later invited us to their home for Christmas dinner.

By the end of the year Julie and I had over 100 friends. Today I say "Hi" to someone everywhere I go. I still see Lisa everywhere, too. She's our daughter's Girl Scout leader. I coach against her daughter's soccer team.

This close-knit atmosphere makes Sanibel different than any other place I've ever lived. Surrounded by water, with only one exit, the islands have an unavoidable intimacy. "I have never been to Bailey's without seeing someone I know," says Melissa Con-

---

**Facing page:** Enjoying his new electric car lifestyle, software entrepreneur Keith Cruickshank sold his San Diego-based company and moved with his family to Sanibel in 2000

**A joke** popular among Sanibel schoolgirls:

*Three boys are out fishing. Out of the blue, they catch a mermaid. She says if they will set her free, she will grant each of them a wish.*

*"OK," says the first boy, "then double my I.Q." The mermaid says "Done." Suddenly, the guy starts reciting all the Harry Potter books, line by line.*

*The second guy says to the mermaid "Triple my I.Q." She says "Done." He starts to say the answers to* every *division problem... 234 divided by 17, 2345 divided by 32, 6548 divided by 13...*

*The last boy says to the mermaid "Quintuple my I.Q." She says "You know, I normally don't try to change people's minds when they make a wish, but please ask for something else." The guy says "Nope, I want you to increase my I.Q. five times, and if you don't, I won't set you free." She says "But you don't know what you're asking. It'll change your entire view of the universe!"*

*But the boy insisted on having his I.Q. increased by five times. So the mermaid sighed and said: "Done!"*

*And he became a girl.*

**Facing page:** Leandra Carriero, 9, boogies in a dance contest at Sanibel's annual Baileyfest

gress, a 14-year Sanibel resident who helps run her family's jewelry store. "When I had a baby people made me food, even people I didn't know that well."

Of course, this small town is also a subtropical island. You really can go to the beach every day, or ride your bike, paddle your kayak or head out in your boat.

Your wardrobe is almost exclusively T-shirts and shorts. "My husband's goal is to wear shorts 365 days a year," says Charlotte Harlow, an island mom. "So far he's made it to 363." "You only wear socks when you go off the island," adds Melissa Congress. "My husband hasn't bought a suit since we got married."

The "real world" seems far away. You forget about reality TV, talk radio and shock jocks. When Charlotte mentioned to me how her hometown of Denver has become so polluted, I forgot for a moment what "polluted" meant. Only newcomers fear crime. Kids roam freely on the bike paths; some ride their bikes to school. Many of us don't lock our cars, or even our homes.

And you stay happy. Surrounded by excited, appreciative visitors, you're always reminded how special it is here. And how fortunate you are to call these islands home.

# Who lives here

Sanibel has 6,064 official residents; Captiva has 379. The islands are a mix of retirees and families.

Forty percent of Sanibel residents are over 65, as are a third of those on Captiva. "I just couldn't help picturing living here," says Jim Sprankle, a retired major league baseball pitcher who moved here in 1995. Today he's a nationally-famous waterfowl wood carver. Some of Jim's birds hang in the refuge visitors center.

Most retirees live here only half the year, from October through March. Malcolm and Susan Harpham make the trek each fall from Connecticut. They volunteer at the refuge and belong to the local fishing club, Power Squadron and Audubon Society. "We love it here," says Susan, a former Harlem schoolteacher. "The people are so optimistic, so stimulating and interesting." They bought their Sanibel condo in 1998, on their first visit here. "We fell in love immediately — the beaches, the golfing, the biking, the refuge," says Malcolm, a retired steel-company executive. "We signed a contract before we flew back."

Of those who live here year-round, nearly half are middle-aged couples. They share a zest for life, and aren't afraid to be who they are. They ride electric cars and motorcycles. Men have pony tails, or crew cuts. Women fish, coach sports or run restaurants.

More than 1,000 35- to 54-year-olds make their permanent homes on Sanibel. Most have children, having moved here specifically to raise kids.

Rudy and Sandy Zahorchak moved here from New Jersey in 1995. Looking for a place to raise their newborn son, Rudy Jr., they first refused to consider Florida. "We thought it was too hot and full of old people," says Rudy, a pilot for Northwest Airlines. But then they came here for vacation, and discovered Sanibel's intimate culture. "I grew up in a small town in Wisconsin," Sandy says. "I knew everyone in my school, and if I went to the grocery store I'd always see someone I knew. It's like that on Sanibel. I like that little Rudy gets to grow up in a small town."

New Yorkers Steven and Susan Wener had vacationed on Sanibel for years. They moved here in 1993, when their son Matthew was born. "Long Island was no place to raise a child," Susan says. "It was so stressful, with a 90-minute commute to town." A physician, Steven gave up his private practice for a job in a Fort Myers veterans hospital. "It was absolutely worth it," he says.

The islands have few young adults. Only five percent of the island population is aged 20 to 34. Sky-high real estate prices, combined with only a handful of apartments, make Sanibel and Captiva difficult to afford if you're still building your career.

**Facing page:** Sanibel's George Lederman takes his parrot, Howie, for a beach walk. **Above:** Mules in Sanibel's 4th of July parade. **Below:** Parade participant and preschool teacher Lu Sares protects herself from a former student's squirt gun.

# Island Recipes

## Fish in Coconut Milk

By Jean Bair

4   fillets of fish
    freshly ground black pepper
2   cups milk
3   large tomatoes, sliced thin
    salt
1   cup fresh grated coconut
2   large onions, cut in rings

Sprinkle fish with salt and pepper on both sides. Arrange in a single layer in a buttered casserole. Refrigerate until ready to bake. Rinse coconut under cold water, combine in saucepan with milk. Bring to a boil, remove from heat, let stand 30 minutes. Run mixture in a blender or strain pressing out all liquid. Spread onions over the fish, cover with tomatoes. Pour coconut milk over all. Bake in a preheated oven, 375° for 45 minutes. Serve from casserole. *Do not use sugar-added coconut.*

## Sea Grape Jelly

1   quart sea grape juice
5   tablespoons lemon or lime juice
1   package powdered pectin
5   cups sugar

To prepare juice: Wash sea grapes and measure. Put in fairly large, wide pot with half as much water (1 cup water to 2 cups sea grapes). Bring to boil. Mash often with a potato masher, continue boiling until fruit is reduced to a soft pulp (25–30 minutes). Drain through a jelly bag or several layers of cheesecloth. Do not squeeze.

Place one quart juice in a wide kettle. Turn heat high and add lemon or lime juice and pectin. Bring mixture to a rolling boil. Stir in sugar and return to a rolling boil. Boil hard for 1 minute, stirring constantly. Remove from heat. Skim foam if necessary. Pour hot into hot, sterilized jars, leaving ¼-inch head space. Adjust caps. Process 5 minutes in boiling water bath.

## Prickly Pear Cactus Jelly

10  deep garnet cactus pears, very ripe
1¾ cups sugar
2   tablespoons fresh lemon juice
1½ ounces liquid pectin
½   cup dry red wine
Paraffin (optional)

Cut pears in half lengthwise and scoop out pulp. Place in food processor; whirl for 1 minute. Press mixture and liquid through a strainer to remove seed and pour liquid into a sauce pan. Add sugar and lemon juice. Stir. Bring mixture to boil. Reduce heat and simmer for 5 minutes. Stir in pectin and wine; bring to boil. Remove from heat after boiling 30 seconds; let stand 30 minutes. Pour into sterilized jars. Seal with paraffin if not using immediately.

## How to open a coconut

You'll need a hammer and a large flat-blade screwdriver. Use a coconut with no cracks, with milk you can feel sloshing inside. The process takes four minutes, tops:

**1. Drain the liquid.** Hold the coconut firmly on a hard surface. Using the hammer, tap the screwdriver about two inches into one, or two, of the nut's "eyes." Remove the screwdriver; pour out the milk.

**2. Crack the shell.** Place the coconut on a flat surface, and locate its natural fracture point, about a third of the way from the smaller end. Using the hammer, give that spot a light whack. Rotate the coconut slightly, and whack it again, the same distance from the end. Repeat several times as you rotate it on the surface. Once you see a crack develop, insert the tip of the screwdriver into it and pry up. The coconut should separate in such a way that you can easily get at the white meat.

**Facing page:** Sanibel's Terri Cummins casts for bait, which she'll use to catch a fish dinner for her family

FL 7773LZ

# Thoughts While Waiting To Make a Left Turn onto Periwinkle Way at Height of Season

**By Joseph Pacheco**

Creating the paradise is easiest:
You pick a place everyone overlooked,
That goes against the current fashion,
Has some very special things: beaches
Filled with shells, a great big sanctuary
For animals, birds, trees and man
To be as close as they can ever be
And a panoramic bridge
    to get you there.

Then you pick out your spot
    and build on it
For far less the cost you hope
It will someday be worth,
And you revel in the restrictions and the
    limitations
You would never have put up with
    elsewhere:
Government telling people what to do
To keep other people from pouring in
And ruining your Eden.

Maintaining the paradise is harder:
The place is discovered, it's hot,
    everyone wants it,
The price of land and houses,
    everything, rises
Like the Australian Pines
    you want to topple;
Builders burst out of their woodwork

Building like beavers before a flood,
Demolishing and replacing
    the bungalows
Of those who loved paradise first —
The battle to contain them rages
And you choose the side of
    necessary ordinance
And the drawbridge dragon guarding
    the moat of your island.

Travel magazines put you
    on their covers
And lists of the 50 best places
    to live and to go,
Everyone's renting and buying
    and suddenly
There are never vacancies and
    the whole world,
It seems, wants to taste and drink
The milk of your paradise.

Leaving the paradise is hardest —
The anaconda of pick-up trucks,
    campers and convertibles
Slowly choking Periwinkle Way
Suddenly relaxes,
A tiny space appears
    between two SUVs
And like a wild animal set free,
You make your left turn.

But a few Generation X'ers are here. Daniel Dix, 32, and his wife, Monica, 31, own and operate The Bean, a popular Sanibel restaurant and coffeehouse.

Living in Ohio in the mid '90s, Daniel and Monica had visited the islands often, but never thought of moving here. Their plans were to start their own business in Ohio, specifically to start a coffee shop. But the location they wanted was too expensive. Then Daniel's parents, who were vacationing here, called with some news: The Bean was for sale. "I remember we were standing in the kitchen," Monica says. "I said, 'Let's do it! Let's buy it!'"

They've never looked back. The couple often works seven days a week, but "our business is clicking," Daniel says, "and I love the environmental focus here." Monica agrees. "It's frustrating sometimes seeing everyone else on vacation when you're not. But where else can I drive to work and watch an osprey fight a kestrel for a fish?" The couple spends much of its spare time at the beach, often with their border collie, Bisou, and chihuahua, Jupa de la Vega. They've just had a baby girl, Isabella Ray.

With no major job market nearby, many islanders work out of their homes, connected to the business world by a computer and a FedEx account. Some, like Daniel and Monica, have opened restaurants, shops, service companies or other businesses. Others work as waitresses or fishing guides. A few, like Steven Wener, commute to the mainland. And yes, some islanders don't work at all. Some got lucky in the stock market. A few are blessed with wealthy parents.

# Education and government

Children in kindergarten through 8th grade attend the Sanibel School. With a little over 400 students, the school is known for its test scores — among the best in Florida — and the incredible devotion of its parents. Older kids attend high school in Fort Myers.

Most toddlers attend the Children's Education Center, a remarkable parent-owned co-op preschool. About 60 kids paint, cook, play and sing with wide-eyed enthusiasm on the five-acre campus, which parents have filled with everything from a state-of-the-art computer lab to a pedal-car race track. When we recently stopped by the kids were singing to each other, in English, Spanish, French, Japanese and *sign language.*

The entire island of Sanibel was incorporated as the city of Sanibel in 1974. It's run by an all-volunteer city council. The city places a priority on environmental issues. It protects all native vegetation, has banned drive-

**'It's raining fish!'** It's true: islanders occasionally see fish falling from the sky. They're dropped by osprey flying overhead. Fish are common on the youth sports fields, as osprey nest on top of the adjacent light poles.

**Same-day delivery.** A local letter mailed early in the morning at the Sanibel post office will be delivered that same day.

**Sanibel is the only** U.S. city that contains a national wildlife refuge within its boundaries

**With an average height** above sea level of only 4 feet, minor flooding is common on the islands, but hurricanes are the real threat. Hurricane Georges was headed directly for the islands in 1998; forecasters predicted storm surges up to 12 feet. The storm changed course just a few hours before landfall, sparing islanders major damage.

**The islands' drinking water** comes from an underground river 750 feet beneath the surface. It's processed through a reverse-osmosis system, the same as most bottled water. The islands use 3.5 million gallons of water a day; 25 percent goes for pools and landscaping.

through restaurants, and has a Dark Skies ordinance that fights light pollution. "On Sanibel environmental issues are addressed first, before people issues," says Natural Resources Director Dr. Rob Loflin.

Lee County controls parts of Sanibel, including the causeway and school. Captiva is an unincorporated county area.

# Real estate

"Wouldn't it be nice to live here?" Over a million visitors come to the islands each year, and many, if not most, ask themselves that question. But real estate prices are high.

Older, two-bedroom homes start at about $350,000. Most real-estate ads show houses in the $450,000 to $650,000 range. Homes on the bay and Gulf start in the millions. The few lots left are demanding premium prices, too. A picturesque lot on Sanibel's Dinkin's Bayou, off San Carlos Bay, was $250,000 in 2000. In 2001 it was listed again — at $450,000. "Many couples ask me 'What can we get for $250,000?'" says real-estate agent Bob Radigan. "The answer is maybe a vacant lot."

You can build a 1,600-square-foot house for about $365,000, but it'll take some work. Lots on Sanibel now start at $150,000 (Captiva land costs far more). Construction starts at $135 a foot, but the best contractors are busy at twice that rate.

Some decent existing homes — two bedrooms, on unpaved roads, away from the beach — are still available at an affordable price. But they're getting hard to find. Some fall victim to land appreciation; the lot becomes worth more than the house, so owners sell to newcomers who bring in the bulldozers. Others get remodeled and enlarged, increasing their value.

In response to high real estate costs, Sanibel officials have created the Below Market Rate Housing program. Fifty homes and apartments rent for as little as $445 a month; tenants include more than 50 children. Unlike most public housing, these units are located throughout the community, indistinguishable from the "regular" homes next door. Prospective residents have to live or work on the island and meet strict income limits.

**Above:** Samia Islam, 8, after a talent show performance. **Facing page:** Joel Mitchell, 11, competes for Sanibel's U14 soccer championship. **Below:** Kayla Weber, 8, sings in the school Christmas pageant.

# Restaurants

"Where to eat?" is a tougher question here. Sanibel and Captiva restaurants are mainly mom-and-pop affairs, each with its own take on menu, service, decor and pricing.

To write this chapter we ate at nearly every restaurant on the islands and jotted down our impressions (but note our biases: we're a middle-class couple with a 10-year-old daughter, prefer simple dishes over gourmet food, and don't eat much meat). We also surveyed hundreds of island residents, and added their preferences to ours.

**Color codes** reflect the average cost of dinner for one adult including entree, beverage and dessert (tax, tip, or alcoholic beverages not included):
    **Green** = under $10
    **Blue** = under $20
    **Purple** = under $35
    **Red** = $35 and up

**Credit cards** are indicated as follows:
V = Visa                        D = Discover Card
MC = MasterCard          DC = Diners Club
AE = American Express

 Ⴤ = **Full bar**

All restaurants are non-smoking.

## Reviews

**Amy's Over-Easy Cafe.** American *(Breakfast and lunch daily, takeout dinner available; kid's menu; in the Olde Sanibel shops, 630 Tarpon Bay Rd., Sanibel, 472-2625; V, M, D).* If you want a meal like mom used to make, you'll love Amy's. Nothing's too fancy here, but everything's good. For breakfast, the pancakes are hot (try them with blueberries) and the eggs aren't greasy. For lunch it's more of the same — grilled ham and cheese sandwiches and hot dogs — as well as fancier items like a good Summer Salad (greens with fruit, cheese, nuts and noodles) and a classic Hot Brown (an English muffin topped with turkey, cheddar, bacon, tomato and Welsh rarebit). Amy's also offers elaborate prepared dinners to go (with 24 hours notice), including grilled salmon, shrimp scampi, and South Beach Diet meals.

**Beachview Steakhouse.** American Ⴤ *(Lunch and dinner daily; kid's menu; in the Beachview Estates subdivision (no beach view) at 1100 Parview Dr., Sanibel; 472-4394; V, MC, AE, D; reservations suggested).* Steak lovers say this country-club restaurant "is like Sanibel Steakhouse with less ambiance and lower prices." Try the cowboy steak, the Chateaubriand, or the rack of lamb.

**The Bean.** American *(Breakfast, lunch, dinner daily; no table service; kid's menu; next to the SCA Periwinkle Playhouse at 2240 Periwinkle Way, Sanibel; 395-1919; V, MC).* The best coffee and light-breakfast spot on the islands is also a great stop for sandwiches, snacks and ice cream. Owners Daniel and Monica Dix bring a passion for quality to everything they do. Daniel makes the oatmeal each morning from scratch, cooking unprocessed oats for 90 minutes. Add cream, brown sugar and a sliced banana and you're in heaven. Monica bakes the banana bread (a must, if they still have any when you get there). They squeeze the juice to order, and clean the coffee machines 10 times a day. We love the Mr. Bean bagel (grilled ham, an egg, cheese and vegetables stacked inside a large bagel with a side of hashed browns and a couple of slices of fruit — the entire food pyramid), the roasted pepper panino and the butter pecan ice cream. The Bean has a high kid-friendly quotient, with chalk for the sidewalk. It's also a Wi-Fi Hot Spot — sign on the internet with either your own computer or the one in the corner.

**Bubble Room.** American Ⴤ *(Lunch and dinner daily; kid's menu; 15001 Captiva Dr. at Andy Rosse Ln., Captiva; 472-5558; V, MC, AE, D, DC).* A ramshackle assortment of small crowded rooms, the Bubble Room has notorious lines but is a must-see landmark. The rooms are filled with every old kitschy item you can imagine: Christmas bubble

---

**Facing page:** Lazy Flamingo is the local restaurant champ, the islands' most popular place to eat

lights hang on the walls, a toy train runs under the ceiling, each table is a glass-topped display. Servers ("bubble scouts") dress in Boy Scout uniforms. The best food is the bread basket: cream-cheese Bubble Bread and sticky buns. We get the Tiny Bubble sampler: a salad, choice of appetizer (try Moons over Miami) and a dessert. Desserts are huge; two or three people can share one. After your meal, walk around to marvel at all the memorabilia, which includes a 7-foot stuffed Mickey Mouse from a 1930s Disney float and a Macy's Santa's Workshop window display. To avoid the longest lines, come here for lunch.

**The Bungalow.** American ☎ *(Lunch and dinner daily; kid's menu; open until 1 a.m.; 975 Rabbit Rd. at Sanibel-Captiva Rd., Sanibel; 395-3502; V, MC, AE, D).* This working-class sports bar and locals hangout has finger foods, sandwiches and a raw bar. Families are welcome; kids like the games.

**Captiva Garden & Gourmet.** American *(Breakfast and lunch daily; no table service; across from the South Seas Resort in Chadwick's Square, Captiva; 395-0354; V, MC).* This charming cafe/gift shop/flower shop has no official place to sit, but there are three patio tables out front. Breakfast means pastries, bagels or croissants and coffee. For lunch try the special, especially if it's the duck-breast sandwich.

**Chadwick's.** American ☎ *(Lunch and dinner daily; kid's menu; at the entrance to the South Seas Resort, Captiva; 472-7575; V, MC, AE, D, DC).* Buffets feature reassuring food such as fried chicken and prime rib. Desserts have loads of whipped cream.

**Cheeburger Cheeburger.** American *(Lunch and dinner daily; kid's menu; 2413 Periwinkle Way, Sanibel; 472-6111; V, MC, AE, D, DC).* The burgers are good, have lots of cheese and come as big as you want 'em. The creamy shakes and malts are served in big frosty tins. Expect a long wait at peak hours. This is the original Cheeburger Cheeburger, which is now a Florida chain.

**Chocolate Expressions.** Snacks and desserts *(No tables; in Periwinkle Place, 2075 Periwinkle Way, Sanibel; 472-3837; V, MC).* Yummy treats tempt you everywhere you look: hand-dipped chocolate strawberries, imported chocolates and candies, homemade fudge, gelato, yogurt and 40 flavors of jellybeans. Our picks here are the Sun Harvest lemonade and the rich and creamy fruit smoothies, the best on the islands.

**Dairy Queen.** Fast food *(No indoor seating; 1048 Periwinkle Way, Sanibel; 472-1170, debit cards).* A friend calls this the best Dairy Queen in the U.S. We want to agree, though the prices are high and the food is, well, Dairy Queen. But coming here at night, sitting out on a concrete picnic table and licking down a drippy Dilly Bar does have its charms. Adults are free to relax, as the crowds are exclusively island and tourist families — no carloads of teens. Grandfathered in as the only fast-food restaurant on the islands (now *there's* a business), this DQ is prohibited from modernizing. So it's still just a walk-up, with the exact architecture it had in the 1960s. Somebody ought to declare it a landmark.

**Doc Ford's Sanibel Rum Bar & Grille.** American/Caribbean ☎ *(Lunch and dinner daily; kid's menu; 975 Rabbit Rd. at Sanibel-Captiva Rd., Sanibel; 472-8311; V, MC, AE, D; call-ahead seating suggested, reservations available for parties of six or more).* The Deep South and tropical influences recall Sanibel's heritage as a farming community and Cuban fishing outpost. But there's nothing old or tired here — the tables and booths are clean, the sports-bar TVs are crisp and clear and the menu is full of creative dishes. Tropical sauces and spices highlight the best choices. A mango-and-corn chutney makes the shrimp sausage quesadillas a light, zesty appetizer. For an entree, try the fish tacos (chunks of grouper tossed with cilantro and papaya) or the pan-fried grouper sandwich, topped with slaw and a yummy remoulade. For kids, our daughter says skip the kid's menu and get

---

**Color code:** Avg. cost of dinner for one adult: **Under $10. Under $20. Under $35. Over $35.**

an appetizer. The bar serves over 40 brands of rum and some imaginative rum drinks. The best is the Mojito, a Cuban concoction of rum, sugar and soda served in a canning jar, with slices of lime and mint leaves. For straight rum try the smooth Zaya, from Guatemala. Or impress your friends and order a Dark and Stormy, a not-on-the-menu specialty made with Gosling's Black Seal (a sailor's favorite, from Bermuda) and ginger beer. Doc Ford, by the way, is an ex-CIA spy turned local marine biologist — and completely fictional. He's the main character in a series of novels by local mystery writer Randy Wayne White, who drops in here a few times a week.

**Dolce Vita.** Northern Italian ☥ *(Dinner nightly; 1244 Periwinkle Way, Sanibel; 472-5555; V, MC, AE, D, DC; reservations suggested).* Attracting a well-heeled older crowd, this cosmopolitan restaurant features dueling pianos each night until 12:30. For appetizers try the fritto misto, escargot or shrimp and avocado cocktail. Popular entrees include veal chops, rigatoni and a rustic Italian quesadilla. Dolce Vita gets mixed reviews in our islander survey. "Its specials are very good and the waitstaff is phenomenal," says one, but another calls it "snooty, overpriced and much too noisy." Repeat customers can store a case of wine in the locker and drink from it each visit.

**East End Deli.** American/British takeout *(Breakfast and lunch daily, dinner daily in season; kid's menu; free delivery 12:30 p.m. to 2:30 p.m. in local area; no tables; near the lighthouse at 359 Periwinkle Way, Sanibel, 472-9622; V, MC, AE).* An enormous menu of good food at fair prices makes the East End Deli a great mom-and-pop find. In this case, mom and pop are Kim and Rob Price, recent transplants from Winchester, England. Their menu board lists 43 subs, sandwiches, salads and soups — and the case in front has another dozen or so sides and desserts — all homemade and all priced like you're in Ft. Myers, not on Sanibel. Everything's good, but our favorites are the British recipes — the Welsh egg (a hard-boiled egg in a thick coating of potato and egg breading, deep fried), the Sticky Tof-

fee pudding (served hot, with dates and butterscotch sauce) and the Banoffee pie (a banana cheesecake topped with toffee and meringue, so sinfully sweet two should share it). There's breakfast too, from coffee and muffins to a secret-family-recipe rarebit (an English muffin covered in hot cheese sauce). No tables, but you can sit down on the benches outside. Chances are you'll meet Kim, Rob, or maybe even their kids when you stop in. They're some of the hardest-working folks on Sanibel.

**Ellington's.** Continental/American ☥ *(Breakfast and dinner daily, seasonal Sunday jazz brunch; kid's menu; at the Sanibel Inn, 937 East Gulf Dr., Sanibel, 337-5299; V, M, AE, D, DC; reservations suggested; formerly Portofino).* Thanks to the efforts of new chef Amy Visco, the cuisine here easily rivals that of Sanibel's more established gourmet bistros. Appetizers include a shrimp cocktail with fruit salsa and a corn-and-crab chowder seasoned with a touch of jalapeño peppers. For entrees, try the ahi tuna with pineapple-citrus sauce or the duck breast with pickled cherry compote. Other items include steak, sea bass and lobster. With live jazz (sometimes with famous guests) nightly, Ellington's mix of quality food and entertainment shouldn't be overlooked.

**Gramma Dot's Seaside Salon.** Seafood *(Lunch and dinner daily; kid's menu; at the Sanibel Marina, 634 North Yachtsman, Sanibel; 472-8138; V, MC).* This dockside institution has "such a quaint seaside feel," says a regular. Screened windows and sea-dog decor complement the seafood — try the coconut or bacon-wrapped shrimp, mesquite grouper or Maine lobster (reserve one in advance). Homemade potato chips come with all lunches.

**The Green Flash.** Seafood ☥ *(Lunch and dinner daily; kid's menu; early-bird specials; 15183 Captiva Dr., Captiva; 472-3337; V, MC, AE, D; reservations suggested).* This bayside restaurant has a good lunch sandwich: the Green Flash features turkey or vegetables and cheese on grilled focaccia. Or try the BBQ shrimp and bacon. Good starters for dinner include oysters Rockefeller and shrimp bisque. For dinner try the garlicky grouper Cafe de Paris or the salmon with dill Bernaise sauce. Watch for otters in back.

**Greenhouse Grill.** Mediterranean *(Lunch and dinner daily; kid's menu; outside patio dining; 2407 Periwinkle Way, Sanibel; 472-6882; V, MC, AE; reservations suggested).* As soon as you walk in, the subtle lighting and great aromas from the kitchen tell you this is a special place. As modern and sophisticated as restaurants in New York or San Francisco, the Greenhouse is true (not superficial) gourmet, using the freshest ingredients. Locals swear by the bouillabaisse and the escargot, a 16th-century recipe discovered from the Borgia family. Our favorites: the mozzarella and tomato appetizer with buffalo cheese and basil dressing, the pasta specials, the desserts flown in from Milan and the homemade skin-on fries and lemonade at lunch. Actually, it's worth a trip just for the crusty bread and spicy oil dip.

**Greenside Grille at the Dunes.** American ☥ *(Lunch Mon.–Sat., dinner Wed.–Sat.; kid's menu; 949 Sandcastle Rd., Sanibel; 472-3355; V, MC, AE, D, DC; reservations suggested).* Everyone's welcome at this relaxed restaurant on a golf course. Wednesday is all-you-can-eat pasta night. For lunch try the Oriental chicken salad or grilled Reuben.

**Gully's.** American *(Breakfast, lunch and dinner daily; kid's menu; in the Periwinkle Place shopping center, 2075 Periwinkle Way, Sanibel, 472-2525; V, M, AE, D; reservations suggested; formerly the Periwinkle Place Bistro; formerly the Sanibel Island Chowder Co.).* The new owners of this venerable Periwinkle Place eatery are working hard to have it finally fulfill its promise. Renee and Richard Prestipino have expanded the menu to include everything from Buffalo wings to New York strip steak, and have replaced this spot's infamous zombie waitresses with a helpful, friendly staff. For lunch, try the Cobb salad or Sanibel Island wrap. For dinner, we like the Ropa Vieja (Cuban shredded beef simmered in onions and peppers) and chicken pasta. The soothing chowder is a good holdover from the past.

**Hungry Heron.** American *(Breakfast, lunch and dinner daily; kid's menu; across from Eckerd at 2330 Palm Ridge Rd., Sanibel; 395-2300; V, MC, AE, D).* Kids love the TVs tuned in to Nickelodeon and the Disney Channel here. The food comes in generous portions; the menu has over 250 selections. Best bets include the baked Beach Bread and roast beef or Hot-to-Trot sandwiches. Monday-night prime rib specials and a seasonal weekend breakfast buffet are good values.

**Huxter's Market and Deli.** Takeout *(Breakfast, lunch and dinner daily; no tables; 1203 Periwinkle Way, Sanibel; 472-6988; V, MC, AE, D).* This family-owned store features fried chicken, salads, generous sandwiches and homemade desserts. Huxter's says it sells the coldest beer on the island, at 28º F.

**Island Cow.** American ☥ *(Breakfast, lunch, dinner daily; kid's menu; 2163 Periwinkle Way, Sanibel; 472-0606; V, MC, AE, D).* One of the most hospitable place on the islands, live music fills the air here most evenings. You can eat outside, but we love an inside booth — the state-of-the-art cooling system is refreshing any time of year. Our favorites on the gazillion-item menu: the catfish Reuben sandwich and the messy patty melt. Locals swear by the salads and seafood quesadillas. You can fill up on the black beans and rice appetizer ($5.95), which includes sour cream and salsa. For breakfast get the special (a sure thing) or the breakfast quesadilla.

**Island Inn.** American *(Breakfast and (seasonal) dinner daily; 3111 West Gulf Dr., Sanibel; 472-1561; V, MC, AE, D, DC; reservations suggested).* Those staying here always have first priority, but squeezing in breakfast or a formal dinner at this Sanibel landmark will be one of your more unique experiences. This is true Old Florida; not much has changed for decades. Breakfasts are a fixed $11, dinners $36 (including appetizer and dessert); the menu changes daily. All the food is homemade. Call first.

---

**Island Pizza and Pasta.** Italian *(Lunch and dinner daily; kid's menu; delivery; 1619 Periwinkle Way, Sanibel; 472-1581; V, MC).* The tight booths of this 1970's-era hangout remind you how much you've fattened up, but it's rarely crowded and the food is fine. Try the garlic bread, spaghetti carbonara, penne San Remo or angel hair Caprese.

**Jacaranda.** Seafood ☝ *(Dinner nightly; early-bird discounts; 1223 Periwinkle Way, Sanibel; 472-1771; V, MC, AE, D; reservations suggested).* A loyal, affluent crowd keeps the Jacaranda packed. This civilized restaurant boasts an outdoor patio and attentive service. Start with Sancap Shrimp, four jumbos sauteed with spiced rum, coconut cream and Florida orange juice. Top entrees include Florida snapper en papillote and chicken Giovanni. After dinner there's live music and dancing in the Patio Lounge.

**Jean Paul's French Corner.** French *(Dinner Mon.-Sat. Dec.-April; next to the Sanibel Post Office at 708 Tarpon Bay Rd., Sanibel; 472-1493; V, MC; reservations suggested).* Jean Paul's is only open now and then. But when it is, this intimate getaway offers cuisine prepared with care and imagination. Try the duck with black-currant sauce, sea scallops with saffron sauce or salmon with dill sauce.

**Jerry's Restaurant.** American *(Breakfast, lunch and dinner daily; kid's menu; inside Jerry's Supermarket, 1700 Periwinkle Way, Sanibel; 472-9300; V, MC, AE, D).* The no-nonsense waitresses have accents straight from Minnesota (Jerry's home base) at this 1970s-era supermarket diner, where the value is tough to beat. The BLTs have big tomato slices; the coconut cream pie is delicious. Kids love the spaghetti and the Bodacious Brownie. The fresh salad bar is a plus, too. For breakfast try French toast. Giant booths overlook a tropical courtyard.

**Johnny's Pizza.** Takeout *(Lunch and dinner daily; free delivery; no tables; 2496 Palm Ridge Rd., Sanibel; 472-1023).* Our picks at this Chicago-style pizzeria are the garlicky white pizza and the Grandma Rose Pizza (with a romano and parmigiana base covered with crushed plum tomatoes and topped with cheddar and mozzarella).

**Keylime Bistro.** New American ☝ *(Lunch and dinner daily; live outdoor entertainment; 11509 Andy Rosse Ln., Captiva; 395-4000; V, MC, AE, D, DC; reservations suggested for larger parties).* Gourmet funk? Where else can you eat crab cakes with a key-lime aoli (spicy and garlicky), or stuffed shrimp in a lobster sauce (rich and creamy), while you sit outside listening to reggae music under a tiki hut? Keylime Bistro makes its own sushi; the tuna tataki and inside-out tuna roll are standouts. The creative salads are first-rate. The light-as-air key lime cheesecake is the best dessert on the islands, and enough for three people. On weekends the restaurant serves until midnight.

## Where islanders eat

We asked 337 Sanibel and Captiva residents to name the three island restaurants where they eat the most. The top 10 answers:

1. Lazy Flamingo
2. Trader's
3. Timbers / Sanibel Grill
4. Island Cow
5. Doc Ford's
6. Pippin's
7. Hungry Heron
8. Lighthouse Cafe
9. R.C. Otter's
10. Matzaluna

We also asked island kids (ages 5 to 18) to name their favorite restaurants:

1. Lazy Flamingo
2. Island Cow
3. Hungry Heron
4. Doc Ford's
5. Matzaluna
6. Schnapper's Hots
7. Subway
8. Bungalow
9. Timbers / Sanibel Grill
10. Mona Lisa's

*Note: Lazy Flamingo is far and away the top place to eat among locals, getting twice the votes of any other restaurant.*

**Latte da Coffee Shop & Deli.** American *(Breakfast, lunch, dinner daily; outdoor cafe seating; next to R.C. Otter's at 11508 Andy Rosse Ln., Captiva; 472-0234; V, MC, AE, D, DC).* This tiny hideaway is the little sister to the Keylime Bistro across the street. It offers coffee, homemade breads and pasta, sandwiches, smoothies, homemade ice cream and daily specials.

**La Vigna.** Italian *(Dinner daily; 1625 Periwinkle Way, Sanibel; 472-5453; V, MC, AE, D).* This comfortable white-tablecloth restaurant is run by two Italian brothers. The quality food is well priced and pretension-free. Dinner starts with terrific secret-recipe crusty bread (the server would only mention fennel) with a dipping sauce. Locals recommend the vegetable lasagna, the shrimp dishes and any special. The bargains here are the imaginative 10-inch pizzas; almost too big for one person. Half-portions of pasta dinners are available for children. Don't miss the moist, cheesy tiramisu: the mangos for the puree come from the owner's own trees.

**Lazy Flamingo II.** American/Seafood *(Lunch and dinner daily; kid's menu; just west of the Sanibel Causeway at 1036 Periwinkle Way, Sanibel; 472-6939).* "Friendly, easy to get to, great prices, food is always consistent." That's what others say. We say this is the best seafood on the islands. If we had to choose our last meal, it would be served in a big booth here and involve blackened grouper and a few bottles of the frigid beer they keep iced behind the bar. We substitute a small Caesar salad for the fries that come with every meal. Or just order a special off the board, sure bets that the manager makes up that morning (don't dare pass up the sliced pork sandwich). In our surveys, islanders rave about nearly everything else on the menu, too: the conch fritters and chowder, cheeseburgers, mussels, peel-and-eat shrimp, teriyaki hot wings. Island kids say the Buffalo wings are the best things to eat in any island restaurant. As you can guess, everyone, regardless of age or class, eats here, so expect a wait anytime from 5 to 8 p.m. during season, and maybe a short delay in other months. Don't let the raw bar/sports bar theme fool you, this is a true family restaurant. The original **Lazy Flamingo I** *(at Blind Pass, 6520 Pine Ave., Sanibel; 472-5353; V, MC, AE, D)* has a similar menu in a tiny 7-booth setting. It fills quickly after sunset.

**Lighthouse Cafe.** American *(Breakfast, lunch and (seasonal) dinner daily; kid's menu; in the Seahorse Shops, 362 Periwinkle Way, Sanibel; 472-0303; V, MC; call-ahead seating).* Sanibel native Mike Billheimer's island landmark serves all three meals, but there's a reason the sign out front says "The World's Best Breakfast." Bring a hearty appetite for rich Eggs Benedict, whole wheat granola hotcakes, coconut french toast, or the Lighthouse Special, an omelet with turkey, broccoli, mushrooms and cream cheese topped with homemade hollandaise sauce. Ask for a booth; they're big and worth a wait. The fast service will get you in and out in no time, but in season get here before 8 a.m. to avoid a long wait. For lunch try a fish sandwich, hamburger or salad. Reasonably-priced dinners are served from mid-December through Easter.

**Mad Hatter.** New American *(Seasonal lunch and dinner daily; at the western tip of Sanibel at Blind Pass, 6467 Sanibel-Captiva Rd., Sanibel; 472-0033; V, MC, AE, D; reservations suggested).* Don't let the tiny barn-like exterior fool you. Like Alice through the looking glass, you'll soon walk into a pink, white and green dining room with a view of the Gulf. An ideal place for a romantic dinner with a bottle of wine, the Mad Hatter has an innovative flair with California, Southwest and Southern cuisines, using recipes that combine strong and mild flavors. The menu changes monthly, with no dish repeated, but you'll always get a wonderful basket of crusty breads (our favorite is the sun-dried tomato). Islanders recommend the lamb chops, tuna or scallop dishes. "Not quite as good as it had been," one writes,

---

**Color code:** Avg. cost of dinner for one adult: **Under $10. Under $20. Under $35. Over $35.**

"but still an interesting menu and a lovely decor." We loved the Seacakes appetizer (lump crab meat, crawfish, red bell pepper and onion, served with honey mustard sauce and mango salsa). The Crème Brûlée is made with real vanilla bean, not extract, so there's no hint of bitterness. There's no kid's menu, but the kitchen keeps some basic pasta and chicken on hand.

**Mama Rosa's Pizzeria.** Italian *(Lunch and dinner daily; kid's pizza; no table service; delivery; across from the South Seas Resort in Chadwick's Square, Captiva; 472-7672; V, MC, AE, D).* Come to this small pizzeria for its decadent Beach Bread: garlic bread layered with ricotta cheese and tomato, topped with melted Monterey jack and cheddar cheese. The pizza's good too; hand-tossed with sun-dried tomatoes, artichoke hearts and other toppings. Any pizza can be prepared "white," without tomato sauce. The menu also has calzones, subs and salads.

**Matzaluna.** Italian ϒ *(Dinner daily; kid's menu; 1200 Periwinkle Way, Sanibel; 472-1998; V, MC, AE; call-ahead seating).* Decorated with food stock and Italian flags, this upbeat two-story restaurant fills up early during season. The crusty bread with garlic dipping sauce is a hit; the freshly grated Romano cheese is sharp. The pizzas are cooked in a wood-burning oven and have good crusts. The superb item is the rich crab bisque, available only on Fridays and Saturdays. Two diners told us to mention the "best eggplant parmigiana you will get anywhere." Island kids go for the ravioli, hamburgers and ice cream. Butcher-paper tablecloths and crayons inspire would-be artists; customer drawings on the walls include a sketch from Stephen King.

**McT's Shrimp House.** Seafood ϒ *(Dinner daily; kid's menu; early-bird discounts; next to the 7-Eleven at 1523 Periwinkle Way, Sanibel; 472-3161; V, MC, AE, D; call-ahead seating).* Everyone raves about the mud pie: an infamous concoction of Oreo cookies, chocolate fudge, coffee ice cream, heavenly hash ice cream and whipped cream. Of course shrimp is the main entree, especially the all-you-can-eat steamed platter, but the crab's

good too. The first 100 persons after 4 p.m. qualify for early-bird specials. In the back, McT's Tavern has a pinball machine, a huge TV, appetizers and light dinners. Notice the bar ceiling, built of Australian pine roots.

**The Mermaid Kitchen and Cake Factory.** New American/Seafood. ϒ *(Lunch and dinner daily; kid's menu; in the Forever Green Shops, 2055 Periwinkle Way, Sanibel, 472-1242; V, M, AE; reservations suggested).* In another slab of restaurant space that seems to change owners every few years, The Mermaid Kitchen and Cake Factory is the new version of Katie Gardenia's. An eccentric island icon who founded Captiva's Bubble Room, Katie also created

## Our Best Bets

### Breakfast

1. Pancakes and eggs, Sunset Grill
2. Mr. Bean bagel, The Bean
3. Breakfast quesadilla, Island Cow

### Lunch

1. Crab and corn chowder, Sunset Grill
2. Blackened tuna sandwich, Lazy Flamingo
3. Catfish Reuben, Island Cow

### Dinner

1. Blackened grouper, Lazy Flamingo
2. Any special, La Vigna
3. Shrimp and pasta, Greenhouse Grill

### Dessert

1. Key lime cheesecake, Keylime Bistro
2. Key lime pie, Mucky Duck
3. White chocolate bread pudding, Tropical Temptations

### Kid's picks*

1. Clam chowder, Lazy Flamingo
2. Vanilla malt, Cheeburger Cheeburger
3. Poached eggs, Sunset Grill
4. Bread pudding, East End Deli
5. Mr. Bean bagel, The Bean
6. Dirt Cup, Pinocchio's
7. Ravioli, Matzaluna

* Choices of Micaela Neal, age 10

this place, an upscale cafe decorated with hundreds of examples of mermaid kitsch. Some of her recipes live on here, including the Salmon Escalade (with a sun-dried bing cherry sauce) and the chiffon Mermaid Cake (once called Katie Kake), which features an icing made of whipped cream and pralines. The prices often outweigh the portions here, but the unique, romantic atmosphere is worth a stop for visitors, especially for a light lunch.

**Mona Lisa's Pizzeria and Deli.** Italian *(Lunch and dinner daily; free delivery; 2440 Palm Ridge Rd., Sanibel; 472-0212; V, MC, AE, D, DC).* Set in a small strip center next to Goodwill, this pizza parlor has a spare atmosphere but good service. Order by honest pizza by huge slices or by the pie. Unusual toppings include meatballs, ricotta cheese, breaded eggplant and spinach. The subs have lots of meat and cheese; also available are pastas, salads, Italian tiramisu and, of course, key lime pie. The $1.95 pizza slice is a bargain, as are the $3.99 lunch specials.

**Morgan's Forest.** American ♈ *(Breakfast and dinner daily; kid's menu; at the Holiday Inn, 1231 Middle Gulf Dr. at Donax St., Sanibel; 472-4100; V, MC, AE, D).* Younger children get a kick out of this dense "forest" of plastic plants. Stuffed animals, ground-level fog and thunder and lightning effects add to the kitsch. Popular dinner entrees include grouper, shrimp, shrimp-stuffed tenderloin and crab cakes. Bacon and eggs are the best selections on the breakfast buffet.

**Mozella's Foodworks.** American *(Breakfast, lunch, dinner daily; takeout; near Hungry Heron at 2330 Palm Ridge Rd., Sanibel; 472-2555; V, MC).* Long-time favorite island caterer Mozella Jordan finally has opened her own place, offering her delicious homemade food to go. Try the pumpkin soup, cold strawberry-cream soup or sweet potato pie (our mouths water as we write). The onion sandwich (much better than it sounds) and bok choy salad are island institutions. Look for the purple door in the Hungry Heron plaza, across from Eckerd.

**Mucky Duck.** American/British/Seafood *(Lunch and dinner Mon.–Sat.; kid's menu; 11546 Andy Rosse Ln., Captiva; 472-3434; V, MC, AE, D, DC).* Victor Mayeron and his family always have a kind greeting for you at their waterfront restaurant, which combines a warm, friendly atmosphere with cheeky British humor (don't complain if you don't sit by the window). The fare is comfort food and fresh seafood. At lunch, go for the charred and tasty Pub burger, a great value. At dinner it's all good; islanders especially like the crab cakes. Don't miss the fluffy and creamy key lime pie. It's made with fresh whipped cream daily by Mrs. Mayeron, and we think it's the best on the islands (though Victor often parades around the room with free forkfuls of other desserts at dinner time). With its low ceilings, bare-wood floors and corny signs and posters, this little hideaway on the Gulf could pass for a cozy country inn. In fact it used to be the Gulf View Inn, back in the 1930s. A current real-estate boom has torn down much of Andy Rosse Lane, but the Mayerons march on, refusing to sell. Don't miss the patio and beach, where there's live music every night but Sunday.

**Nick's Place.** Takeout ice cream and coffee *(Snacks daily except Sunday; no tables; in the Bailey's Shopping Center at 2477 Periwinkle Way, Sanibel; 472-0770).* This literal hole-in-the-wall offers Columbo yogurt, frozen custards and ice cream treats. Coffees include cappuccino, espresso and latte.

**Noopie's.** Japanese *(Dinner nightly; kid's menu; at the Sundial Resort, 1451 Middle Gulf Dr., Sanibel; 395-6014; V, MC; reservations required).* The authentic Teppanyaki Japanese dining here features seafood and steaks prepared on a table-grill in front of you. Noopie's Special Dinner is a good choice if you'd like to try a variety of dishes; a sushi appetizer, Japanese soup, Oriental salad, shrimp complement, two entree choices, stir-fry vegetables, fried rice, bean sprouts, pea pods and Noopie's sundae for $28.95. The servers prepare the sizzling fare with style and flourish.

---

**Color code:** Avg. cost of dinner for one adult: **Under $10. Under $20. Under $35. Over $35.**

**Old Captiva House.** Continental/Seafood ℧ *(Breakfast and dinner daily; kid's menu; at 'Tween Waters Inn, 15951 Captiva Dr., Captiva; 472-5161; V, MC, AE, D; reservations suggested).* The new chef here has made an excellent restaurant even better. The very definition of Old Florida, everything here is green and white, with hardwood floors, shaded candles on the tables, French doors and windows all around, and a live piano. "Ding" Darling and his wife ate here routinely; his original drawings hang on the walls. If you are on the islands over Thanksgiving or Christmas, come here for the buffet (you *must* have the pumpkin pie). We can't imagine a better holiday meal.

**Pinocchio's.** Ice cream *(No tables, benches outside; near the lighthouse at 362 Periwinkle Way, Sanibel; 472-6566).* This tiny shop's claim to fame is its not-too-sweet Sanibel Krunch ice cream, with nuts and coconut. All the ice cream is homemade. The pistachio uses whole nuts. Kids can't resist the Dirt Cup; soft-serve chocolate and vanilla, crushed Oreos and chocolate sprinkles, with gummi worms peeking through. The coffee bar serves espresso, cappuccino, Cuban and iced coffee as well as the regular cup of joe, all ground and brewed to order. Other choices include root beer floats, hand-dipped chocolates and fudge, and fresh baked shortbread.

**Pippin's.** American ℧ *(Dinner nightly; early-bird specials; kid's menu; in Tahitian Gardens, 1975 Periwinkle Way, Sanibel; 395-9111; V, MC, AE, D, DC; reservations suggested).* This 1970s throwback features steaks, prime rib, ribs, seafood and a big salad bar. The homemade Death by Chocolate Cake is an indulgence. Kids love the tropical fish tanks.

**R.C. Otter's.** American *(Breakfast, lunch and dinner daily; kid's menu; 11506 Andy Rosse Ln., Captiva; 395-1142; V, MC, AE, D; call-ahead seating).* Lots of island feel here: A funky painted building, live laid-back music and front-porch and patio dining. The huge menu has items to please anyone. We recommend starting with the cold strawberry bisque, or the black beans and rice topped with salsa, sweet onions and sour cream. Good sandwiches include the Cuban, barbecue pork and grouper Reuben. For bigger appetites try the crab-and-black-bean burrito or the blackened scallops.

**Riviera.** Mediterranean/Northern Italian ℧ *(Dinner nightly; kid's menu; ½ mile west of Tarpon Bay Rd. at 2761 W. Gulf Dr., Sanibel; 472-1141; V, MC, AE, D, DC; reservations suggested).* A dark, live-piano island institution. Appetizers include baked oysters (with spinach, ouzo, cream and Swiss cheese) and pistou soup (vegetables, cranberry beans, pasta and spinach pesto). For an entree try the Lamb Tajine, stewed in terracotta, ginger, coriander, onions, prunes and couscous. Kids love the rock candy dessert.

**Rosie's Island Market & Deli.** Takeout *(Breakfast, lunch and dinner daily; no tables; free delivery 11 a.m. to 2 p.m.; next to the Lighthouse Cafe at 362 Periwinkle Way, Sanibel; 472-6656; V, MC, D).* Leslie Barker has a true restaurant-to-go inside her small market on Sanibel's east end. Breakfasts feature fresh bakery items, pancakes and omelets; lunches include seafood baskets, deli sandwiches (big enough for two, with soft buns), hamburgers, hot dogs and pizza. For dinner it's meatloaf, mashed potatoes, fried chicken and Tex-Mex. Specials vary daily. For dessert try a Pelican Poop, a cream-cheese ball covered in chocolate.

**Sanibel Cafe.** American *(Breakfast, lunch and dinner daily; kid's menu; in the Tahitian Gardens shopping center, 2007 Periwinkle Way, Sanibel; 472-5323; V, MC; call-ahead seating.)* Each table is a shadow box of shells at this cozy cafe. The banana pancakes and the coconut French toast are good for breakfast, as is the black raisin bread with cream cheese and homemade jam. The lunch and dinner menus feature sandwiches, meatloaf and similar items.

**Sanibel Steakhouse.** American ℧ *(Dinner nightly; 1473 Periwinkle Way, Sanibel; 472-5700; V, MC, AE, D, DC; reservations suggested).* The hand-cut USDA Prime steaks here are the island's most expensive, and its standard of excellence. Good crab cakes, too. Try the peanut butter pie for dessert.

**Sunset Grill** at Santiva

**Schnapper's Hots.** Takeout *(Breakfast, lunch and dinner daily; kid's menu; no tables; 1528 Periwinkle Way, Sanibel; 472-8686).* These friendly NEW Yorkers love, honor and cherish hot dogs (and cheesy bumper stickers). They char-grill dogs, burgers and sausages so well they pop when you bite them (try the Polish sausage or bratwurst). Also on the menu: tasty chicken wings, a fish-and-chips-style grouper sandwich, and, new for 2004, pizza (pies up to 18 inches). There's hand-dipped ice cream, too.

**The Seafood Factory.** American ☿ *(Lunch and dinner daily; kid's menu; in the Bailey's Shopping Center, 2499 Periwinkle Way, Sanibel; 472-2323; V, MC, AE, D, DC; reservations suggested).* The standout here is the Carolina she-crab soup. At the adjacent Factory Lounge bar, try the tuna.

**The Shoppe.** Takeout *(Lunch and dinner daily; no tables; at the Sundial Resort, 1451 Middle Gulf Dr., Sanibel; 472-4151 ext. 3840).* This well-stocked store has deli specials such as fresh-baked pizza, hot entrees, sandwiches, salads, pastries, bagels and gourmet coffees. It's a great spot to grab a bite while cruising Sanibel on a bike.

**Subway.** Takeout *(Lunch and dinner daily; no tables; 2496 Palm Ridge Rd., Sanibel; 472-1155).* A rare island franchise, this Subway has sporadic hours. The attendant takes a break a couple times a day, and closes up for a half-hour or so. Otherwise, it's healthy sandwiches and salads at a good price. Breads are baked fresh four times a day.

**Sunset Grill.** Seafood/Steakhouse ☿ *(Breakfast, lunch and dinner daily; at Blind Pass at 6536 Pine Ave., Sanibel; 472-2333; V, MC, AE, D; reservations suggested).* An antique copper ceiling, open-air kitchen and pecky-cypress paneling gives this tiny place a relaxed charm. Every table faces Turner Beach. This is Lazy Flamingo-founder Larry Thompson's "serious" restaurant, with an impressive wine selection and chef John Feagans preparing gourmet-quality meals. Any nightly special is a good choice, but our favorite dinner is straight off the menu: the beef tenderloin, a melt-in-your-mouth steak wrapped in proscuitto ham and served with gorgonzola potatoes. For appetizers try the crab cakes or bruschetta with goat cheese. The terrific black bean soup is topped with sour cream. Lunches are a good value: quality sandwiches and killer soup. The real secret here is breakfast: it's the best on the islands. Quality ingredients and a first-class kitchen combine for terrificly light pancakes and perfect eggs. There's never a morning crowd except on Saturday, when the bike club treks up here.

**Sunshine Cafe.** American/Steakhouse *(Lunch and dinner daily; kid's menu; Captiva Village Square, Captiva; 472-6200; V, MC, AE, D; reservations suggested).* An open-air kitchen adds to the feel at this intimate eatery. The menu changes frequently and offers a handful of fresh selections for dinner. Lunches include Thai salad, hamburgers and wood-grilled pork loin. Dinners include sesame-crusted yellowfin tuna salad, Colorado lamb chops, and nightly fish specials.

**Thistle Lodge.** American/Seafood ☿ *(Lunch and dinner daily; kid's menu; early-bird specials; at the Casa Ybel Resort, 2255 West Gulf Dr., Sanibel; 472-9200; V, MC, AE, D, DC; reservations suggested).* A great view with a beachfront sunset awaits you at the quiet, classy Casa Ybel restaurant. A new chef in 2002 has really improved the food. Try the chipotle BBQ chicken breast sandwich for lunch. Interesting dinner entrees include scallops glazed with potato lattice and pan roasted Maine lobster.

---

**Color code:** Avg. cost of dinner for one adult: **Under $10. Under $20. Under $35. Over $35.**

**Timbers/Sanibel Grill.** Seafood and Steak-house/Sports Bar ℹ *(Dinner daily; kid's menu; across from the post office at 703 Tarpon Bay Rd., Sanibel; 472-3128; V, MC, AE; call-ahead seating).* This light and airy casual restaurant offers no surprises: just seafood and steaks, cooked to order, in a nice, comfortable atmosphere. There's a long list of fresh catches and specials daily; the coconut cake is a good dessert. Next door the Sanibel Grill sports bar (open until midnight) offers good pizza and sandwiches (the best is the char-grilled chicken sandwich with mango chutney sauce), "chicken lips," and a tasty spinach dip.

**Trader's.** New American/Seafood *(Lunch and dinner daily; kid's menu; 1551 Periwinkle Way, Sanibel; 472-7242; V, MC, AE, D; reservations suggested).* The dining room has cool, clean air and the food is fresh, interesting and unusual. No need to look at the menu; the specials are what you want, especially the Cajun scallops. Other specials can be macadamia grouper with a Thai peanut sauce and mango salsa, blackened mahi-mahi with roasted corn salsa and a lime remoulade, and horseradish-crusted swordfish with a roasted red pepper sauce. If they are serving a crisp for dessert, get it hot with vanilla ice cream. After your meal explore the spacious store filled with unique furnishings, accessories, books and gifts.

**Tropical Temptations.** Ice cream and bakery *(No tables; in the Tahitian Gardens shopping center, 2003 Periwinkle Way, Sanibel; 472-6577; cash or personal checks).* Owner and baker Sandy Owens dishes up a combination of homemade ice cream with mouth-watering bakery items. Best are the white chocolate bread pudding, macadamia fudge torte, cinnamon buns, cream cheese-based Pelican Poops and key lime pie. Good espresso, too. Open from 8 a.m. to 9 p.m. daily.

**Twilight Cafe.** Fusion/New American/Vegetarian *(Dinner Mon.–Sat.; kid's menu; behind Tower Gallery at 751 Tarpon Bay Rd., Sanibel; 472-8818; V, MC; reservations suggested.)* Local artists have hand-carved the walls and ceilings at this whimsical but romantic cafe, the best gourmet restaurant on the islands. For starters try the homemade corn and crab chowder, or bruschetta with gorgonzola and a petite salad. Imaginative dishes include grilled tuna on Chinese greens and mushrooms, grilled steak with sweet mashed potatoes and a roasted green apple glaze, and a grilled veal chop in a caramelized onion and sherry reduction with corn and crawfish mashed potatoes. Islanders recommend the grilled pork chops and the Beef Medallions of Diane with grilled broccoli. There are novel vegetarian entrees, too. An open-air kitchen and wood-fired grill add a homey touch.

**Village Cafe.** French *(Dinner nightly; 14970 Captiva Dr., Captiva; 472-1956; V, MC, D, DC; reservations suggested).* With curved white stucco walls and an open kitchen, this intimate restaurant serves good French food with an extensive wine list. Good choices include any special, the foie gras, duck or free-range chicken.

**Windows on the Water.** Florasian/Seafood ℹ *(Breakfast, lunch and dinner daily; kid's menu; at the Sundial Beach Resort, 1451 Middle Gulf Dr., Sanibel; 395-6014; V, MC; reservations suggested.)* This long, narrow room has a wall of windows looking out over the Sundial's large swimming pool and the Gulf. Stepped levels ensure there's no bad seat in this calm Asian-influenced restaurant. The "Florasian" menu ("Florida favorites with a Pacific Rim flavor") features a good Sanibel Dim Sum (seasoned shrimp and chicken wrapped in steamed wonton, served with a sweet soy and garlic sauce). Other top choices include Marathon Mahi-Mahi (sesame crusted with a light honey garlic sauce) and Chicken Cayo Costa (with sun-dried tomatoes, mozzarella and wild mushroom ragout). Even if you're not staying at the Sundial, we recommend coming here for breakfast. The $10 buffet is a fine eye-opener, and the morning view is terrific.

---

**Tell us what you think** of Sanibel and Captiva restaurants. Be honest, specific and descriptive. E-mail your experiences and opinions to: mike@coconutpress.com

# Shopping

Shopping on the islands is special. And that's both good and bad.

Competing for the fickle tourist dollar, each store tries to be unique. You'll have no trouble finding unusual tropical shirts and dresses, sand dollar earrings and hand-painted furniture. But need something mundane — a camcorder battery, a pair of plain jeans — and you may have to hunt.

That gripe aside, the stores and galleries offer all sorts of hidden delights and one-of-a-kind keepsakes, and the quality is first-rate. Nearly all are mom-and-pop shops. The owners' passion for their hand-picked merchandise is contagious.

## Art galleries

**Aboriginals: Art of the First Person** (in the Village, 2340 Periwinkle Way, Sanibel; 395-2200) features museum-quality tribal art from Africa, Aboriginal Australia, native America and the Arctic people of Canada and Alaska, authentically sourced from tribal culture. Selections include ancestral carvings, pottery, baskets, textiles, jewelry and ceremonial masks.

You'll find one of Southwest Florida's largest selections of museum-quality antique and period jewelry at the charming **Albert Meadow Antiques** (across from the Bubble Room at 15000 Captiva Dr., Captiva; 472-8442). The impressive variety of diamond, gold and platinum estate pieces complements original Maxfield Parrish lithographs and collections of Art Nouveau glass from Tiffany, Steuben, Daum and Galle.

Contemporary art is the focus of the **Black Orchid Gallery** (in the Timbers Center, 705 Tarpon Bay Rd., Sanibel; 472-8784). Styles range from the vibrant colors of Hessam and Sabzi to the subtle tones of Picasso. Also available are dozens of Limoges boxes, exotic dolls, whimsical frogs, the delicate hand-blown glass of Novano, and the etched crystal of Sanibel's Luc Century.

---

**Facing page:** The Bubble Room Emporium

Operating in an old island cottage, the **Hirdie Girdie Gallery** (2490 Library Way at Tarpon Bay Rd., Sanibel; 395-0027) offers Sanibel-themed oils, watercolors, pastels, acrylics, baskets, tiles and wood carvings.

**Island Style** (in Periwinkle Place, 2075 Periwinkle Way, Sanibel; 472-6657) has high-end handmade furniture, glass, pottery, jewelry, sculpture, and wall art. Most have a tropical folk-art theme that reflects the relaxed style of the islands. The fanciful wooden tables, in particular, are unique pieces.

Huge metal sculptures rest in the trees outside of **Jungle Drums** (11532 Andy Rosse Ln., Captiva; 395-2266). Inside, the collection includes animals in bronze, wood, ceramics and glass, plus jewelry, framed art, prints, books, furniture and music.

Kelly Murphy showcases unusual and beautiful art at **Kelly's Cocoons** (14830 Captiva Dr., Captiva, 472-8383; 2496 Palm Ridge Rd., Sanibel; 395-0422): her own butterfly art, Diane Mannion's pottery and hand-painted floor cloths, John Mannion's painted furniture, and blown glass by Kellmis Fernandez.

The **Ikki Matsumoto Gallery** (in the Village, 2340 Periwinkle Way, Sanibel; 472-2941) is the best spot to check out island favorite Ikki's whimsical graphic wildlife paintings. The gallery also offers furniture, mobiles and ceramics created by other artists. Don't miss the colorful T-shirts with Ikki's designs.

**McEnroe Gallery** (next to the Hungry Heron restaurant, 2330 Palm Ridge Rd., Sanibel; 472-1118) stocks quality paintings and painted furniture. Owner Denise McEnroe also does first-class custom framing.

Invitational and juried shows feature works from many Florida artists at the **Phillips Gallery** (inside the Barrier Island Group for the Arts (BIG Arts), 900 Dunlop Rd., Sanibel; 395-0900). The exhibits change monthly; all the art is for sale. The gallery and receptions are free. BIG Arts is a nonprofit arts center.

**Sanibel Art and Frame** (2460 Palm Ridge Rd., Sanibel; 395-1350) offers a large selection of prints, photos and posters. Services include next-day custom framing, shipping and free island delivery and hanging.

## Island Artists

**Ikki Matsumoto** is an island institution. His playful wildlife prints and soft watercolors hang in businesses and homes throughout the area. Ikki illustrated the 1972 edition of "The Joy of Cooking" and was one of 50 artists chosen by First Lady Nancy Reagan to design an Easter egg in 1985. It's now at the Smithsonian. Today he has his own island gallery.

**Marty Stokes** and his family use the ancient Japanese art form of Gyotaku ("fish impressions") to create unusual and beautiful paintings. Developed as a way of measuring the exact size of a caught game fish, Gyotaku obtains a printed impression of a fish by painting the animal with block inks and pressing absorbent paper over it. Marty's variation uses handmade rice papers with water-based inks. He uses seahorses and other sea life to create underwater scenes. His work is sold at the Tower Gallery and other island shops.

**Bryce McNamara** uses discarded tin and other metals to create whimsical and functional objects. His lamps, lanterns and luminaries feature punched designs that cast intricate light patterns. Fanciful fish and animals are popular for children's rooms. See Bryce's work at his gallery and workshop, Tin Can Alley.

**Luc Century** uses a photo-stenciling process to etch wildlife images onto glass sculpture, paperweights, glassware and wall art. It's available at the refuge gift shop and many island galleries. The Vietnam Memorial used his technique to etch its names onto stone.

**Teri Causey** makes funky hand-painted furniture and wall hangings, featuring tropical motifs. We bought a mermaid-themed chest to use as a coffee table.

We should also point out that world-renowned artist **Robert Rauschenberg** lives on the islands, and participates occasionally in local exhibitions.

The oldest island gallery, the **Sanibel Gallery** (in the Heart of the Island Shops, 1628 Periwinkle Way, Sanibel; 472-3307) represents over 170 artists and craftspeople. Oils, watercolors, clay, glass, wood, metal, paper and the annual Sanibel Christmas ornament reflect the island environment.

**The Seaweed Gallery** (in the Forever Green shops, 2055 Periwinkle Way, Sanibel; also next door to the Keylime Bistro at 11509 Andy Rosse Ln., Captiva; both stores: 472-2585) has an eclectic collection of island art. Mermaids are a common theme.

Artist Bryce McNamara hammers, punches, and sculpts pieces of recycled tin into fish, suns and other objects at **Tin Can Alley** (2480 Library Way, Sanibel; 472-2902). The luminaries produce magical patterns of light. Lamps and tropical folk art are also for sale.

**A Touch of Sanibel Pottery** (1544 Periwinkle Way, Sanibel; 472-4330) features functional and decorative stoneware and porcelain, and colorful raku. Local and nationally-recognized potters are featured, so there's a wide choice of colors and designs.

Filling both stories of a brightly painted historic beach house, **Tower Gallery** (751 Tarpon Bay Rd., Sanibel; 472-4557) is a co-op of 20 local artists. A well-chosen assortment of quality paintings, prints, raku ceramics, baskets, painted furniture, photography, stained glass and handcrafted jewelry is constantly changing. One of the artists usually sits behind the counter.

A gallery and gift shop, the **Tree House Gallery** (in the Olde Sanibel shops, 630 Tarpon Bay Rd., Sanibel; 472-1850) features paintings, photos and pottery, including Shelligrams, Hilda Kaihlanen's Island Primitives and Cat's Meow Village miniatures.

## Beach paraphernalia

**Beach Stuff** (14900 Captiva Dr., Captiva; 472-3544) has the best floats on the islands; many hang from the overhang outside the store (they'll blow up your floats and rafts for you after you buy them). Inside are swimsuits, skim boards, towels, beach shoes and sandals, kites, beach toys, masks, hats, sunglasses, sunscreen and many T-shirts. Gifts include the Sanibel lighthouse ornament, hand-painted "Soul Fish" by Bonnie Murray, and classic Florida kitsch souvenirs.

**Sanibel Surf Shop** *(in Jerry's Shopping Center, 1700 Periwinkle Way at Casa Ybel Rd., Sanibel; 472-8185)* has a terrific selection of island T-shirts, with sizes up to 6X. But it's also packed with moderate-priced beach supplies and equipment, and a good selection of books, games, toys and puzzles.

**Winds** *(2353 Periwinkle Way, Sanibel; 395-0091)* has the largest selection of beach stuff: inexpensive and moderate-priced suits and T-shirts for all ages, as well as boogie boards, masks, fins, beach towels, totes, sunscreen, floats, even a few seashells.

## Bookstores

The three island bookstores overflow in Sanibel spirit. Each has its own personality.

Primarily a paperback exchange, the **Island Book Nook** *(2330 Palm Ridge Rd., Sanibel; 472-6777)* has over 10,000 paperbacks. Joan Simonds puts her recommendations on a front table. She stocks a thorough list of local books and field guides, and *rents* hardcover bestsellers for $5 a week.

**MacIntosh Book Shop** *(2365 Periwinkle Way, Sanibel; 472-1447)* has been Sanibel's main bookstore for decades. Owner Jim Dowling has a friendly, knowledgeable staff. He will search the world to find the book you want. "We find the most remote books on earth!" he says. The shelves include local fiction, field guides and children's books.

Hollie Smith's **Sanibel Island Bookshop** *(across from Jerry's Supermarket, 1711 Periwinkle Way, Sanibel; 472-5223)* reflects her laid-back sensibility: her dog may greet you when you walk in. Her shop is filled with every definition of a "beach-read" — local authors, field guides, bestsellers. The children's section is especially appealing.

Four Sanibel attractions also sell books. The **Bailey-Matthews Shell Museum** gift shop *(3075 Sanibel-Captiva Rd., Sanibel; 395-2233)* has great shelling books, plus gifts and decorative items with a shell theme. The

**Practicing** on his new skim board, Minnesota's Ned Hartfiel, 8, works on his skills. Skim and boogie boards (for the waves) are sold at island beach shops.

children's section has some terrific items. The bookstore at the **J.N. "Ding" Darling National Wildlife Refuge** *(inside the visitors center, 1 Wildlife Drive, Sanibel; 472-1100)* has a great selection of nature and field guides. The **Sanibel-Captiva Conservation Foundation** *(3333 Sanibel-Captiva Rd., Sanibel; 472-2329)* has hard-to-find guides. Finally, the **Sanibel Historical Village and Museum** *(950 Dunlop Rd., Sanibel; 472-4648)* sells books on Sanibel history (some out of print) inside the old Bailey's General Store.

## Clothing

You'll find a huge selection of swimwear and accessories at the **Beach House** *(in Periwinkle Place, 2075 Periwinkle Way, Sanibel; 472-2676; and across from the South Seas Resort in Chadwick's Square, Captiva; 472-4665)*. Over 5,000 suits for men, women and children pack the store. The women's selection is a Godsend: coverage options from tiny bikinis to conservative, yet still flattering, choices; sizes up to 30; mastectomy, long-torso and D-cup styles; and you can buy tops and bottoms separately.

**C. Turtles and Company** *(next to The Bean, 2242 Periwinkle Way, Sanibel; 472-1115)* has colorful casual clothes. Brands include Jams World, Tori Richards and Tommy Bahama.

**Candace at Frangi-Pani** *(across from the South Seas Resort in Chadwick's Square, Captiva; 395-0717)* stocks upper-end beach and resort wear for women, including pieces by Lilly Pulitzer, Polo, Lauren, Sigrid Olsen and Calvin Klein. Also available are intimates and some great casual shoes.

**Caribbean Coast** *(in Periwinkle Place, 2075 Periwinkle Way, Sanibel; 472-2993)* carries tropical clothing, with a good selection of Tommy Bahama apparel and shoes.

**Casual Attitude** *(in Tahitian Gardens, 2001 Periwinkle Way, Sanibel; 472-0088)* has classic outdoor clothing, plus jewelry. Brands include Royal Robbins, Hook & Tackle, Tori Richards and Brighton.

No wonder women love **Chico's** *(in Periwinkle Place, 2075 Periwinkle Way, Sanibel; 472-0202; at Palm Ridge Place, 2330 Palm Ridge Dr., Sanibel; 472-3773; and across from the South Seas Resort in Chadwick's Square, Captiva; 472-4426).* Here you're a size 2, even though you're really a 12! The store's unique sizes run 0-3, matching the traditional range of 6-16. The lightweight clothes are versatile and fashionable. The Sanibel Chico's are the original stores of this chain.

Comfort is the name of the game at **Coastal Cotton Co.** *(in Periwinkle Place, 2075 Periwinkle Way, Sanibel; 472-8887).* The all-cotton women's clothing is matched with accessories, hats, sandals and scarves. Long, flowing cotton halter dresses from Miami's Cotton Connection are perfect for the island heat. Plus sizes are available, too.

**Comfort by Design** *(in the Lime Tree Center, 1640 Periwinkle Way, Sanibel; 395-0666)* offers quality shoe and sandal brands such as Birkenstock, Mephisto and Ecco. Inserts are available; shipping is free.

Manager Sally Kopplow stocks the **Cricket Shop** *(in the Anchor Point Shopping Center, 1633 Periwinkle Way, Sanibel; 395-2277)* with thoughtful choices. Swimsuits include father/son and mother/daughter designs,

and all children's sizes. There's a good selection of contemporary sportswear and classic dresses. We like the crushable straw hats and "no-headache" visors.

**Dockside Quality Clothing and Shoes** *(in Periwinkle Place, 2075 Periwinkle Way, Sanibel; 472-9098)* carries upscale, outdoor men's clothing, with a few items for women. Most pieces have a fish or outdoor theme. Brands include Timberland (shoes and clothing), Reyn Spooner, Cutter & Buck, Hook & Tackle, Newport Blue, Ex Officio, Guy Harvey (shirts and hats), Teva (sandals), Freestyle (watches) and Costa del Mar (sunglasses). It's a great-looking store, too.

The classic cut of the apparel at **Eileen Fisher** *(in the Forever Green shops, 2055 Periwinkle Way, Sanibel; 472-4655)* flatters all shapes and sizes, in neutral colors and lightweight, comfortable fabrics.

You'll find island-casual footwear for the whole family at **Footloose** *(in Jerry's Shopping Center, 1700 Periwinkle Way, Sanibel; 472-4717; and across from the South Seas Resort in Chadwick's Square, Captiva, 472-1707).* Brands include Sperry, NAOT, Minnetonka (moccasins), Teva (sandals), Speedo and Costa del Mar sunglasses.

**Fresh Produce** *(in Periwinkle Place, 2075 Periwinkle Way, Sanibel; 395-1839)* sure has the island spirit, though the chain is actually based in Boulder, Colo. The bright, cotton clothing often has matching socks or caps. Many pieces feature nature designs.

**H20 Outfitters** *(in Periwinkle Place, 2075 Periwinkle Way, Sanibel; 472-8890; and across from the South Seas Resort in Chadwick's Square, Captiva; 472-7507)* stocks outdoor apparel, including T-shirts, shorts, jeans and sandals. Quality brands include Tommy Bahama, Weekender, Nautica, Ex Officio, Guy Harvey and Royal Robbins. Shoes include NAOT, Sperry and Teva. They also carry Costa del Mar sunglasses.

**Her Sports Closet** *(in Periwinkle Place, 2075 Periwinkle Way, Sanibel; 472-4206)* features casual island sportswear in sizes 2 through 18 and with many mother/daughter coordinates. Brands include Lilly Pulitzer. Check out the unusual belts and purses.

**I Can Too Sport** (in Tahitian Gardens, 1979 Periwinkle Way, Sanibel; 395-2511) has comfortable clothes for women and girls, mix and match cotton separates in concentrated colors. Owners Alan and Ali Duenas have T-shirts, shorts, tanks, sundresses and beach coverups, plus hats and great funky sandals. The "Under the Sea" collection has fun fish designs. Check out the lotions, too.

Beach boutiques **Island Beach Co.** and **Island Beach, Too** (14820 Captiva Dr., Captiva; 472-3272) offer resort clothing for the entire family, featuring Quiksilver, Roxy and Fresh Produce. Pick up a T-shirt while the kids shop for games and toys.

The upscale apparel at **Island Pursuit** (in Periwinkle Place, 2075 Periwinkle Way, Sanibel; 472-4600) includes soft island suits for men. Brands include Helen Kaminski, Tommy Bahama, Brighton and Axis. Shoes from Sperry, Cole Haan and Bragamo, and purses and belts round out the selection.

Glamorous, arty, Moroccan, Indonesian… many adjectives describe **I-Spy** (2340 Periwinkle Way, in the Village, Sanibel; 472-2221). Owner Pat St. Cyr hand-picks women's clothing and jewelry that have a definite exotic style. Unusual accessories include delicate shawls, 1920s-era Bakelite jewelry and mah-jongg tile bracelets.

Brigh cotton separates for women and kids stock the **Keylime Clothing Co.** (across the street from the Lighthouse Cafe, 359 Periwinkle Way, Sanibel; 395-1870). You'll also find funky T-shirts and hats, books, gifts, cookbooks, sandals, beach toys, sterling silver palm tree jewelry and picture frames.

The upscale children's clothes at **Lads & Lassies** (in Periwinkle Place, 2075 Periwinkle Way, Sanibel; 472-1180) include many unusual pieces, some handmade. Accessories and toys are tucked in, too.

Jackets are a specialty at **Lookin Good** (in the Olde Sanibel shops, 630 Tarpon Bay Rd., Sanibel; 472-6888). Unusual choices include hand-painted canvas and decorated denim. Also note the soft ribbon shirts from Korea.

**Lucky Dog of Sanibel** (2359 Periwinkle Way, Sanibel; 395-9999) carries casual and classy

apparel for men and women. Carol and Vince Damico, new to Sanibel from Rochester, N.Y., also have shoes and sandals, bags, scarves and Thymes body lotions. The straw hats are perfect for the islands.

**Maddison and Me** (across from the South Seas Resort in Chadwick's Square, Captiva; 395-8777) is as girly a shop as you'll find: feminine clothing, wonderful scents and beautiful accessories. Brands include Crabtree & Evelyn and April Cornell. Both big and little girls can shop here; the store even has mother/daughter matching outfits. Most of the clothing is soft cotton or linen; some is sumptuous velvet. The sleepwear, robes, tablecloths and bedding evoke an old-fashioned, genteel era.

**Maggie Elliott** (in Periwinkle Place, 2075 Periwinkle Way, Sanibel; 472-2230) offers clothes that combine a big-city elegance with a vacation spirit. The boutique also has Brighton accessories, jewelry and shoes.

**Mango Bay** (in Jerry's Shopping Center, 1700 Periwinkle Way at Casa Ybel Rd., Sanibel; 472-6678) carries clothing and beach items. The selection is good but not unique; the chain also has stores in Florida malls.

**Memories of Sanibel** (in the Olde Sanibel shops, 630 Tarpon Bay Rd., Sanibel; 395-1410; and next to the Bean at 2240 Periwinkle Way, Sanibel; 395-0990) carries shorts, hats and accessories, as well as quality T-shirts, including many embroidered styles.

High-end children's apparel for lucky children 0 to 14 fills **Nanny's** (in the Village, 2340 Periwinkle Way, Sanibel; 472-0304). The store has exquisite handmade items, plus shoes, jewelry, books, toys, even dress-up clothes.

The soft, breezy fabrics at **Oh Mango!** (in the Village, 2340 Periwinkle Way, Sanibel; 472-2223) are made for island living. The muslin, gauze, and 100-percent cotton pieces for men and women are lightweight and come in dozens of colors. The hand-painted dresses from Southern Mexico are one-of-a-kind, as are the purses made of coconuts.

**Paradise of Sanibel** (in Periwinkle Place, 2075 Periwinkle Way, Sanibel; 472-3020) has one of the best selections of island T-shirts.

**Quality apparel** at the T-shirt Hut

You'll also find big tropical shirts for men, cotton sweaters for women, plus clothes for kids and babies. Other items include Beanie Babies, jewelry, frames, chimes and toys. Parrot Heads will feel at home: the store plays Jimmy Buffett music constantly, sells Buffett's T-shirts (to size 4X), beach towels and note cards, as well as nearly every Buffett album (even some hard-to-find discs). The shop is worth a look just for the decor: Owners Roger Digby and his sister Marilyn Bodimer have made the walls and floor a matching landscape; flamingos wrap around you in the dressing room.

**Peach Republic** *(in Periwinkle Place, 2075 Periwinkle Way, Sanibel; 472-8444)* has double the room of most stores in Periwinkle Place, so there is plenty of room for their lovely women's clothes and accessories. Our favorites are the colorful funny handpainted T-shirts by Diane Wat and the elegant Sigrid Oldsen Sport all-cotton sweaters. The store also has the islands' largest selection of women's shoes.

The only plus shop here, **PlusPerfect** *(in the Forever Green shops, 2055 Periwinkle Way, Sanibel; 472-8110)* stocks stylish, lightweight tropical attire from Emme, Karen Kane, Amanda Gray, CMC Cotton, Kedem Sasson and Flax. Separates let you mix and match. Don't overlook the nice lingerie and jewelry selected by owner Judy Dearborn.

The **Sporty Seahorse** *(362 Periwinkle Way, Sanibel; 472-1858)* is a department store from the 1950s, a true throwback. Much bigger than it looks, it has a large selection of apparel and accessories, including over 2,000 swimsuits. Look for bargains: clearance merchandise is tucked in everywhere.

Say hi to Nick and Stan at the **T-Shirt Hut** *(1504 Periwinkle Way, Sanibel; 472-1415)*, the oldest T-shirt shop on Sanibel. The shirts run the gamut from classy and embroidered to silly and silk-screened. The children's selection has a treasure hunter's map of Florida. The terrycloth beach pillows are a great idea. The store is open til 9 p.m. (that's late) Monday through Saturday, 6 p.m. Sunday.

At the **T-Shirt Place of Sanibel** *(in Periwinkle Place, 2075 Periwinkle Way, Sanibel; 472-2392)* the name says it all: a good group of funky T-shirts for men, women and kids. They also carry shorts, hats, soft cotton separates, beach totes and fun jewelry.

The **Tahitian Surf Shop** *(in Tahitian Gardens, 2015 Periwinkle Way, Sanibel; 472-3431)* has apparel for men, women and children, including Tommy Bahama. The swimsuit collection includes daring styles not found elsewhere. Brands include Ray Ban, Freestyle (watches) and Reef (beach shoes).

**Trader Rick's** *(in Periwinkle Place, 2075 Periwinkle Way, Sanibel; 472-9194)* specializes in youthful women's apparel and funky accessories, with jewelry, belts, purses, shoes and gifts. The handmade glycerin soaps are nice, as is the bed and body dust and tile art.

We probably buy more T-shirts from **West Wind Surf Shop** *(in Periwinkle Place, 2075 Periwinkle Way, Sanibel; 472-3490)* than anywhere else. The organized store also sells sunglasses, skim boards, water toys, hats, books and jewelry. Brands carried include Billabong, Tommy Bahama, Oakley, Freestyle, and Reef and Quiksilver (sandals).

**Why Knot** *(in the Village, 2340 Periwinkle Way, Sanibel; 472-3003)* sells lightweight natural-fiber womenswear. Brands include Eileen Fisher. The washable linens are especially popular. The solid-color T-shirts are worth a look, too. Accessories include Jeanine Payer sterling silver jewelry.

## Convenience stores

Both **7-Eleven** stores *(1521 Periwinkle Way, Sanibel; 472-9197; and at intersection of Tar-*

pon Bay Rd., 2460 Periwinkle Way, Sanibel; 472-8696) have a good supply of ice cream, bakery products and hot dogs. The Tarpon Bay Road store has gas at off-island prices.

**Hess Express** (at Tarpon Bay Rd., 2499 Palm Ridge Rd., Sanibel; 472-2198) has pay-at-the-pump gas at off-island prices, too. The tire air is free. Inside are to-go sandwiches, hot dogs and ice cream.

**Huxter's Market and Deli** (near the causeway at 1201 Periwinkle Way, Sanibel; 472-2151) has all the standard convenience items plus beach supplies, video rentals, liquor, cigars, paperbacks, newspapers and an old-fashioned deli with sandwiches, salads and desserts. Try the fried chicken.

Captiva's tiny **Island Store** (11500 Andy Rosse Ln., Captiva; 472-2374) is packed with stuff: hard-boiled eggs over here, frozen bait over there. Groceries, rental videos, gifts, apparel and sandwiches fill every space. Don't overlook the homemade ice cream. Next door is an even tinier liquor and cigar store.

**Rosie's Island Market & Deli** (in Old Town Sanibel, 362 Periwinkle Way, Sanibel; 472-6656) serves Sanibel's east end, offering groceries, convenience items, Old Town Sanibel posters and postcards, baked goodies and ice cream. There's good take-out food, too.

The wood floors, reasonable prices and clean, friendly atmosphere tell you the **Santiva General Store** (across from Turner Beach at 6406 Sanibel-Captiva Rd., Sanibel; 472-5556) is owned by an islander, in this case Larry Thompson, who sells the same fish here they cook at his Lazy Flamingo and Sunset Grill restaurants next door. His sister creates the pasta and bean salads. Boars Head meats are priced less than Publix. For kids there are ice cream cones and lots of doo-dads. The ultra-expensive Hal's Grocery used to be here. What an improvement!

Hidden inside the lobby of the Sundial resort, **The Shoppe** (1451 Middle Gulf Dr., Sanibel; 472-4151) is a good small convenience store, handy for bikers riding down East Gulf Drive. Selections include international cheeses and freshly-baked cookies.

## Gifts

You can tell from the name that you won't find the same old stuff at **Area 51 Design Imports** (at Palm Ridge Place, 2330 Palm Ridge Rd., Sanibel; 472-3643). The exotic furniture, gifts and accessories are imported from the Philippines and Honduras. A bamboo and iron bar table is popular; the braided bamboo lamp with beaded shade is interesting. Owner Gail Barden keeps her prices low by ordering the pieces direct.

**Arundel's Hallmark Shoppe** (in the Heart of the Island shops, 1626 Periwinkle Way, Sanibel; 472-8317) is a one-hour photo shop, a FedEx shipping center, and the island's office supply store. Oh yeah, it's also a Hallmark shop, with the usual quality greeting cards, ornaments, gifts and photo albums.

**Bandanna's at Sundial** (inside the Sundial Resort, 1451 Middle Gulf Dr., Sanibel; 472-4151) features swimwear, tennis apparel, cover-ups, casual dresses, shorts, accessories, shoes and tennis equipment.

After (or before) stuffing yourself at the restaurant, visit the **Bubble Room Emporium** (15001 Captiva Dr., Captiva; 472-6545). Manager Michaela Sustrova has stocked an eclectic selection of art, keepsakes and toys, including Pam Webb's paintings of the Bubble Room, Teri Causey's wooden fish and furniture and inspired dress-up hats and masks for kids.

We lived on Sanibel for years but never stopped in **Caloosa Canvas** (1616 Periwinkle Way, in the Heart of the Island shops, Sanibel; 472-2218) until researching this book. We figured it sold awnings or tents. But "canvas" here refers to its stock of bags, beach chairs, hammocks, umbrellas and pillows. They also have some fun metal garden accessories and painted bird houses.

Island-themed stained glass and lots of local paintings and prints fill **Captiva's Finest** (across from the South Seas Resort at 110 Chadwick's Square, Captiva; 472-8222). There's sculpture, too, as well as replica Sanibel and Captiva street signs.

Enjoy a cup of coffee while you shop at **Captiva Garden & Gourmet** (across from the South Seas Resort in Chadwick's Square, Captiva; 395-0354). This combination cafe/gift shop/florist has gourmet food, handmade napkins and candles, birdhouses that look like hats, Italian tile coasters and other upscale items. Olive lovers should check out their olive bar, including citrus, garlic and martini olives. The full-service floral department can wire flowers worldwide as well as handle weddings and other special events.

Carmen Lombardo has turned his 1950s cottage into the **Confused Chameleon** (11528 Andy Rosse Ln., Captiva; 472-0560), a whimsical gift shop. Carmen and his partner, Constantine Stratos, sell standout items like retro balancing toys, votive candle holder birds, spiritual cards by Susan Miller and delicate mermaid watercolors. Each time we're here we find something new.

When you enter the **Enchanted Fairy** (in Tahitian Gardens, 1999 Periwinkle Way, Sanibel; 472-1144) you first notice the giant tree, then you see the delicate artwork displayed on it. Artist Josanne McAfee and husband Bruce spent eight years going to art shows and festivals. Tiring of being constantly on the move, they opened this shop, featuring her clay and polymer fairies and mermaids, plus candles, frames, children's toys, note cards, Christmas ornaments and costume jewelry. Don't miss the gossamer fairy wings for little girls to play dress-up.

Standouts at **End Result** (in Periwinkle Place, 2075 Periwinkle Way, Sanibel; 395-3333) include delicate hanging glass balls, sterling-silver jewelry, Indian paper lamps, beaded barrettes, ceramics, wind chimes and funky Christmas ornaments. Every time we're here we feel like adding a rec room to our house.

The eclectic collection at **Il Crocodile** (at Palm Ridge Place, 2330 Palm Ridge Dr., Sanibel; 472-9166) includes furnishings, hostess gifts, toys, Vera Bradley handbags, handcrafted skirts by Ruth Comes, ethnic and trouves jewelry by Lannie Cunningham and the Fitz and Floyd Gallery of dinnerware, gifts and Christmas accessories.

You'll go back in time at the **Islander Trading Post** (1446 Periwinkle Way, Sanibel; 395-0888). Old signs, radios, kitchen items, curios and seemingly every other old thing is for sale here, at modern prices. Why oh why didn't we hang onto Grandma's stuff! New items include some great candles.

**Island Gifts and Shells** (1609 Periwinkle Way, Sanibel; 472-4318) is an old-fashioned gift shop, with many shells, shell bottles and shell-themed gifts, books, postcards, towels, knickknacks and Florida T-shirts.

The owner of **Jonna's of Sanibel** (at Palm Ridge Place, 2330 Palm Ridge Dr., Sanibel; 472-2302) laughs as she describes her pieces as "wearable art," but that's what it is: Lovely hand-painted clothing and jewelry. Jonna's is the exclusive shop on the island for Lunch at the Ritz jewelry. Each pin, necklace or pair of earrings is one-of-a-kind. The White House ordered some pieces a few years ago; so did Janet Jackson. Jonna also has some wild painted sculpture and collander–teaspoon lamps and mobiles.

Pamela Kirby Rambo offers functional gifts and decorative accents at her **Kirby Rambo Collections** (in the Village, 2340 Periwinkle Way, Sanibel; 472-4944). Many of the unusual pieces come from local artists. Check out the beaded wire wall geckos, recycled light-bulb ornaments, tiny flower purses and painted-animal bike bells. Pamela's own handmade door stops and wine stoppers come in gorgeous bright colors.

One of the first stores you see as you come onto Sanibel, the **Lion's Paw** (1025 Periwinkle Way, Sanibel; 472-0909) has been transformed from a dress shop to a furniture store. The unique pieces include tables and other furniture made from 100-year-old recycled Eastern European pine. There are many unusual dishes, lamps, trivets and mirrors. Don't miss the prayer chairs from Russia, complete with scribbles on the back.

Beautiful glass sculptures catch your eye at **The Mole Hole of Sanibel** (in the historic Cooper house in the Olde Sanibel shops, 630 Tarpon Bay Rd., Sanibel; 472-2767). Choose from dolphins, elephants, lovebirds, even multicolored sun catchers. The jewel-toned perfume bottles are worth a look, too, as are the hollow witches balls to hang in the window (they ward off "evil spirits").

Quirky figurines, statues, mobiles, ornaments, jewelry, glass, ceramics, kid's books and teddy bears fill every nook and cranny of **Pandora's Box** (in Periwinkle Place, 2075 Periwinkle Way, Sanibel; 472-6263; also near the lighthouse at 455 Periwinkle Way, Sanibel; 395-2400). Greeting cards are upstairs. One-of-a-kind pieces abound, many homemade.

Hold a candle up to one of the lights in the **Sanibel Candle Co.** (in Tahitian Gardens, 1985 Periwinkle Way, Sanibel). The cutouts in each softball-sized candle glow with beautiful color when the wick is lit. The outside won't melt, and you can refill the inside with votives and tea lights. You can watch the candles being made.

The **Sandpiper of Sanibel** (next to the Hungry Heron restaurant at 2330 Palm Ridge Rd., Sanibel; 472-4645) features sterling silver jewelry and accessories for the home, wall hangings, bird carvings, baskets, pottery, gifts, cards and lamps.

Wall-size maps are just some of the unique items at **Sanybel's Finest** (in Jerry's Shopping Center, 1700 Periwinkle Way at Casa Ybel Rd., Sanibel; 472-6776). Watercolor artist Barney Baller is well represented, as is carver Rod Becklund. Other items include mirrors, fountains and shell bottles and lamps.

A top-of-the-line apparel and gift boutique, the **South Seas Shoppe** (South Seas Resort, Captiva; 472-1994) features shirts with the South Seas logo or that say "Captiva." The artistic items include whimsical studio glass from Anna Ornberg, unusual hand-painted bed linens from Susan Sargent, hand-painted furniture and jewelry boxes for children. They also do custom apparel work for groups, and welcome baskets.

Unique primitive furniture and artifacts from Mexico, Indonesia and Morocco surround the diners at **Trader's Store and Cafe** (1551 Periwinkle Way, Sanibel; 472-7242). The large store also includes scented candles, clothing, books, toys and aromatherapy bath essentials.

**Tuttle's Sea Horse Shell Shop** (next to the Lighthouse Cafe at 362 Periwinkle Way, Sanibel; 472-0707) is packed with kitschy Florida souvenirs. But there's more serious stuff, too, such as local artist "Apple Annie" Rothwell's hand-painted wooden benches and Sanibel's Dave Terlap's handmade wooden seahorse tables and crab benches. Rounding out the goods are beach paraphernalia, T-shirts, sweats, hot sauces, Florida's Fabulous books, shells, sunglasses, 14-karat gold jewelry and some nice Sanibel Christmas ornaments.

**Valhalla** (in Periwinkle Place, 2075 Periwinkle Way, Sanibel; 472-2795) is the place to find a shell bottle to hold those great beach treasures you've found. Many are shaped like fish. Also check out the mobiles, funny clay birds, sea-life jewelry and etched glass pieces from local artist Luc Century.

**Wilford & Lee** (in Tahitian Gardens, 2019 Periwinkle Way, Sanibel; 395-9295) has many interesting home accents and gifts. Choose from wood and metal wildlife sculptures, hostess trays, tile-topped tables, shell bottles, framed island-themed art and those omnipresent Ty Beanie Babies. UPS shipping is available.

## Food

Founded in 1899 by Frank Bailey and run today by his sons, **Bailey's General Store** (in Bailey's Shopping Center, Periwinkle Way at Tarpon Bay Rd., Sanibel; 472-1516) is the heart and soul of the islands. From the street it looks like a simple grocery-and-hardware store. But Bailey's is a catch-all for whatever islanders need. Here they'll change your watch battery, send your telegram, fill your prescription, propane tank or fishing line, ship your fruit, or repair your vacuum cleaner. They ship UPS packages and develop film. Don't miss the to-die-for homemade fudge (at the coffee bar in front), made daily with cream and butter. The bakery has excellent key lime pie (it should; the Baileys used to farm key limes). The hardware side of the store sells fishing supplies, bait shrimp, fishing licenses and a few appliances, toys and gifts. Every Sanibellian seems to have different reasons to love Bailey's. Ours: they have handles on their paper bags, and they give kids free cookies. Bailey's charm is most visible during Baileyfest, the free-food carnival it throws for islanders each fall, and during a tropical storm, when it's one of the few places that stays open. And, yes, the Bailey brothers are still here running it all. The thin one is Sam, the jolly one is Francis.

Addicted to cheese? **Cheese Nook** (in Periwinkle Place, 2075 Periwinkle Way, Sanibel; 472-2666) has a tempting selection and daily specials. There's a separate wine room, and a whole row of hot sauces. If they have a sun-dried tomato and pesto-cheese "party pie," either run for cover or give up your diet — it's so addictive you literally can't stop eating. We buy the tasty crab spread (almost always in stock) to give to guests at our book signings. Owner Steve Corbin also sells cookbooks and a good selection of gifts. A true island find.

**CW's Market & Deli** (South Seas Resort, Captiva; 472-5111) serves South Seas guests. It has a little of everything, including an extensive deli, liquor, and video rentals. Fresh-ground coffee is sold by the cup or the bag.

Macrobiotic, organic and natural foods fill the shelves of **Island Health Foods** (1640 Periwinkle Way, Sanibel; 472-3666). They've got takeout, too: fresh carrot juice, protein drinks and organic snacks. Also here: organic free-range eggs, soy milk, aromatherapy supplies and homeopathic herbs.

Besides typical supermarket goods, **Jerry's Foods** (in Jerry's Shopping Center, 1700 Periwinkle Way at Casa Ybel Rd., Sanibel; 472-9300) has a good salad bar, hot and cold takeout, a varied cheese selection, unique juices and a post office branch. We like it for the "underground" parking out of the sun (and thunderstorms) and unique service: After you check out, a conveyor belt sends your groceries down to the parking area, to a drive-through lane. You pull up, clerks load your trunk, and off you go!

The cozy **Sanibel Produce Co.** (next to The Bean at 2242 Periwinkle Way, Sanibel; 472-9696) has quality fresh fruit, Sun Harvest juice, vegetables and specialty foods such as blue-corn chips, fruit dips, Tuscany flatbread, sauces, olives and salad dressings.

## Hardware

**Bailey's True Value Hardware** (in Bailey's Shopping Center, Periwinkle Way at Tarpon Bay Rd.; Sanibel; 472-1516) is part of Bailey's General Store. See listing under Food.

**Forever Green Ace Hardware** (in the Forever Green shops, 2025 Periwinkle Way, Sanibel; 472-5354) has more than paint and hardware. There's a good selection of imported pottery and an extensive lawn and garden shop. Unusual Mosquito Magnets kill mosquitoes and no-see-ums without chemicals (a portion of profits go to SCCF). And if you need a snook mailbox (the door is the mouth), Sanibel's Ace is the place.

## Jewelry

**A Slight Indulgence** (in the Bailey's shopping center, 2439 Periwinkle Way, Sanibel; 395-4100) has gold and silver rings and pendants, as well as coins and medallions.

**Cedar Chest Fine Jewelry** (in Tahitian Gardens, 1993 Periwinkle Way, Sanibel; 472-2876) has vintage jewelry, including yellow diamonds. New pieces include sea-life designs.

Island-themed creations are the trademark of **Congress Jewelers** (in Periwinkle Place, 2075 Periwinkle Way, Sanibel; 472-4177). The largest jewelry store on the islands, it also carries Rolex, Cartier, Tag Heuer, Raymond Weil, Philippe Charriol, Quadrillion and Mikimoto brands. They repair watches, too.

Island motifs at **Friday's Fine Jewelers** (in Jerry's Shopping Center, 1700 Periwinkle Way, Sanibel; 472-1454) include sandals, pail and shovels, and sea turtles. Friday's also has pre-owned Rolexes and Rolex upgrades, Fabergé eggs and Waterford crystal.

**Rene's Artisans of Fine Jewelry** (in the Olde Sanibel shops, 630 Tarpon Bay Rd., Sanibel; 472-5544) offers diamond and gold jewelry, gemstones and sea-life themes.

Master coin maker Gene Gargiulo creates unique treasures at **Sanibel Coin and Jewelry** (in Bailey's Shopping Center, 2439 Periwinkle Way at Tarpon Bay Rd., Sanibel; 395-3899). Our favorites: his 14K gold sea creatures perched on reefs of freshwater pearls.

The roomy **Sanibel Goldsmith Gallery** *(2407 Periwinkle Way, Sanibel; 472-8677)* offers fine gold pieces, gemstones and beach glass. Kevin Greten hand crafts gold sea life pieces as well as real-shell jewelry, sterling silver chains, and glass beads. Formerly Sanibel Island Goldsmith, the gallery has relocated next to the Greenhouse Grill.

Bill Wilson creates hand-crafted jewelry at his intimate workshop and showroom, **William E. Wilson Fine Jewelry Design & Diamond Broker** *(in the Village, 2340 Periwinkle Way, Sanibel; 472-8590)*. He specializes in remounts and custom rings, using his 37 years of experience.

## Liquor and wine

Manager Joe Suarez makes sure the **Grog Shop** *(in Bailey's Shopping Center, Periwinkle Way at Tarpon Bay Rd., Sanibel; 472-1682)* carries just about any wine and liquor you could want, including French champagne. He has the islands' only walk-in cigar humidor, stocked with 15 brands (Arturo Fuente is the most popular; others include Macanudo, Partagas and Montecristo).

**Huxter's Liquors** *(near the causeway at 1201 Periwinkle Way, Sanibel; 472-3333)* has over 2,000 bottles of wine, champagne, liquor and beer (including micro-brew and imported brands), and imported cigars. Limited delivery is available on Sanibel.

**Sanibel Spirits** *(in Jerry's Shopping Center, 1700 Periwinkle Way at Casa Ybel Rd., Sanibel; 472-8668)* has the islands' largest selection of single malt scotch. Choose a Merlot, Chardonnay or Cabernet Sauvignon from the fine wine department, or pick up premixed cocktails. The new cigar department carries Macanudo, Partagas and H. Upmann, among others.

## Pharmacies

**Bailey's Corner Pharmacy** *(in Bailey's Shopping Center, Periwinkle Way at Tarpon Bay Rd., Sanibel; 472-4149)*, a section of Bailey's General Store, fills prescriptions Monday through Friday, 9 a.m. to 5 p.m. *See Bailey's listing under Food.*

**Barrier Island Pharmacy** *(across the street from Jerry's Shopping Center at 1721 Periwinkle Way, Sanibel; 472-8866)* is just that: an old-school, friendly pharmacy straight out of the 1950s, with no magazines, books, candy aisle or other merchandise that clutter today's modern "drug stores." It prides itself on helping visitors who have left their prescription at home.

**Eckerd Drugs** *(across from the Hungry Heron at 2331 Palm Ridge Rd., Sanibel; 472-1719)* has the best prices on soft drinks and beer. The islands' only chain drug store, it offers one-hour photo processing and lots of film, batteries, cards and sunscreen.

## Seashells

**Island Gifts and Shells** *(1609 Periwinkle Way, Sanibel; 472-4318)* has a good supply of shells and shell bottles, as well as shell-themed gifts and books.

**Neptune's Treasures** *(across from Dairy Queen, 1101 Periwinkle Way, Sanibel; 472-3132)* is a real find, hidden among some business condos just west of the causeway. It has an excellent assortment of shells (including the world-record horse conch), fossils, dinosaur teeth and eggs, Spanish treasure coins, native American artifacts and the largest selection of shark teeth in the region. The passion and care devoted to the store is evident in owner Ed Hanley's painstakingly hand-printed display notes.

The unassuming **Sanibel Seashell Industries** *(just off Periwinkle Way at 905 Fitzhugh St., Sanibel; 472-1603)* is a seashell conglomerate. Inside it's packed with bins and buckets of shells from Sanibel and around the world, plus specimen shells and preserved sea-life. National decorating magazines, including Martha Stewart Living, buy their supplies here. Owners Bill Strange and Gary Greenplate also sell shell lamps, paraphernalia and sailor's valentine kits.

**She Sells Sea Shells** *(1157 Periwinkle Way, Sanibel; 472-6991; and 2422 Periwinkle Way, Sanibel; 472-8080)* offers local and world-wide shells, corals and exotic sea-life, shell mirrors, gifts, jewelry, lamps, craft supplies and T-shirts. Ask to see their homemade Christmas ornaments and novelties; they'll even customize items for you.

Word of mouth must be the secret of the **Shell Net** *(in Bailey's Shopping Center, Periwinkle Way at Tarpon Bay Rd., Sanibel; 472-1702)*. It's hidden back in the corner of Bailey's Shopping Center, but has been in business for 32 years. Island-themed gifts and decorative items fill the shelves, as well as shells, shell craft, ornaments, wood carvings, Beanie Babies and jewelry. All the crafts are made locally — nothing here is stamped "Made in China."

**Showcase Shells** *(in the Heart of the Island shops, 1614 Periwinkle Way, Sanibel; 472-1971)* offers specimen shells, aquarium and decorative coral, jewelry, gifts and lamps.

## Secondhand stores

You'll find rare items at terrific prices at **Designer Consigner** *(near Tarpon Bay Rd. at 2460 Palm Ridge Rd., Sanibel; 472-1266)*. Manager Phyllis Marten focuses on furniture (especially unusual decorator pieces) and offers designer clothing (often new, but selling for half price or less), artwork, lamps, unusual gift items and accessories.

A few doors down is the **Goodwill Boutique** *(near Tarpon Bay Rd. at 2440 Palm Ridge Rd., Sanibel; 395-1225)*. Goodwill Industries calls this store a "boutique" because it stocks higher-quality items than a regular Goodwill store. Clothing for men and women is grouped in easy-to-find sections, including a rack for plus sizes. The bed, bath and kitchenware section is especially popular.

**Noah's Ark** *(behind the Episcopal Church, 2304 Periwinkle Way, Sanibel; 472-3356)* is a treasure. The large store is packed with ever-changing donated merchandise from islanders, with all proceeds going to charity. Electronics, clothing, bedding, suitcases — it's all here. The Designer Boutique has the finest of labels, with even the most expensive dresses only about $30. The Barnes and Noah book section has paperbacks and hardbacks. Another area features furniture, large items and artwork. During the season Noah's Ark gets new items every day. But get here early: in-the-know locals arrive when the doors open, and the best finds go right away. In-season hours are 9:30 to noon weekdays.

## Toys

The favorite store of island kids, **Needful Things** *(in Tahitian Gardens, 1995 Periwinkle Way, Sanibel; 472-5400)* is a groovy collection of kid's stuff — stickers, sports cards, ornaments, retro candy and other irresistible goodies. Brands include Ty Beanie Babies, Betty Boop, Pokemon cards, Dragonball Z, Hello Kitty and Barbie. "I recommend Needful Things because they have useless stuff," says Sanibel School student Kory Phillips. Formerly a retro "junk" shop, it still carries antique jewelry and handkerchiefs.

**Toys Ahoy** *(in Periwinkle Place, 2075 Periwinkle Way, Sanibel; 472-4800)* offers many educational games, books, kites, stuffed animals and brands including Playmobil, Madeline, Thomas the Tank Engine and Madame Alexander. A second location upstairs, Toys Ahoy Collectibles, has collector's cards, dolls, bears, tin toys, nesting dolls, Dover books and other retro items.

## Video rentals

The **Island Store** *(11500 Andy Rosse Ln., Captiva; 472-2374)* is the rental source on Captiva. Not a huge selection, but very convenient for Captiva visitors.

**Little Nancy's Sunrise Video** *(near the lighthouse, 359 Periwinkle Way, Sanibel; 472-6364)* rents videos, VCRs and camcorders.

Owner Peter Palazzotto recently opened **Michele's Video & DVD** *(in the Olde Sanibel shops, 630 Tarpon Bay Rd., Sanibel; 472-7222)*, which offers 8,300 movies to rent and 2,500 previously viewed movies to buy. The movie rental rates are $3 for two days. VCRs and Playstation games are also available.

**Video Scene** *(in Bailey's Shopping Center, Periwinkle Way at Tarpon Bay Rd.; Sanibel; 472-1158)* is the islands' largest video and DVD rental store. It also rents VCRs and video games.

## Miscellaneous

**Amy's Something Special** *(in the Olde Sanibel shops, 630 Tarpon Bay Rd., Sanibel; 472-4421)* is a charming, eclectic collection of gifts and antiques. Amy Horton's store has English teas, porcelain dolls, pancake mixes, great retro chandeliers and even funky shoe racks (the hooks are high heels).

**CopiKats** *(in Tahitian Gardens, 1983 Periwinkle Way, Sanibel; 395-4040)* offers whimsical accessories geared to a young, sophisticated crowd: tiny dressy purses, jeweled hair clips, butter-soft leather handbags, a coat scarf that velcroes on the back and tucks into your jacket or blouse. Young girls love the ponytail holders, beaded anklets and pick-a-bead necklaces. The best island store for perfume, CopiKats has fragrances from Sanibel to Bulgari to Obsession at good prices (co-owner Mary Benzrihem's family has been in the biz for years).

Temptations at **Chocolate Expressions** *(in Periwinkle Place, 2075 Periwinkle Way, Sanibel; 472-3837)* include rich homemade fudge, Godiva chocolates and hand-dipped chocolate strawberries. Those with willpower may settle for some imported candy, Jelly Belly jellybeans or a fruit smoothie.

Wonderful aromas abound at **Escentials** *(in the Village, 2340 Periwinkle Way, Sanibel; 472-7770)*. Items include lotions, cosmetics, oils, bath crystals, incense and candles, with dozens of samples to try. Sleepwear and handmade jewelry is also available.

Pet owners love **Island Critters** *(in Tahitian Gardens, 2019 Periwinkle Way, Sanibel; 395-1125)* and its unusual pet accessories and specialty gifts. The dog sunglasses are perfect for island pooches, as is the special doggie sunscreen featured on the Today Show. Other items include organic catnip toys, Catopoly and Wild Animonopoly games, and yummy-smelling bake-at-home pet treats. The pet spa section has colognes for dogs, with clever names like Tommy Holedigger, Pucci, White Dalmatians and Miss Claybone. Most items are for dogs and cats, but Dana and Brett Gowdy's store has interesting must-haves for other pets, too.

**Mel Fisher's Sanibel Treasure Company/ Treasures of the Atocha Exhibit and Gift Shop** *(in the Winds Plaza, 2353 Periwinkle Way, Sanibel; 395-5376)* offers original and replica pieces from the shipwrecked Spanish galleon Atocha, including jewelry and silver and gold coins.

The islands' only dedicated sunglass store, **Sunglasses Internationale** *(next to Cheeburger Cheeburger at 2427 Periwinkle Way, Sanibel; 472-7866)* has a wide range of quality shades, from classic to trendy, for grownups and kids. Paul and Toni Primeaux also have T-shirts, watches and caps. (If Seth is there ask for a soccer demo; he's our team's midfield coach.)

The items at **Tarpon Bay Explorers** *(900 Tarpon Bay Rd., Sanibel; 472-8900)* run the gamut from dolphin masks to handpainted linen napkins, frozen candy bars to fishing equipment. Most souvenirs have a nature theme. There is a great selection of T-shirts and hats, and lots of nature books for adults and kids. Check out the huge new aquarium and touch tank, filled with local creatures.

**Terry's Tennis Shop** *(in the Dunes Golf and Country Club, 949 Sandcastle Rd., Sanibel; 472-3522)* is stocked with racquets, tennis clothes, shoes and accessories. Brands include Boast, Descente, Snauwaert and Marcia Originals. They restring rackets, too.

Trudie Prevatt and the other sweet women at **Three Crafty Ladies** *(in the Heart of the Island shops, 1620 Periwinkle Way, Sanibel; 472-2893)* have a shop full of arts and crafts supplies, fabric, notions and shellcraft. They give free craft demonstrations every Tuesday and Thursday during the winter season.

**The Write Stuff** *(in the Village, 2340 Periwinkle Way, Sanibel; 472-8289)* is a stationery store with a terrific selection of fun and classy paper products: notecards, greeting cards, napkins, gift bags, calendars, photo albums, journals, diaries, address books and more. We love the unusual and imaginative pens, including the "Sparkling Rocket" that lights up when you write. Owner Jennifer Lessinger will help you order custom engraved invitations and Christmas cards.

# Accommodations

Sanibel and Captiva have places to stay suitable for all tastes. Small inns line Sanibel's Gulf shore. Most were built in the 1960s and early 1970s and retain the look and feel of that era. Other options: small family-owned operations off the Gulf, rustic campsites, high-end resorts and fully equipped apartments. Don't expect many familiar names. The only franchises on the islands are Holiday Inn and Best Western.

**Color codes** reflect the lowest quoted rates per night, including tax and service charges, during high season (February, March and April). Other months are much cheaper; summer rates can be 50 percent less.

    **Green** = under $100
    **Blue** = under $200
    **Purple** = under $300
    **Red** = under $400

**Superior Small Lodgings.**
*SSL* denotes an inn or hotel accredited by the Superior Small Lodging program. It has passed an annual inspection and meets SSL criteria for cleanliness, comfort, privacy and safety (and, by definition, has less than 51 rooms).

## Sanibel

**Anchor Inn of Sanibel** *(1245 Periwinkle Way; 395-9688; fax 395-2411. Pool.)* Formerly the Anchorage Inn, this small operation has hotel rooms, efficiencies and A-frame cottages. All have refrigerators. A-frames have spiral staircases. Close to stores, restaurants.

**Beach Road Inn** *(764 Beach Rd.; 395-1314 or 877-501-7600; fax 395-1921. BBQ grills, hot tub, laundry. SSL)* This four-suite inn is a short walk to the Gulf. The two-bedroom units sleep four, with a living room, dining room, 1 1/2 baths and two screened lanais. Video players, washers and dryers and ironing boards provided.

**Beachview Cottages** *(3325 West Gulf Dr.; 472-1202 or 800-860-0532; fax 472-4720. Ten*

*BEACHVIEWSANIBEL.COM*

**Facing page:** Christmas at 'Tween Waters

percent discount for seven-night stay in summer. BBQ grills, laundry, pool. On Gulf. SSL) Studio apartments and one- and two-bedroom cottages, each with screened porch. Daily towel service; weekly maid service. Shell and fish service area. Beach sundeck and tiki hut. Cribs available.

**Best Western Sanibel Island** *(3287 West Gulf Dr.; 472-1700; for reservations call 800-645-6559; fax 481-4947; Germany, Austria and Switzerland 069-44-60-02, fax 069-43-96-31. Packages available. Rates include continental breakfast. BBQ grills, bicycles, daily maid service, laundry, picnic tables, pool, shuffleboard and tennis courts. On Gulf.)* These 45 rooms have microwaves, refrigerators or kitchenettes, and free HBO. Most have screened terraces and garden or Gulf views. Two-bedroom suites have fully-equipped kitchens. Complimentary use of chaise lounges and tennis equipment.

**Blue Dolphin** *(4227 West Gulf Dr.; 472-1600 or 800-648-4660; fax 472-8615. BBQ grills, bicycles, laundry. On Gulf. SSL)* These casual Gulf-front cottages are run by 20-year island residents. The nine efficiency and one-bedroom units have kitchens with microwaves, individually controlled air conditioning, telephones and sun decks. Guests have complimentary use of lounge chairs, beach umbrellas and bicycles. The last business along West Gulf Dr., in a quiet area.

**Brennen's Tarpon Tale Inn** *(367 Periwinkle Way; 472-0939 or 888-345-0939; fax 472-6202. Rates include continental breakfast. Bicycles, laundry. SSL)* Each unit in this 40-year-old, five-bungalow inn has its own theme; all have tile floors, whitewashed wicker and antique oak furniture. Landscaped grounds hide the inn from the street. Near the lighthouse, it's a four-minute walk (or two-minute bike ride) to the beach. Free use of videos, beach chairs and umbrellas. Ask owners Joe and Dawn Ramsey for advice on restaurants, activities.

**Buttonwood Cottages** *(1234 North Buttonwood Ln.; 395-9061 or 877-395-COTTAGE; fax 395-2620. BBQ grills, bicycles, laundry. SSL)* These one- and two-bedroom suites, efficiencies and studio cottages have king beds, screened porches and video players. Guests have use of beach chairs, towels, umbrellas and fishing equipment. Grounds include hammocks and hot tubs.

**Caribe Beach Resort** *(2669 West Gulf Dr.; 472-4526 or 800-330-1593. BBQ grills, bicycles, horseshoe pit, hot tub, laundry, pool, shuffleboard and volleyball courts. Pets 25 lbs. and under allowed. On Gulf. SSL)* In a shady location, Caribe offers 19 efficiency apartments, five one-bedrooms, a one-bedroom and a two-bedroom cottage. Efficiencies include a Murphy bed and a double pullout couch. All units have a deck or balcony, private phone, cable TV and video player.

**Casa Ybel Resort** *(2255 West Gulf Dr.; 472-3145 or 800-276-4753; fax 472-2109. Packages available. BBQ grills; bicycles; daily maid service; laundry; pool; restaurant; shuffleboard, tennis and volleyball courts. On Gulf.)* Now a modern, 114-unit resort, Casa Ybel has been a major Sanibel destination for over 100 years. Located on 28 acres, it features one- and two-bedroom suites (all beachfront), each with a sleeper sofa in the living room. For families, the resort has a children's play area, a children's pool and a Kid's Club, with programs on shelling, the beach, nature and treasure hunts. Adult classes available, too. The Olympic-sized main pool has an adjacent whirlpool.

**Castaways at Blind Pass** *(6460 Sanibel-Captiva Rd.; 472-1252 or 800-375-0152; fax 472-1020. Ten percent discount for seven-night stay during summer months. Packages available. BBQ grills, bicycles, laundry, pool. Three-night minimum stay during holiday periods. Some pets OK. Some units on Gulf.)* The Castaways sits on a small bay off Blind Pass. It includes water-view cottages, efficiencies and motel units. Daily towel service; weekly maid service. Public telephones available. The small marina offers rentals, charters, bait and sundry items.

**Colony Resort** *(419 East Gulf Dr.; 472-5151 or 800-342-1704. BBQ grills, laundry, picnic tables, pool. Three-night minimum stay during holidays. On Gulf.)* The Colony features

single and duplex cottages and one-bedroom condos, which sleep four. Linen service is free; maid service optional. Condos have screened porches.

**Driftwood Inn** *(711 Donax St.; 395-8874; fax 472-6935. Some pets allowed.)* These efficiency, one-bedroom, and two-bedroom cottages have a living room, dining area and screened-in porch with a dining table. One-bedrooms accommodate four people; two-bedrooms sleep six. Bedrooms have queen-size beds; living rooms queen-size sofa beds. Beach chairs, umbrellas and linens, except for beach towels, are provided.

**Forty-Fifteen Resort** *(4015 West Gulf Dr.; 472-1232. Weekly rentals only. Laundry, pool, tennis courts. Not handicap accessible. Non-smoking. On Gulf. SSL)* These nine vacation cottages are on the uncrowded end of West Gulf. Seven accommodate four people, two sleep six, one sleeps two. Kitchens have microwaves. Complimentary linens.

**Gulf Breeze Cottages** *(1081 Shell Basket Ln.; 472-1626 or 800-388-2842; fax 472-4664. Laundry, shuffleboard courts. On Gulf. SSL)* These 13 one-room efficiencies and one- and two-bedroom cottages are at the end of a private lane. Each has a kitchen and refrigerator. Cottage No. 7 has a two-way view of the Gulf. Babysitting available.

**Holiday Inn Beach Resort** *(1231 Middle Gulf Dr.; 472-4123. Bicycles, pool, restaurant, tennis courts. On Gulf.)* All 98 rooms include two double beds or one king-size bed, small refrigerator, iron and ironing board, coffee maker, hair dryer and safe. Pool-side snack bar, gift shop. Free use of beach cabanas.

**Hurricane House Resort** *(2939 West Gulf Dr.; 472-1696 or 800-448-2736; fax 472-1718. BBQ grills, bicycles for rent, laundry, pool, tennis courts. On Gulf.)* These two-bedroom townhouses have video players and screened balconies. Whirlpools and picnic areas on grounds. Guests get tennis, golf privileges at the Dunes Golf & Tennis Club.

**Island Inn** *(3111 West Gulf Dr.; 472-1561 or 800-851-5088; fax 472-0051. Two-night mini-*

**Color code:** Lowest rate, peak season: **Under $100. Under $200. Under $300. Under $400.**

mum for efficiency units and for all units on weekends. Daily maid service; laundry; pool; restaurant; table tennis; croquet, shuffleboard, tennis, volleyball courts. Butterfly garden. On Gulf.) Established in 1895, this genteel inn has three lodges and several cottages. All units have refrigerators. Modified American plan (breakfast and dinner included in the room rate) Nov. 15 to May 1. The blowing of the conch summons you to dinner (jackets for men) during the season.

**Kona Kai Motel** (1539 Periwinkle Way; 472-1001 or 800-820-2385. Rates include continental breakfast. BBQ grills, bicycles, pool. Some pets allowed.) The Kona Kai has motel rooms, efficiencies, and suites that sleep six. Free linen service. Stores and restaurants nearby; Sanibel River in back. Canoes available. The beach is 3/4 mile away.

**Lighthouse Resort & Club** (210 Periwinkle Way; 472-4526 or 800-456-0009; fax 472-0079. Weekly rentals only. BBQ grills, bicycles, laundry, pool, shuffleboard and tennis courts. SSL) Each of these bayfront 1,800-sq.-ft. apartments has a king and two twin beds, a pull-out couch and a washer and dryer.

**Mitchell's Sand Castles By The Sea** (3951 West Gulf Dr.; 472-1282. No credit cards. Laundry, pool. Some pets allowed. On Gulf.) Owned by islander Roxanne Palmer, these relaxed one- to four-bedroom cottages have kitchens and screened porches.
*mitchellSSANDCastle.com*

**Ocean's Reach Condominium** (2230 Camino del Mar Dr.; 472-4554 or 800-336-6722. Weekly rentals only. BBQ grills; bicycles; covered parking; laundry; picnic tables, pool; basketball, shuffleboard and tennis courts. On Gulf.) These one- and two-bedroom units each have a Gulf-front lanai, washer, dryer, dishwasher and video player.

**Palm View Motel** (706 Donax St., 472-1606; fax 472-6733. BBQ grills, laundry. Some pets allowed.) Motel rooms, efficiencies and one- and two-bedroom apartments all have kitchens (except two rooms which can connect). Picnic area, fish cleaning facilities. A block from the beach.

**The Palms of Sanibel** (1220 Morningside Dr.; 395-1775 or 877-749-5093; fax 395-3379.

Weekly rentals only. BBQ grills, bicycles, laundry, pool. SSL) Near the lighthouse, these cottages each have a ceramic-tile floor, breakfast bar, queen bed, queen sleeper sofa, two TVs, a video player, screened-in porch and deck. Fresh towels daily. Complimentary umbrellas, beach towels, chairs.

**The Parrot Nest Old-Sanibel Resort** (1237 Anhinga Ln.; 472-4212. BBQ grills, daily maid service, laundry. SSL) Talking parrots are the attraction at this six-room inn near the lighthouse. Each room has a refrigerator, microwave, stove and patio. Each sleeps up to three with one king bed and one single bed. A cafe, deli and shops are next door. The Gulf is a five-minute walk away.

**Pelican's Roost Condominium** (605 Donax St.; 472-2996 or 877-757-6678; fax 472-0317. Weekly rentals only. No credit cards. BBQ grills, horseshoe pit, laundry, pool, shuffleboard and tennis courts. On Gulf.) Each of these 21 two-bedroom, two-bath apartments has a Gulf-view screened porch. On 3 1/2 acres.

**Periwinkle Cottages** (1431 Jamaica Dr.; 472-1880; fax 472-5567. No walk-ins accepted; some pets allowed. SSL) These cottages are off Sanibel-Captiva Road, not on Periwinkle Way. Each has a screened porch, video player and hair dryer. Free linen service. Beach chairs, umbrellas, floats, beach towels furnished. Grounds have a secluded pond, gazebo and climbing equipment for small children. The Sanibel Recreational Complex, with a pool, tennis courts and other amenities, is a short bike ride away.

**Periwinkle Park and Campground** (1119 Periwinkle Way; 472-1433. Children under 6 free. No credit cards. BBQ grills, laundry, picnic tables. Some pets allowed, but not dogs.) Periwinkle Park accepts trailers, motor homes, truck campers, tent campers, tents and vans. It has electricity, sewer and water hookups, as well as restrooms and showers. Ice and LP gas are available. The park also has a collection of exotic animals, including tropical birds and monkeys. Attracting an upscale crowd, the campground has guests who've been coming annually for decades. About a dozen people live here year-round. The Sanibel River is in back.

**Pointe Santo de Sanibel** *(2445 West Gulf Dr.; 472-9100 or 800-824-5442; fax 472-0487. Weekly rentals only. BBQ grills, hot tub, laundry, pool, shuffleboard and tennis courts. On Gulf.)* Each one- to three-bedroom condo has a breakfast area, dining room, screened lanai, washer and dryer. Some have rooftop decks. Tiki huts, activity program.

**Sandalfoot Condominium** *(671 East Gulf Dr.; 472-2275 or 800-725-2250; fax 472-5135. Minimum stay three nights off season, one week in season. BBQ grills, laundry, pool, tennis court. On Gulf.)* Sixty fully equipped one- and two-bedroom Gulf-front or Gulf-view units. Lushly landscaped grounds. Elevators, on-site management.

**Sanddollar Condominium** *(1785 Middle Gulf Dr.; 472-5021 or 800-794-3107; fax 466-0514. Minimum stay: one week during the winter season, two weeks rest of the year. BBQ grills, laundry, pool, tennis courts. On Gulf.)* All 36 two- and three-bedroom units have a washer and dryer and a screened lanai.

**Sandpiper Inn** *(720 Donax St.; 472-1529 or 877-227-4737; fax 472-0967. BBQ grills, bicycles, laundry, picnic tables. SSL)* These one-bedroom, one-bath suites have living rooms and dining rooms. Complimentary beach towels and beach chairs.

**Sandy Bend** *(3057 West Gulf Dr.; 472-1190; fax 472-3057. Weekly rentals only. Daily maid service, laundry, tennis courts. On Gulf.)* Eight two-bedroom apartments each have a living and dining room, dishwasher and screened Gulf-front porch. Individually decorated. Complimentary linens.

**Sanibel Arms Condominium** *(805 East Gulf Dr.; 472-2259 or 800-806-7368; fax 472-2420. Weekly rentals only. Extended-stay discounts. No credit cards. BBQ grills, laundry, pool, shuffleboard courts. On Gulf.)* These units have individually controlled air-conditioning and screened porches or balconies. Free linens. Clubhouse library, beach shower, fish-cleaning facilities. Canal boat dock.

**Sanibel Arms West Condominium** *(827 East Gulf Dr.; 472-1138 or 800-950-1138.*

*Minimum stay four nights. Laundry, pool, tennis courts. On Gulf.)* Each of these 13 two-story units has over 1,000 square feet, with two bedrooms, two baths, a living room, dining room, balcony and screened porch.

**Sanibel Beach Club I and II** *(626 Nerita St. and 265 Periwinkle Way; 800-456-0009. Weekly rentals only. BBQ grills; bicycles; horseshoe pit; hot tub and sauna; laundry; pool; basketball, shuffleboard, tennis and volleyball courts. On Gulf.)* Each two-bedroom, two-bath condo includes a microwave, linens and dishes, washer and dryer, video player and screened-in porch. The 6.3-acre complex also includes a children's play area.

**Sanibel Inn** *(937 East Gulf Dr.; 472-3181 or 800-965-7772; fax 481-4947. BBQ grills, bicycles, daily maid service, pool, restaurant, room service, tennis courts. On Gulf.)* Most of these 96 units are hotel rooms with a king or two queen beds, refrigerator, microwave, a screened balcony or patio, coffee service and a video player. One-bedroom suites have king beds and queen sleepers. Two-bedroom suites sleep six, and come with a dishwasher, refrigerator, stove, microwave and living room with sleeper. Free daily newspaper, HBO and Disney Channel. Poolside cabana, on-site rentals of umbrellas, cabanas, floats and kayaks; free rental of tennis gear. Gardening, beach, shell and dolphin programs. Children's programs, crafts and parties. The eight acres are landscaped to attract butterflies and hummingbirds, and have over 500 palms.

**Sanibel Moorings Condominium** *(845 East Gulf Dr.; 472-4119 or 888-FLA-ISLE; Germany and U.K 800-237-5144. One-week minimum stay during peak season. BBQ grills, laundry, pool, tennis courts. On Gulf.)* Located between the Gulf and a canal, this six-acre resort has a canal dock. Free use of beach chairs, lounges. Business center with PC, fax.

**Sanibel Siesta** *(1246 Fulgur Street; 472-4117 or 800-548- 2743; fax 472-6826. Minimum stay three nights. Laundry, pool, shuffleboard and tennis courts. On Gulf.)* Each of these 64 two-bedroom, two-bath units has a living

---

**Color code:** Lowest rate, peak season: **Under $100. Under $200. Under $300. Under $400.**

room, dining area, microwave and screened lanai. Beachview Country Club nearby.

**Sea Shells of Sanibel Condominium** *(2840 West Gulf Dr.; 472-4634 or 800-533-4486; fax 472-0724. Minimum stay one week during winter, three days rest of year. BBQ grills, laundry, pool, shuffleboard and tennis courts.)* These two-bedroom units are divided into Group A (1,050 square feet) and Group B units (1,350 square feet). Each has a dishwasher, disposal, self-cleaning oven, microwave, telephone, screened porch. Some have video players and stereo receivers.

**Seahorse Cottages** *(1223 Buttonwood Ln. North; 472-4262; fax 466-6149. No children. BBQ grills, bicycles, laundry, pool. SSL)* Each cottage has a living room, bedroom, porch, front and back entrance, antique oak furnishings, paddle fans, ceramic-tile floors, individually controlled air conditioning and video player. Kitchens have solid-carbon water filters. Hammock on grounds. Free use of beach towels, chairs, umbrellas. A few blocks from the Gulf; 200 feet from the bay.

**Seaside Inn** *(541 East Gulf Dr.; 472-1400 or 800-831-7384; fax 481-4947. Rates include continental breakfast. BBQ grills, bicycles, laundry, picnic tables, pool, shuffleboard courts. On Gulf.)* This 33-unit inn has one-, two-, and three-bedroom cottages with separate dining areas and living rooms and video players. Poolside studios have small refrigerators and microwaves. Some units have private porches or balconies. Free use of books, videos.

 **Shalimar Resort** *(2823 West Gulf Dr.; 472-1353 or 800-995-1242. Ten percent discount to AAA and AARP members. Packages available. Laundry, pool, basketball and shuffleboard courts. SSL)* Thirty-three one- and two-bedroom cottages and efficiencies feature microwaves and furnished linens.

**Signal Inn** *(1811 Olde Middle Gulf Dr.; 472-4690 or 800-992-4690; fax 472-3988. Minimum stay three nights. Hot tub, laundry, pool, sauna, air-conditioned racquetball court. Some pets OK. SSL)* All 19 elevated one- to four-bedroom units have three-sided exposures. Each has a screened porch, video player, washer, dryer and parking underneath. Gazebo, outdoor foot showers. On a dead-end road 200 yards from the beach.

**Song of the Sea** *(863 East Gulf Dr.; 472-2220 or 800-231-1045; fax 472-8569; Germany, Austria and Switzerland 069-44-60-02, fax 069-43-96-31. Rates include outdoor continental breakfast. BBQ grills, bicycles, laundry, pool, shuffleboard and tennis courts, whirlpool. On Gulf.)* Song of the Sea offers 10 pool-view rooms, 12 Gulf-view rooms and eight one-bedroom Gulf-front suites. Each has a kitchen, dining area and screened terrace. Pool-view rooms have two queen beds; Gulf-view rooms have one king bed; one-bedroom suites have one king bed and a queen living room sleeper sofa. All are nonsmoking. Guests get a bottle of wine, fresh-cut flowers, bottled water, daily newspapers and use of the inn's book and video library, video players, beach umbrellas and chaise lounges. Popular with Europeans.

**Sundial Beach Resort** *(1451 Middle Gulf Dr.; 472-4151 or 800-965-7772. BBQ grills, bicycles, fitness room, laundry, pools, restaurants, tennis courts, whirlpool. On Gulf.)* The 33-acre, 270-unit Sundial has studio, one-bedroom and two-bedroom condos. All have a dining area, living room and safe; some have a den and/or screened balcony or patio. Catamaran, sea kayak and boogie-board rentals. The 12-court tennis facility holds guest tournaments. Private lessons, group clinics available. Organized activities for children, teens, adults and groups. Kids camps available for half days, full days and evenings. Kid's activities include shell crafts, tennis clinics, aquacize. Environmental programs have hands-on learning. Business center has PCs, printing, typing service, cell-phone and pager rentals.

*SunDial resort · Com*

**Sunshine Island Inn** *(642 East Gulf Dr.; 395-2500. BBQ grills, laundry, pool.)* This family-operated five-room inn is across the street from the beach. Each room has Mexican tile and Berber carpet, a sliding glass door that leads out to the pool, a video player and either an efficiency or full kitchen.

**Surfrider Beach Club** *(555 East Gulf Dr.; 472-2161. Two-night minimum stay. BBQ grills, bicycles, hot tub, laundry, pool, shuffle-*

**South Seas Resort**

board, tennis courts. On Gulf.) The Surfrider has 30 small one-bedroom condos and one two-bedroom unit. Each has a microwave and video player. Guests get free use of beach chairs and umbrellas.

**Tropical Winds Motel** (4819 Trade Winds Dr.; 472-1765. Pool. On Gulf.) Six units are on the beach (four more are a short walk away in a separate building) at this old-time, quiet property. All units are efficiencies, with coffee makers and dishes.

**Waterside Inn On The Beach** (3033 West Gulf Dr.; 472-1345 or 800-741-6166. Wedding and family reunion packages available. BBQ grills, bicycles, laundry, pool, shuffleboard courts. Some pets OK. On Gulf.) These rooms, efficiencies, cottages and condos are nestled among palms. Cottages have dining nooks. Bedrooms have king beds, dressers, large closets. Efficiencies have queen beds, microwaves and private patios or balconies. A honeymoon cottage has a double Jacuzzi and a fireplace. Non-smoking rooms available. Beach umbrellas for rent.

**Westend Paradise of Sanibel** (1389 Tahiti Dr.; 472-9088; fax 472-8009. Two-bedroom suites have a two-night minimum. During holidays winter rates apply with a three-night minimum. BBQ grills, bicycles, laundry. SSL) This small inn is in a quiet subdivision 1,000 feet from a secluded beach. One- and two-bedroom suites have individually controlled air conditioning, telephones. Shady gazebos in garden. Complimentary beach chairs, umbrellas.

, com

**West Wind Inn** (3345 West Gulf Dr.; 472-1541 or 800-824-0476; fax 472-8134; U.K. 00-800-897-44321, U.K. fax 0800-9625-67; Germany fax 0130-810990. Group rates available. Minimum stays required during certain holiday and peak-season periods (call for details). Bicycles, laundry, pool, restaurant, tennis courts. On Gulf.) All rooms have refrigerators, data ports and screened lanais; many have kitchens. Driftwood Building rooms are larger, include upgraded appointments and video players. Non-smoking rooms have king beds or two double beds. Complimentary cribs with advance notice. Beach games and rentals. Pool area includes bar, splash pool for toddlers. Free tennis, tennis clinics. Complimentary 24-hour coffee and tea, daily newspapers. Gift shop, concierge service. On the quiet end of West Gulf Dr.

## Captiva

**Captiva Island Inn** (11509 Andy Rosse Ln.; 395-0882 or 800-454-9898; fax 395-0862. Rates include breakfast. Bicycles. SSL) Down the street from the beach, this B&B is next to shops, restaurants and art galleries. Six one- and two-bedroom cottages each have a living room with a sleeper sofa. Complimentary beach chairs and sunscreen.

**Jensen's On The Gulf** (15300 Captiva Dr.; 472-4684. Minimum stay may be required. On Gulf.) These nine shady beach homes and apartments are in the center of Captiva.

**Jensen's Twin Palm Resort** (15107 Captiva Dr.; 472-5800. Minimum stay may be required. SSL) This historic bayside retreat has 14 cottages and apartments. The Twin Palm marina is adjacent.

**Maddison Suites** (11508 Andy Rosse Ln.; 472-3113 or 800-472-0638. Weekly rates available. Breakfast included. Bicycles. Some pets OK. SSL) Located in the Old Captiva Village, this four-suite B&B is a two-minute walk from the beach. Suites sleep two to four. Shops, restaurants nearby.

**South Seas Resort** (Captiva Dr.; 472-5111 or 800-965-7772; fax 481-4947. Packages available. BBQ grills, bicycles, daily maid ser-

---

**Color code:** Lowest rate, peak season: **Under $100. Under $200. Under $300. Under $400.**

vice, 9-hole golf, laundry, pools, restaurants, tennis courts, water-sports center. On Gulf.) This 330-acre resort covers the north end of Captiva. Over 600 accommodations include hotel rooms; one-, two- and three-bedroom condos; cottages; and private homes with their own pools and tennis courts. Complete marina. Twenty-one tennis courts; 18 swimming pools. Offshore Sailing School. Free trolley service.

'Tween Waters Inn *(15951 Captiva Dr.; 472-5161 or 800-223-5865; fax 472-0249. Packages available. Rates include continental breakfast buffet. Rates based on occupancy of 1–2 in rooms and efficiencies and 1–4 in suites. Daily maid service, fitness center, laundry, pool, restaurants, tennis courts.)* On a narrow strip of land between the Gulf and Roosevelt Channel, this inn has a marina in back and sandy beaches in front. Three restaurants, poolside bar and grill, free tennis and tennis clinics, and (extra-cost) private lessons. The marina has boat, canoe and kayak rentals. Fishing, shelling, sailing and kayaking guides available. Clothing store.

## Off the islands

These places are just minutes from Sanibel:

**Country Inns & Suites** *(13901 Shell Point Plaza, Ft. Myers; 454-9292. Rates include continental breakfast. Daily maid service, heated pool, workout room.)* Opened in the fall of 2001, this 112-room facility has special rates for extended stays. Each room has a coffee maker and hair dryer. At the entrance to the Shell Point retirement village.

**Hampton Inn & Suites** *(11281 Summerlin Square Dr., Ft. Myers; 437-8888. Rates include continental breakfast. Daily maid service, heated pool. Nonsmoking rooms available.)* The closest location of this respected chain to the islands.

**Radisson Inn/Sanibel Gateway** *(20091 Summerlin Rd., Ft. Myers; 466-1200. Daily maid service, hot tub/Jacuzzi, pool, restaurant, room service.)* Rooms come with a king-size bed and a double bed or sofa sleeper. Each has a small refrigerator, coffee maker, iron, ironing board and hair dryer. Renovated in the summer of 2001.

**Sanibel Harbour Resort & Spa** *(17260 Harbour Pointe Dr., Ft. Myers; 466-4000. Daily maid service, pool, restaurant, spa, tennis courts, watersports. Many extras. On San Carlos Bay.)* This internationally famous resort has 417 guest rooms, suites and condos. Special program for kids.

## Rental agencies

Rental homes and condos are scattered throughout the islands. Each agency below represents a large number of properties.

■ **1-800-Sanibel**
2000 Periwinkle Way, Sanibel; 472-1800
■ **At Sanibel Vacation Reservations**
P.O. Box 1553, Sanibel; 472-9700
■ **Central Reservations SW Florida**
1633B Periwinkle Way, Sanibel; 472-0457
■ **Cottages to Castles**
2427 Periwinkle Way, Sanibel; 472-6385
■ **Gopher Enterprises**
P.O. Box 186, Sanibel; 472-5021
■ **Grande Island Vacations**
1506 Periwinkle Way, Sanibel; 472-5322
■ **Island Vacations**
1101 Periwinkle Way, Sanibel; 472-7277
■ **Kenoyer Real Estate Corp.**
2669 West Gulf Dr., Sanibel; 472-4526
■ **North Captiva Island Club Resort**
P.O. Box 1000, Pineland; 395-1001
■ **Priscilla Murphy Vacation Rentals**
1177 Causeway Rd., Sanibel; 472-4883
■ **ReMax of the Islands Rentals**
2400 Palm Ridge Rd., Sanibel; 472-5050
■ **Reservation Central**
695 Tarpon Bay Rd. #1, Sanibel; 395-3682
■ **Royal Shell Vacation Properties**
1200 Periwinkle Way, Sanibel; 472-9111
■ **Sanibel Accommodations**
2341 Palm Ridge Rd., Sanibel; 472-3191
■ **Sanibel Holiday**
1630A Periwinkle Way, Sanibel; 472-6565
■ **Sanibel One**
1633G Periwinkle Way, Sanibel; 395-2610
■ **VIP Realty Rental Division**
1560 Periwinkle Way, Sanibel; 472-1613

**Tell us what you think** of island accommodations. Be honest, specific and descriptive. E-mail your experiences and opinions to: mike@coconutpress.com

# Resources

## Important phone numbers

Emergencies ................................. 911
Sanibel Police Department ........ 472-3111
Lee County Sheriff (Captiva) ...... 477-1200
Sanibel Fire Department ............ 472-5525
Captiva Fire Department ............ 472-9494
HealthPark of the Islands ............ 395-1414
C.R.O.W. (for injured animals) .... 472-3644
Florida Highway Patrol ................ 278-7100
Florida Marine Patrol .................... 332-6966
U.S. Coast Guard ............................ 463-5754
Lee Memorial Hospital ................ 332-1111
Poison Control ........................ 800-282-3171
Local directory inquiries .......................... 411
International directory inquiries ............. 00
International operator assistance ........... 01

**For long-distance information:** dial 1, then the appropriate area code, then 555-1212. **For direct-dial calls** to another area code: dial 1, the area code and then the 7-digit number. For international calls dial 011, the country code then the local area/city code (minus the first 0) and number.

## Florists

- **Captiva Garden & Gourmet**
14830 Captiva Drive, Captiva; 395-0354
- **Floral Artistry**
2400 Palm Ridge Rd., Sanibel; 472-3040
- **Flower Shop of the Islands**
2449 Periwinkle Way, Sanibel; 472-3707
- **Periwinkle Florist & Gift Baskets**
1719 Periwinkle Way, Sanibel; 472-3125
- **Weeds and Things**
2330 Palm Ridge Rd., Sanibel; 472-2112

## Gasoline and auto service

- **Amoco ServiceCenter**
1015 Periwinkle Way, Sanibel; 472-2125
- **Hess Express**
2499 Palm Ridge Rd., Sanibel; 472-2198
*No auto service*
- **Island Garage**
1609 Periwinkle Way, Sanibel; 472-4318
*No gasoline*

---

**Facing page:** Captiva Post Office mailbox

- **Sanibel Shell**
2435 Periwinkle Way, Sanibel; 472-2012
- **7-Eleven**
2460 Periwinkle Rd., Sanibel; 472-8696
*No auto service*

## Hair and nail salons, day spas

- **Beverly Hills Hair Design**
2340 Periwinkle Way, Sanibel; 395-3116
- **Cape Nails**
2407 Periwinkle Way, Sanibel; 472-4145
- **Harry Ruby Salon**
975 Rabbit Rd., Sanibel; 395-0910
- **Island Winds Coiffures**
695 Tarpon Bay Rd., Sanibel; 472-2591
- **New Spirit Hair Design**
630 Tarpon Bay Rd., Sanibel; 472-2371
- **Pat's Hair Kair**
2248 Periwinkle Way, Sanibel; 472-2425
- **Sanibel Barber Shop**
2467 Periwinkle Way, Sanibel; 472-5626
- **Sanibel Beauty Salon**
2467 Periwinkle Way, Sanibel; 472-1111
- **Sanibel Day Spa**
2075 Periwinkle Way, Sanibel; 395-2220
- **Sbarra's Captiva Day Spa**
11508 Andy Rosse Ln., Captiva; 472-5337
- **Scarlett O'Hair's Beauty Salon**
1711 Periwinkle Way, Sanibel; 472-5699

## Massage therapists

- **New Spirit Hair Design**
630 Tarpon Bay Rd., Sanibel; 472-2371
- **Sanibel Beauty Salon**
2467 Periwinkle Way, Sanibel; 472-1111
- **Sanibel Day Spa**
2075 Periwinkle Way, Sanibel; 395-2220
- **Sanibel Wellness**
1717 Periwinkle Way, Sanibel; 395-1100
- **Sbarra's Captiva Day Spa**
11508 Andy Rosse Ln., Captiva; 472-5337

## Medical services

- **Auditory Associates Hearing Center**
2418 Palm Ridge Rd., Sanibel; 395-1700
- **Coral Veterinary Clinic**
1530 Periwinkle Way, Sanibel; 472-8387
- **Drs. Eyecare Centers**
1571 Periwinkle Way, Sanibel; 472-4204
- **Eye Centers of Florida**
1723 Periwinkle Way, Sanibel; 395-1999

**Sanibel fire trucks**

■ **HealthPark of the Islands**
1699 Periwinkle Way, Sanibel; 395-1414
■ **San-Cap Medical Center**
4301 Sanibel-Captiva Rd., Sanibel; 472-0700
■ **Sanibel Chiropractic**
1717 Periwinkle Way, Sanibel; 472-0900
■ **Stevens Family Chiropractic**
2400 Palm Ridge Rd., Sanibel; 472-9830

## Newspapers and magazines

■ **Island Reporter / Captiva Current**
2340 Periwinkle Way, Sanibel; 472-1587
■ **Island Sun**
1640 Periwinkle Way, Sanibel; 395-1213
■ **Sanibel-Captiva Islander**
695 Tarpon Bay Rd., Sanibel; 472-5185
■ **Times of the Islands magazine**
1630 Periwinkle Way, Sanibel; 472-0205

## Photo processing

■ **Arundel's Hallmark Shoppe**
1626 Periwinkle Way, Sanibel; 472-0434
■ **Eckerd Drugs**
2331 Palm Ridge Rd., Sanibel; 472-0085
■ **MotoPhoto & Portrait Studio**
1719 Periwinkle Way, Sanibel; 472-4414

## Photographers

■ **David Meardon** *(P.O. Box 1213, Sanibel; 472-2346, www.sanibelphoto.com)* creates family beach portraits and is a well-known nature photographer. He also handles special-event, business and commercial photography. His photographs have appeared in newspapers, books, magazines and calendars locally and nationally and have won awards in nature, newspaper, and advertis-ing competitions. Some of the wildlife photos in this book are from David, including the shot of the oystercatcher.

## Postal services

■ **Sanibel Post Office**
650 Tarpon Bay Rd., Sanibel; 472-1573
8:30 a.m.–5 p.m. Mon.–Fri.; 10 a.m.–noon Sat.
■ **Captiva Post Office**
14812 Captiva Dr.; 472-1674
9 a.m. to 4 p.m. Mon.–Fri.
■ **Jerry's Supermarket** (contract office)
1700 Periwinkle Way, Sanibel; 472-9300
8 a.m.–5 p.m. Mon.–Fri.; 8–10 a.m. Sat.

## Printers

■ **Big Red Q Quickprint Center**
1101 Periwinkle Way, Sanibel; 472-2121
■ **Island Graphics**
459 Periwinkle Way, Sanibel; 472-4437
■ **Sanibel Print and Graphics**
2400 Palm Ridge Rd., Sanibel; 472-4592

## Radio

■ **Adult Contemporary**
WINK-FM, 96.9
WSGL-FM, 104.7
■ **Classical/Jazz**
WGCU-FM, 90.1, NPR/classical
WDRR-FM, 98.5, Smooth jazz
■ **Country**
WIKX-FM, 92.9
WWGR-FM, 101.9
WCKT-FM, 107.1
■ **Easy listening**
WAVV-FM, 101.1
■ **Kids**
WMYR-AM, 1410, Radio Disney
■ **News/Talk**
WINK-AM, 1200, News talk
WRLR-FM, 100.1, Talk
■ **Oldies**
WOLZ-FM, 95.3, '50s–'60s oldies
WJGO-FM, 102.9, '70s rhythmic oldies
■ **Pop**
WXKB-FM, 103.9, Top 40
WBTT-FM, 105.5, Dance Top 40
■ **Rock**
WARO-FM, 94.5, Classic rock
WRXK-FM, 96.1, Classic rock
WJBX-FM, 99.3, Modern rock

■ **Sports**
WWCN-AM, 770
■ **Standards**
WJPT-FM, 106.3
WKII-AM, 1070

## Religious services

*Services are year-round except as indicated*

■ **Bat Yam Temple of the Islands.** *Services at the Sanibel Congregational United Church of Christ, 2050 Periwinkle Way, Sanibel; 472-6684.* Reform services Fri. at 8 p.m.
■ **Captiva Chapel by the Sea.** *11580 Chapin Ln., Captiva; 472-1646.* Services Sun. at 11 a.m Nov.–April.
■ **St. Isabel Catholic Church.** *3559 Sanibel-Captiva Rd., Captiva; 472-2763.* Mass Mon.–Fri. at 8:30 a.m., Sat. at 5:30 p.m.; Sun. at 8:30 and 10:30 a.m. Confession Sat. at 9 a.m.
■ **St. Michael's and All Angels Episcopal Church.** *2304 Periwinkle Way, Sanibel; 472-2173.* Services Advent–Easter: Sat. at 5 p.m.; Sun. at 7:30, 9:30 and 11:30 a.m. Easter–Advent: Sun. at 7:30 and 9:30 a.m. Other services Wed. at 9 a.m.; Thur. at 7:30 a.m. Church school Sun. mornings; youth group Wed. evenings.; adult Bible Study Thur. mornings.
■ **Sanibel-Captiva First Church of Christ Scientist.** *2950 West Gulf Dr., Sanibel; 472-8684.* Services Sun. at 10:30 a.m.; Wed. at 7:30 p.m. Sunday school Sun. at 10:30 a.m. Reading room Mon., Wed., Fri. 10 a.m–noon.
■ **Sanibel Community Church.** *1740 Periwinkle Way, Sanibel; 472-2684.* Services Sun. at 8 a.m. (communion), 9 a.m. (contemporary), 10:30 a.m. (traditional). Sunday school Sun. at 9 a.m. General fellowship Sun. at 10 a.m. in courtyard. LOGOS youth program.
■ **Sanibel Congregational United Church of Christ.** *2050 Periwinkle Way, Sanibel; 472-0497.* Sun. services Nov.–April at 7:45, 9, and 11 a.m.; May–Oct. at 7:45 and 10 a.m.
■ **Unitarian-Universalist Society of the Islands.** *Services at the Congregational United Church of Christ, 2050 Periwinkle Way, Sanibel; 472-1646.* Services Sun. 7:30 p.m. Nov.–April except last Sun. of month.
■ **Unity of the Islands.** *Services at the Congregational United Church of Christ, 2050 Periwinkle Way, Sanibel; 278-1511.* Services first Sun. of month at 4 p.m.

■ **Vineyard Christian Fellowship of Sanibel.** *4115 Sanibel-Captiva Rd., Sanibel; 472-1018.* Interdenominational services Sun. 9 a.m. (time may vary).

## Shipping

■ **Arundel's Hallmark Pack & Ship**
1626 Periwinkle Way, Sanibel; 472-0434
■ **Pak 'N' Ship**
2402 Palm Ridge Rd., Sanibel; 395-1220
■ **Quik Pack & Ship**
1713 Periwinkle Way, Sanibel; 472-0288

**Federal Express drop boxes:**
■ 1101 Periwinkle Way, Sanibel
■ 1626 Periwinkle Way, Sanibel
■ 1648 Periwinkle Way, Sanibel
■ 1713 Periwinkle Way, Sanibel
■ 2244 Periwinkle Way, Sanibel
■ 2402 Periwinkle Way, Sanibel
■ 650 Tarpon Bay Rd., Sanibel
■ 695 Tarpon Bay Rd., Sanibel
■ 11500 Andy Rosse Ln., Captiva

## Television

■ **ABC** WBR-TV, Cable 7
■ **CBS** WINK-TV, Cable 5
■ **FOX** WFTX-TV, Cable 4
■ **NBC** WBBH-TV, Cable 2

## Veterinarians

■ **Coral Veterinary Clinic**
1530 Periwinkle Way, Sanibel; 472-8387
■ **Dr. Suzanne Presley**
Vet care in your home, Sanibel; 392-0072

## Weddings

**You can buy a marriage license** at the Lee County Office of the Clerk of the Circuit Court (335-2273). The cost is $88.50 cash (no personal checks); the license is valid 60 days. Both you and your betrothed must appear in person; you both need a valid photo ID (a driver's license is OK) and Social Security number. Florida does not require a blood test. There is no waiting period except for Florida residents, who must wait three days. Weddings may be performed by a clergy member, Notary Public, judicial member or Clerk of the Court.

# Index

Page numbers in **bold** refer to photographs

1-800-Sanibel, 291
7-Eleven, 277, 293

**A**

Aboriginals: Art of the First Person, 271
Accommodations, 284–291
Ace Performer, 216
Adventure Cat, 209
Adventure Sailing Charters, 209
Adventure Sea Kayak Wildlife Tours, 209
Adventures in Paradise, 177–178
Air Canada, 36
Airlines, 35–37
Airport. *See Southwest Florida International Airport*
AirTran, 36
Air Transat, 36
Alamo, 37
Albert Meadow Antiques, 271
Alcohol, 30, 96
Algiers, 81
Algiers Beach. *See Gulfside City Park*
Allen castor bean farm, 47, 74
Allen, William, 47
Alligator. *See American alligator*
Alligator Curve. *See J.N. "Ding" Darling National Wildlife Refuge*
Alligator Hole, 190
Alphabet cone, 113, **114**
America West, 36
American Airlines, 35, 36
American alligator, 62, 97, 156, **156**, 157, 180–181
American coot, 151
American crocodile, **158, 159**, 160, 188
American Eagle, 35, 36
American Express, 29
American oystercatcher, 143, **144, 145**
American painted lady, 152
American ray, 172
American Revolution, 44
American star shell, **121**, 122
American Trans Air, 36
Ammonicera rota, 106
Amoco ServiceCenter, 36, 293
Anchor Inn of Sanibel, 28, 285
Anderson, Hans Christian, 169
Angel wing, 109, **109**
Angulate periwinkle, 127, **127**
Angulate wentletrap, **126**, 127
Anhinga, 146, 147, **147**
Anholt, Betty, 47
Aphrodite, 169
Apple murex, **116**, 117
Apple Taxi and Limousine Service, 37
Area 51 Design Imports, 277
Arks, 107
Armadillo. *See nine-banded armadillo*
Around the Sound Tours, 209

Art galleries, 271–272
Arundel's Hallmark Shoppe, 277, 294, 295
Atargatis, 169
Athenian shipwreck, 45
Atlantic baby's ear, **115**, 116
Atlantic false jingle, 123, **126**
Atlantic hair triton, 123, **123**
Atlantic kitten's paw, **126**, 127
Atlantic moon snail, **115**, 116, 128
Atlantic slipper shell, **126**, 127
Atlantic strawberry cockle, **111**, 112
Atlantic surf clam, **111**, 112
Atlantic winged oyster, 131
ATM machines, 29
At Sanibel Vacation Reservations, 291
Auditory Associates, 293
Audubon Cooperative Society, 248
Augers, 107
Australian pine, 77, 98, 190, 200, **200**, 201, **201**
Australian trumpet, 106
Auto service, 293
Avis, 37

**B**

Baby's ear. *See Atlantic baby's ear*
Back Country Fishing Charters, 223
Bailey, Francis, 70, **70**, 73, 82
Bailey, Frank, 49, 70, 279
Bailey house, 74
Bailey, John, 70, **70**
Bailey, Sam, 70, **70**, 77, 82
Bailey Road beach, 83
Bailey-Matthews Shell Museum, 17, 29, 31, 75, **75**, 203, 207, 235, 236
    Gift shop, 273
Bailey Tract. *See J.N. "Ding" Darling National Wildlife Refuge*
Bailey's Corner Pharmacy, 281
Bailey's General Store, 21, 70, 75, 178, 227, 236, 247, 279, 280
Bailey's True Value Hardware, 280
Bait Box, 227
Bait Box Guide Service, 223
Bald eagle, 146–148, **148**
Bandanna's at Sundial, 277
Banded tulip, 120, **121**
Bank of America, 29, 74
Bank of the Islands, 29
Baptist Church. *See Sanibel Baptist Church*
Barnacle Phil's, 221
Barnes, Jean, 53, **53**
Barnes, Rev. George, 51–53, 69
Barnes, Georgia, 53
Barnes, Marie, 53
Barnes, William, 53, **53**, 55
Barnum, P.T., 169
Barrier Island Group for the Arts. *See BIG Arts*
Barrier Island Pharmacy, 281
Bat Yam Temple of the Islands, 295
Bay scallop, 119, **119**
Bay of Pigs, 221

Bayside Charters, 223
Beach activities, 89–96
Beach parking, 83
Beaches, 78–99
Beach House, 273
Beach paraphernalia, 272–273
Beach reads, 84
Beach Road Inn, 285
Beach Stuff, 272, 273
Beachview Cottages, 285
Beachview Golf & Tennis Club, 241
Beachview Steakhouse, 259
Bean, The, 25, 33, 255, 259, 265
Below Market Rate Housing, 257
Best Western Sanibel Island, 285
Beverly Hills Hair Design, 293
BIG Arts, 238, **238**, 241, 271
BIG Arts Film Society, 238
Big Dipper, 245
Big Red Q Quickprint, 294
Bike rentals, 207
Bike Route, 207
Biking, 202–207
Biking map, 205
Billheimer, Mike. *See Lighthouse Cafe*
Billy's Rentals, **204**, 207
Binder, William, 49, 62, 75
Birds, 133–151
    American coot, 151
    American oystercatcher, 143, **144**, **145**
    anhinga, 146, 147, **147**
    bald eagle, 146–148, **148**
    black-bellied plover, 143
    black-crowned night-heron, 135, **135**, 146
    brown pelican, 38, 79, 149, **149**, 150
    cattle egret, 138, **138**
    common moorhen, 151, **151**
    double-crested cormorant, 147, **147**
    great blue heron, 133, **135**
    great egret, 133, **134**, 135, 146
    green heron, 97, 135, **135**
    herring gull, 142, **142**
    laughing gull, 142, **142**, 143
    little blue heron, 132, 135, 146
    mangrove cuckoo, 151
    osprey, 146, 148, **148**, 209, 255
    pileated woodpecker, 151
    reddish egret, 138, **138**, 146
    red-shouldered hawk, 148, **148**, 149
    ring-billed gull, 142, **142**, 143
    roseate spoonbill, **16**, 141, **141**, 146, **182**
    royal tern, **26**, **143**, 146
    ruddy turnstone, **143**, 146
    sandwich tern, 146
    snowy egret, **2**, 138, 146
    southeastern snowy plover, 143
    tricolored heron, 138, **138**
    turkey vulture, 151
    western sandpiper, 142, 143, 146

white ibis, **140,** 141
white pelican, 150, **150, 184**
willet, **143,** 146
wood stork, 141, **141,** 150
yellow-crowned night-heron, 135, **136, 137,** 138, 146
Bittersweets, 107, 109
Bivalve, 106
Black-bellied plover, 143
Black Caesar, 45
Black-crowned night-heron, 135, **135,** 146
Black drum, 228, **228**
Black-eyed Susan, 97
Black grouper, 229, **229**
Black mangrove. *See mangrove*
Black mullet, 230, **230**
Black Orchid Gallery, 271
Black sea bass, 228, **228**
Blind Pass, 17, 46, 55, 81, 286
Blue crab, 162
Blue Dolphin, 285
Boating, 208–221
Boat rentals, 212, 213, 216
Bobcat, 154
Boca Ciego, 46
Boca Grande, 40, 45, 68, 104, 213, 221, 226
Boca Grande Pass, 45, 172, 223, 232
Bookstores, 273
Boston Red Sox, 243
Bottlenose dolphin, 25, 79, 162–163, **162, 164, 165,** 180–181, 212
Bougainvillea, 220
Bowman, Robert, 46
Bowman's Beach, 21, **21,** 25, **32,** 33, 46, 65, **78, 80,** 81–83, 89, 93–98, **97, 99, 100,** 143, 177, 190, 196, 200, 201, 204, 207
Brainerd, Ann, 43, 49
Brazilian pepper, 190, 200, 201, **201**
Brennen's Tarpon Tale Inn, 28, 47, 74, 285
Broad-ribbed cardita, 123, **123**
Brown pelican, 38, 79, 149, **149,** 150
Brown scorpion, 154
Brown spiny sea star, 131, **131**
Bubble shell. *See common bubble shell*
Bubble Room, 259, 263
Bubble Room Emporium, **270,** 277
Buck Key, 17, 46, 49, 177, 212
Budget Rent-A-Car, 36, 37
Buffett, Jimmy, 219, 275
Bull shark, 172
Bungalow, 259, 260, 263
Burnap Cottage, 236
Burnsed, Capt. Jim and Jimmy, 226
Burnsed, Capt. Joe, 104, 223
Burr, Raymond, 235
Business hours, 29, 30
Buttercup lucine, 98, **114,** 116
Butterflies, 152, 153, 178
Buttonwood. *See mangrove*
Buttonwood Cottages, 285, 286
Buttonwood Drive beach, 83, 93
Byssus, 107

**C**
C. Turtles and Company, 274

Cabbage Key, 25, 33, 104, 213, 219–220, **219, 220,** 226
Cabbage palm, 155, **192,** 193, 196
Caesar, Henri. *See Black Caesar*
Calcium carbonate, 106
Caldez, José, 46
Calico clam, 109, **110**
Calico scallop, 119, **119**
California condor, 150
Caloosa Canvas, 277
Caloosahatchee River power plant, 167
Caloosahatchee River, 46, 242, 243
Calusa Indians, 43, 44, 46, 74, 75, 188, 220, 221, 235
Candace at Frangi-Pani, 274
Canoe Adventures and Wilderness Tours, 177, 181, 209, 212
Canoe and Kayak magazine, 209
Cape Air, 36
Cape Nails, 293
Cape San Blas, 45, 49
Capt. Jim's Charters, 209
Capt. Joe Burnsed's Charters, 223
Capt. Joe's Charters, 209
"Capt. Mike Fuery's New Florida Shelling Guide," 104
Capt. Randy's Fishy Business Charters, 209, 226
Captiva Beach, 25, 83, 93
Captiva cemetery, **42,** 75
Captiva Chapel by the Sea, 21, 62, 75, 295
Captiva Cruises, 25, 172, 213, **213,** 216, 220
Captiva Current, 294
Captiva Fire Department, 293
Captiva Garden & Gourmet, 260, 277, 278, 293
Captiva History House, 75
Captiva Island Inn, 290
Captiva Kayak & Wildside Adventures, 212, 213
Captiva map, 10
Captiva Memorial Library, 242
Captiva Post Office, **292,** 294
Captiva's Finest, 277
Caribbean Coast, 274
Caribbean milk moon, 116, **116**
Caribe Beach Resort, 286
Carlos, 46
Casa Ybel Resort, 28, 46, 53–59, 65, 69, 70, 75–77, 190, 196, 207, 268, 286
Casa Ybel Shell Day, 55
Cash advances, 29
Castaways at Blind Pass, 286
Castaways Marina, 104, 209, 212
Castor beans, 47, 74, 236
Castor oil, 47
Castro, Fidel, 68
Casual Attitude, 274
Casuarina. *See Australian pine*
Cat's paw. *See Atlantic kitten's paw*
Catch and release, 226, 227
Cattle egret, 138, **138**
Causeway. *See Sanibel Causeway*
Causey, Teri, 272
Cayo Costa, 25, 33, 35, 51, 104,

213, 219–221, **221**
Cedar Chest Fine Jewelry, 280
Central Reservations SW Florida, 291
Century, Luc, 271, 272, 279
Ceriths, 107
Chadwick, Clarence, 62
Chadwick's, 260
Chalky buttercup lucine, **114,** 116
Chamber of Commerce. *See Sanibel-Captiva Chamber of Commerce*
Channel bass. *See redfish*
Channeled duck clam, 109, **110**
Channeled whelk, **121,** 122
Chapel by the Sea. *See Captiva Chapel by the Sea*
Charters, 104, 209, 223, 226
Chase shipwreck, 45
Cheeburger Cheeburger, 33, 260
Cheese Nook, 280
"Cheeseburger in Paradise," 219
Chestnut mussel, 117, **117**
Chestnut turban, **121,** 122
Chico's, 274
Children's Education Center, 255
Chili's Too, 35
Chione elevata, 109, **110**
Chocolate Expressions, 260, 283
Church of the Four Gospels, **52,** 53, 61, 76
City Hall. *See Sanibel City Hall*
City of Palms Park, 243
Civic Center. *See Sanibel Civic Center*
Civil War, 45
Civil War naval station, 74
Clams, 109
Clam Bayou, 93, 177, 190
Clark, Capt. Gary, 226
Clinic for the Rehabilitation of Wildlife. *See CROW*
Clothing, 273–276
Coastal Cotton Co., 274
Cobia, 228, **228**
Cockles, 112
Coconut, how to open, 252
Coconut palm, 193, **193,** 195
Coir, 195
Colorful Atlantic natica, **115,** 116
Collier, Barron, 221
Colonial Bank, 29, 60, 74
Colony Resort, 286
Columbus, Christopher, 44, 130, 169, 195
Comair, 35, 36
Comb bittersweet, 107, **108**
Comfort by Design, 274
Commodore Creek Water Trail, 33, 209, 212
Common American auger, 107, **108**
Common American sundial, 123, **123**
Common bubble shell, 117, **118**
Common egg cockle, **111,** 112
Common fig, 123, **123**
Common moorhen, 151, **151**
Common nutmeg, **126,** 127
Common snook, 231, **231,** 232
Community Association. *See Sanibel Community Association*
Community Center. *See Sanibel Community Center*

Compton, Emily, 89
Conchs, 114
Conde Nast Traveler magazine, 21
Cones, 114
Confused Chameleon, 278
Congress Jewelers, 280
Conservation Land, 182–191
Constellations, 245
Continental Airlines, 35, 36
Continental Connection, 36
Convenience stores, 276–277
CopiKats, 283
Coquina, 104, 109, **110**
Coral, soft or horny. *See sea whip*
Coral snake. *See eastern coral snake*
Coral Veterinary Clinic, 293, 295
Corkscrew Swamp Sanctuary, 242
Cottages to Castles, 291
Cottonmouth snake, 161
Country Inns & Suites, 291
Cow-nose ray, 172
Crabs, 162
Credit cards, lost or stolen, 29
Cricket Shop, 274
Crocodile. *See American crocodile*
Crocodile Sanctuary, 160
Cross-barred venus clam, 109, **110**
Cross Dike Trail. *See J.N. "Ding"
   Darling National Wildlife Refuge*
CROW, 178, 293
Crown conch, **113,** 114
Crucifix shell. *See gafftopsail catfish*
Crutchfield, Russ, 241
Crux, 245
Cuban fish ranch, 74
Currency exchange, 29
Cut-ribbed ark, 107, **107**
CW's Market & Deli, 280

**D**
Dairy Queen, 260
Dark Skies ordinance, 245, 257
Darling, J. Norwood "Ding," 65–69,
   **65, 66, 67,** 74, 75, **188,** 201, 266
Darling Tract. *See J.N. "Ding" Darling
   National Wildlife Refuge*
Day spas, 293
Day trips, 243
Dead man's fingers, 128, **128**
Deet, 28
Delta, 35, 36
Delta Express, 35, 36
Designer Consigner, 282
DeSoto, Hernando, 44
"Ding" Darling. *See J.N. "Ding"
   Darling National Wildlife Refuge*
"Ding" Darling Center for
   Education. *See J.N. "Ding"
   Darling National Wildlife Refuge*
Dinkin's Bayou, 177, 255
Discover Card, 29
Disk dosinia, 109, **110**
Diversions, 234–245
Dixie ferry, 46
Dixie Beach, 46, 83
Doc Ford's, 260
Dockside Quality Clothing and
   Shoes, 274
Drs. Eyecare Centers, 293

Dolce Vita, 260
Dollar Rent-A-Car, 37
Dolphin. *See bottlenose dolphin*
Dosinia. *See disk dosinia*
Double-crested cormorant, 147, **147**
Drawbridge. *See Sanibel drawbridge*
Driftwood Inn, 286
Drum, 228, 229
Duck clam. *See channeled duck clam*
Dugong, 166, 169
Dunes, 93
Dunes Golf & Tennis Club, 241
Dusky pygmy rattlesnake, 16

**E**
East End Deli, 260
East River Trail, 190
Eastern coral snake, 161
Eastern diamondback rattlesnake, 161
Eastern indigo snake, 161
Eastern oyster, **118,** 119
Eastern tiger swallowtail, 152, **152**
Eastvold, Capt. Randy, 223
Echolocation, 162
Eckerd Drugs, 281, 294
Ecliptic, 244
Edison, Thomas, 62, 243
Edison-Ford Estates, 242–243, **243**
Egg cases, 128, **128,** 129, **129**
Eileen Fisher, 274
Elegant dosinia, 109, **110**
Elevation, 21
Emergency numbers, 293
Enchanted Fairy, 278
End Result, 278
Enterprise Rent-A-Car, 36, 37
Episcopal Church. *See St. Michael's
   and All Angels Episcopal Church*
Escentials, 283
Eye Centers of Florida, 29

**F**
Factory Lounge. *See Seafood Factory*
Fallen angel wing, 109, **109**
False angel wing, 109, **109**
Fargo's worm shell, 122, **122**
Farming, 60-62
Federal Express, 295
Ferries, 62
Ferry landing, 74
Fiddler crab, 162
Fig. *See common fig*
Finnimore's Cycle Shop, 207
Fintastic Charters, 223
Fire ant, 153
Fireworks, 83
Fish hawk. *See osprey*
Fishing, 222–233
   black drum, 228, **228**
   black grouper, 229, **229**
   black mullet, 230, **230**
   black sea bass, 228, **228**
   cobia, 228, **228**
   common snook, 231, **231,** 232
   Florida pompano, 230, **230**
   gafftopsail catfish, 128, 228, **228**
   goliath grouper, 229, **229**
   grouper, 229
   king mackerel, 229, **229,** 230

   mackerel, 229, 230
   mangrove snapper, 231, **231**
   redfish, 46, 228, **228,** 229, 233
   red grouper, 229, **229**
   sheepshead, 231, **231**
   Spanish mackerel, 230, **230**
   spotted seatrout, 231, **231,** 233
   tarpon, **50, 51,** 51, 223, 232, **232**
Fishing charters, 223, 226
Fishing license, 227
Fishing pier. *See Sanibel fishing pier*
Fish ranches, 68
Floral Artistry, 293
Florida cerith, 107, **108**
Florida Communities Trust, 190
Florida cone, 113, **114**
Florida fighting conch, 97, **113,** 114
Florida Highway Patrol, 293
Florida holly. *See Brazilian pepper*
Florida horse conch, 106, 113, **115**
Florida lace murex, 117, **117**
Florida Land Company, 47
Florida lucine, **114,** 116
Florida manatee, 25, 166–172, **167,**
   **170, 171**
Florida Marine Patrol, 293
Florida Museum of History, 235
Florida panther, 154
Florida pompano, 230, **230**
Florida prickly cockle, 112, **112**
Florida spiny jewel box, 123, **126**
Florists, 293
Flower Shop of the Islands, 293
Fluke, 163
Flying Fish & Co., 223, 233
Food, 277–280
Footloose, 274
Ford, Henry, 62, 243
Forest of Flowers Christmas Shoppe,
   283
Forever Green Ace Hardware, 280
Fort Myers, 46, 53, 61, 68, 167, 243,
   255
Fort Myers Beach, 79
Forty-Fifteen Resort, 286
Fresh Produce, 274
Friday's Fine Jewelers, 280
Frontier Airlines, 36
Fuery, Capt. Mike, 104

**G**
Gaffney, Capt. John, 209
Gafftopsail catfish, 128, 228, **228**
Gasoline and auto service, 293
Gaspar, José, 44, 45
Gasparilla, 35, 45
Gentrification, 71, 73
George Cooper House, 74, **74**
Getting Here, 34–41
Giant Atlantic cockle, 112, **112**
Giant bittersweet, 107, **108**
Giant clam, 106
"Gift from the Sea," 69
Gift shops, 277–279
Gnarly Woods trail, 81
Godfrey, Capt. Dave, 223
Golden olive, 117
Golden Slipper. *See snowy egret*
Golf, 241

Goliath grouper, 229, **229**
Gonopore, 129
Goodwill Boutique, 282
Gopher Enterprises, 291
Gopher tortoise, 62, 161, **161**
Goss, Porter, 71
Gramma Dot's Seaside Salon, 260
Grande Island Vacations, 291
Gray snapper. *See mangrove snapper*
Great blue heron, 133, **135**
Great Depression, 62
Great egret, 133, **134,** 135, 146
Great Red Spot, 244
Green heron, 97, 135, **135**
Green Flash, The, 28, **28,** 155, 261
Greenhouse Grill, 25, 33, 261, **261**
Greenside Grille at the Dunes, 261
Grog Shop, 281
Grouper, 229
Gulf Breeze Cottages, 74, 286
Gulfside City Park, 75, 81, 154, 187,
    190, **202,** 203, 204
Gulfside Park Preserve, 31, 81, 190,
    **191,** 204
Gulfstream International, 36
Gumbo limbo, 195, **195**
Gyotaku, 272

**H**
H2O Outfitters, 274
Hair and nail salons, 293
Hal's Grocery, 277
Hammerhead shark, 172
Hampton Inn & Suites, 291
Hardware stores, 280
Harry Ruby Salon, 293
Hawk-wing conch, 113, **114**
HealthPark of the Islands, 172, 293,
    294
Hermit crab, 162
Herring gull, 142, **142**
Her Sports Closet, 274
Hertz, 36, 37
Hess Express, 277, 293
Hickey, Capt. Tim, 223
Hiking trails, 188–190
Hinds, Lou, 183
Hirdie Girdie Gallery, 271
"Historia Naturalis," 169
Historical sites, 74–75
History, 42–77
Hobby, Capt. Paul, 223
Ho Ho Ho Show, 236
Holiday Inn Beach Resort, 286
Holiday Water Sports, 25, 216, 218
Homestead Act, 47, 49
Hooked mussel, 117, **117**
Horrible thistle, 195, **195,** 196
Horn shells, 107
Horny coral. *See sea whip*
Horse conch. *See Florida horse conch*
Horseshoe crab, 166, **166**
Hubble Space Telescope, 245
Hungry Heron, 261, 263
Hunter, Ruth, 236
Huntress shipwreck, 45
Hurricanes, 33, 61, 76, **76,** 77
Hurricane Andrew, 77, 193, 200
Hurricane Donna, 77, 201

Hurricane Georges, 255
Hurricane House Resort, 286
Huxter's Market, Liquor and Deli,
    261, 277, 281
Hydenoil Products Co., 62, 74

**I**
Ibis. *See white ibis*
I Can Too Sport, 275
Ida shipwreck, 45
Ikki Matsumoto Gallery, 271
Il Crocodile, 278
Imperial venus, 109, **110**
Incorporation, 71
Indigo snake. *See eastern indigo snake*
Indigo Trail. *See J.N. "Ding" Darling
    National Wildlife Refuge*
Insects, 152–154
Intercoastal Waterway, 40
International Ocean Telegraph Co., 61
International Space Station, 245
Intertidal surf zone, 93
Island Beach Co., 275
Island Beach, Too, 275
Island Book Nook, 84, 273
Island Cinema, 236
Island Cow, The, **24,** 25, 33, 262,
    **262,** 263, 265
Island Critters, 283
Islander. *See Sanibel-Captiva Islander*
Islander Trading Post, 278
Island Garage, 293
Island Gifts and Shells, 278, 281
Island Graphics, 294
Island Health Foods, 280
Island House, 31, 259, 262, 263
Island Inn, 53, **69,** 71, 75, 262, 286,
    287
Island Living, 246–257
Island Pizza and Pasta, 262
Island Pursuit, 275
Island Rental Service, 91
Island Reporter, 294
Island Seniors Program, 242
Island Store, 74, **74,** 277, 282
Island Style, 271
Island Sun, 294
Island Vacations, 291
Island Winds Coiffures, 293
I-Spy, 275

**J**
J. Howard Wood Theatre, 238
J.N. "Ding" Darling National
    Wildlife Refuge, 15, **18, 19,** 25,
    27, 29, 31, 65, 74, 94, 114, 127,
    141, 146, 150–151, 156, 162,
    166, 176–178, 181, **182,** 183–
    188, 195, 196, 204, 207, 255,
    273
    Alligator Curve, 156, 181
    Bailey Tract, 176, **185,** 188, 196,
        196, 207
    bookstore, 184, 273
    Cross Dike Trail, 25, 166, 176,
        188, 204
    Darling Tract, 183–188
    Indigo Trail, 25, 176, 188, 204
    Perry Tract, 94, 187

Red Mangrove Overlook, 114,
    127, 162, 166, 176, 187, **187**
Shell Mound Trail, 74, 176, 188,
    195, **197**
Jacaranda, 262
Jamaica Tall, coconut palm, 195
Jean Paul's French Corner, 262
Jeffrey's Bay, 101
Jellyfish, 98, 116, 166
Jensen's On The Gulf, 290
Jensen's Twin Palm Resort and
    Marina, 21, 75, 172, **208,** 212,
    220, **224, 225,** 290
Jerry's Restaurant, 262, 263
Jerry's Foods, 176, 178, 280, 294
JetBlue Airways, 36
Jewel box. *See Florida spiny jewel box*
Jewelry stores, 280
Jewfish. *See goliath grouper*
Jim's Rentals, 91, 207
Jingle shell, 123, **126**
Joey's snack boat, 92, **92**
Johnny's Pizza, 263
Johns, Glynis, 169
Johnson Shoals, 104
Jonna's of Sanibel, 278
Joyce Rehr's Fly Fishing & Light
    Tackle Guide Service, 226
Jungle Drums, 271
Junonia, 123, **124, 125**
Jupiter, 244, 245

**K**
Kaminski, Capt. Kelly, 223
Katie Gardenia's, 263
Kelly's Cocoons, 271
Kenoyer Real Estate Corp., 291
Keylime Bistro, 33, 263, 264
Keylime Clothing Co., 275
Key West, 45, 47, 61
King mackerel, 229, **229,** 230
Kingfish. *See king mackerel*
King's crown conch. *See crown conch*
Kirby Rambo Collections, 278
Kitten's paw. *See Atlantic kitten's paw*
Kona Kai Motel, 287
Koppel, Ted, **238**
Koreshan State Historic Site, 243

**L**
La Costa. *See Cayo Costa*
Lace murex. *See Florida lace murex*
Ladder horn shell, 107, **108**
Lads & Lassies, 275
Lady Chadwick, 25, **213**
Lady-in-waiting venus, 109, **111**
Land's End Village, 35
Latte da Coffee Shop & Deli, 264
Laughing gull, 142, **143**
La Vigna, 33, 263, 264
Lazy Flamingo, 25, 28, 31, 155, 199,
    226, **258,** 263–265, 268, 277
Leal, Dr. José, 235
Lee County Sheriff, 293
Lee County Sports Complex, 38, 243
Lee Memorial Hospital, 293
Lemon pecten, 120
Lessinger, Capt. Ozzie, 226
Lethal yellowing, 195

Lettered olive, 117, **118**
Library
  *See Captiva Memorial Library*
  *See Sanibel Public Library*
Lighthouse. *See Sanibel lighthouse*
Lighthouse Beach, 25, 30, 33, 79, 81, 127
Lighthouse Cafe, 33, 263, 264
Lighthouse Resort & Club, 287
Lightning whelk, **100, 105, 121,** 122, 128
Lindbergh, Anne Morrow, 62, 69, 75, 116
Lindbergh, Charles, 62, 75
Linesides. *See common snook*
Lindgren, Hugo, 68
Lion's paw, 120, **120**
Lion's Paw, 278
Liquor and wine, 281
Little blue heron, **132,** 135, 146
Little Nancy's Sunrise Video, 282
Loflin, Dr. Rob, 255
Loggerhead turtle, 94, 173–176, **173, 174, 175**
Lookin Good, 275
Louise, Princess Maria, 44
LTU International, 36
Lucines, 116
Lucky Dog of Sanibel, 275
Luminary Night, 31
Lynx Air International, 36

**M**
Mackerel, 229, 230
MacIntosh Book Shop, 84, 273
Maculated ear moon, 116, **116**
Maddison and Me, 275
Maddison Suites, 290
"Mad About Men," 169
Mad Hatter, 264, 265
Magazines, 294
Maggie Elliott, 275
Maine, The, 61
Makin' Waves Charter Services, 223
Malayan Dwarf coconut palm, 195
Mama Rosa's Pizzeria, 264, 265
Manatee. *See Florida manatee*
Mango Bay, 275
Mangrove, 187, 194, **194**
Mangrove cuckoo, 151
Mangrove honey, 194
Mangrove Overlook. *See J.N. "Ding" Darling National Wildlife Refuge*
Mangrove snapper, 231, **231**
Mangrove tree crab, 135, 162
Manhattan, 15
Manta ray, **58, 59**
Maps
  Captiva, 10
  Sanibel, 8–9
  Sanibel bike paths and routes, 205
Marijuana, 71, **71**
Marinas, 40
Mars, 244, 245
Marsh rabbit, 46, 155
Martha M. Heath shipwreck, 45
Massage therapists, 293
Matsumoto, Ikki, 271, 272
Matthews, Charlotta, 53

Matthews wharf, 75
Matthews, Will and Harriet, 53, 69
Matzaluna, 263, 265
Mayer, Claudia, **198,** 199
McCarthy's Marina, 75, 226
McCumber, Mark, 241
McCune, Kevin, 241
McDonald's, 72
McEnroe Gallery, 271
McLane, Roscoe, 65
McNamara, Bryce, 272
McSpoil, 72, **72**
McT's Shrimp House, 265
Meardon, David, 294
Medical services, 293, 294
Mel Fisher's Sanibel Treasure Company, 74, 75, 283
Melaleuca, 200
Memorable Charters, 104
Memories of Sanibel, 275
Menendez de Aviles, Pedro, 44
Mercury, 244
Mercury Marine, 212, **212**
Mermaid, 169, 248
Mermaid's purse, 129
Merritt, Dixon Lanier, 149
Michele's Video & DVD, 282
Middle beach, 93
Middleton, Capt. Sean, 223, 233
Midwest Express, 36
Mike Fuery's Tours, 104, 209
Milky Way galaxy, 244
Millay, Edna St. Vincent, 62
Minnesota Twins, 38, 243
"Miranda," 169
Miss Charlotta's Tearoom, 75
Mitchell's Sand Castles By The Sea, 287
Mole crab. *See sand flea*
Mole Hole of Sanibel, The, 278
Mona Lisa's Pizzeria and Deli, 263, 265
Monarch butterfly, 152, **152, 153**
Money, 28, 29
Money magazine, 21
Moon morning glory, **195,** 196
Moon shells, 116
Moon jellyfish, 166, **166**
Moon snail. *See Atlantic moon snail*
Morgan's Forest, 266
Morning Glories, 236
Morton's egg cockle, 112, **112**
Mosquito. *See saltwater mosquito*
Mosquito Magnet, 280
Mossy ark, 107, **107**
MotoPhoto & Portrait Studio, 294
Mozella's Foodworks, 265
Mucky Duck, 266
Mullet. *See black mullet*
Murexes, 117
Mussels, 117
Myers, Col. Abraham C., 46

**N**
Nacre, 119
Nanny's, 275
Naples, 81
Narváez, Pánfilo de, 44
Natica. *See colorful Atlantic natica*
National Audubon Society, 139, 242
National Public Radio, 242

National Rent-A-Car, 37
National Wildlife Refuge System, 139
Nealon, Kevin, 236
Needful Things, 282
Neptune, 245
Neptune's Treasures, 281
New Spirit Hair Design, 293
Newspapers, 294
Nick's Place, 266
Nine-banded armadillo, 97, 154, **154**
Nine-pointed star, 131
Noah's Ark, 282
Noctiluca scintillans, 94
Noopie's, 266
North Captiva, 35, 46, 104, 221, **221,** 226
North Captiva Island Club Resort, 291
Northwest/KLM, 36
No-see-um. *See sand fly*
Nude swimming, 82
Nuñez Cabeza de Vaca, Alvar, 44
Nurse shark, 172
Nutmeg. *See common nutmeg*

**O**
Oannes, 169
Ocean's Reach Condominium, 287
Offshore Sailing School, 213, **214, 215**
Oh Mango!, 275
O'Keefe, Georgia, 116
Old Blind Pass, 97, 190
Old Captiva House, 75, 266
Old Schoolhouse Theater, **17,** 29, 31, 61, 74, 238, **239**
Olives, 117
Operculum, 106
Opossum, 154
Orion, 245
Ortíz, Juan, 46
Osprey, 146, 148, **148,** 209, 255
Otter. *See river otter*
Out islands, 219
Overview, 14–25
Oyster, 117, 119, 130
Oystercatcher. *See American oystercatcher*

**P**
Pacheco, Joseph, 254
Page Field, 37
Pak 'N' Ship, 295
Palm View Motel, 287
Palms of Sanibel, The, 287
Pandora's Box, 279
Panther. *See Florida panther*
Paper fig. *See common fig*
Paradise of Sanibel, 275, 276
Parasailing, 33, 216, **216,** 218
Parchment tube worm, 129, **129**
Parking, 83
Parrot Nest Old-Sanibel Resort, The, 287
Pat's Hair Kair, 293
Peace Park, 204
Peach Republic, 276
Pear whelk, 122, **122**
Pelican

*See brown pelican*
*See white pelican*
Pelican Bay, 220
Pelican's Roost Condominium, 287
Pen shells, 119
Pepper Busters, 201
Periostracum, 107
Periwinkle Cottages, 287
Periwinkle Florist & Gift Baskets, 293
Periwinkle Park Campground, 176, 203, 287
Periwinkle Place Bistro, 266
Periwinkle Place Shopping Center, 203, 204
Periwinkle Way, 46
Periwinkle Way bike path, 203
Perry Tract. *See J.N. "Ding" Darling National Wildlife Refuge*
Pets, 87
Pharmacies, 281
Phillips Gallery, 238, 271
Phoenix Iron Co., 49
Photographers, 294
Photo processing, 294
Pick Preserve. *See Sanibel-Captiva Conservation Foundation*
Pileated woodpecker, 151
Pine Island, 62
Pine Island Sound, 25, 40, 44, 104, 133, 178, 209, 223
Pinnixa chaetopterana, 129
Pinocchio's, 266, 267, 269
Pippin's, 267
Pirates, 45
Pirate Playhouse. *See SCA Periwinkle Playhouse*
Pishmeri, 169
Planning Your Trip, 26–33
Plant, Bradley, 60
Pliny the Elder, 169
PlusPerfect, 276
Pluto, 245
Pointe Santo de Sanibel, 288
Point Ybel, 46, 47
Poison Control, 293
Polaris, 245
Pompano. *See Florida pompano*
Ponce de Leon, Juan, 15, 40, 44, **44,** 46
Ponderous ark, 107, **107**
Portofino, 267
Port Sanibel Marina, 177, 178
Portuguese man-of-war, 116
Postal services, 294
Potash, 61
Power Squadron, 248
Presley, Dr. Suzanne, 295
Prickly pear cactus, 196, **196,** 252
Prickly pear cactus jelly, 252
Princess venus, 109, **111**
Printers, 294
Priscilla Murphy Vacation Rentals, 291
Pro Air, 36
Prohibition, 65, **65**
Punta Gorda, 51, 55, 60
Punta Rassa, 46, 47, 49, 55, 61, 68, 104
Purple sea snail, 116, **116**
Purplish semele, 109, **111**

**Q**
Quahog. *See Southern quahog*
Quarterdeck. *See Atlantic slipper shell*
Queen butterfly, 152, **153**
Queen Isabella, 44, 46
Quik Pack & Ship, 295

**R**
Rabbit. *See marsh rabbit*
Rabbit Road, 46
Raccoon, 155, **155**
Radio stations, 294, 295
Radisson Inn/Sanibel Gateway, 291
Rainfall, 21, 28
Rauschenberg, Robert, 272
R.C. Otter's, 33, 263, 267
Real estate, 255
Rec Center. *See Sanibel Recreational Complex*
Recipes, 252
Red bass. *See redfish*
Reddish egret, 138, **138,** 146
Red drum. *See redfish*
Redfish, 46, 228, **228,** 229, 233
Redfish Pass, 41, 76
Red grouper, 229, **229**
Red mangrove. *See mangrove*
Red Mangrove Overlook. *See J.N. "Ding" Darling National Wildlife Refuge*
Red-shouldered hawk, 148, **148,** 149
Red tide, 93
Reed, William, 49
Refuge. *See J.N. "Ding" Darling National Wildlife Refuge*
Rehr, Capt. Joyce Fly Fishing & Light Tackle Guide Service, 226
Religious services, 295
ReMax of the Islands Rentals, 291
Rene's Artisans of Fine Jewelry, 280
Rental agencies, 291
Rental cars, 29, 36, 37
Reservation Central, 291
Resources, 292–295
Restaurants, 258–269
Restrooms, 204
Rinehart, Mary Roberts. *See Cabbage Key*
Ring-billed gull, 142, **142,** 143
River otter, 154, 155, **155**
Riviera, 267
Robalo. *See common snook*
Rock oyster, **118,** 119
Rodrigues, Juan, 44
Rogel, Juan, 44
Roosevelt Channel, **22, 23,** 41, 46, 291
Roosevelt, Theodore, 46, 60, **60**
Rose petal tellin, 120, **120**
Rose scallop, 120, **103,** 120, **120**
Roseate spoonbill, **16,** 141, **141,** 146, **182**
Rosie's Island Market & Deli, 267, 277
Rough scallop, 120, **120**
Royal Shell Vacation Properties, 291
Royal tern, **26, 143,** 146
Ruddy turnstone, **143,** 146
Rutland House, 236

**S**
Sabatino, Capt. Bob, 226

Sabal palm. *See cabbage palm*
Sabal Palm Trail, 190
Sabena, 35
Safety Harbor, 221
Sailcat. *See gafftopsail catfish*
Sailor's valentine, **234,** 235
St. Isabel Catholic Church, 295
St. Michael's and All Angels Episcopal Church, 189, 282, 295
Sales tax, 29
Saltwater mosquito, 28, 60, 152, 153
San-Cap Medical Clinic, 172, 294
San Carlos Bay, 40, 46, 47, 51, 53
Sanctuary Golf Club, 241
Sand castle, 94, 96
Sand dollar, 98, 102, 129, **129**
Sand flea, 162
Sand fly, 28, 29, 60, 153, 154
Sandalfoot Condominium, 288
Sandbar shark, 172, **172**
Sanddollar Condominium, 288
Sandpiper Inn, 288
Sandpiper of Sanibel, The, 279
Sand spurs, 93
Sandwich tern, 146
Sandy Bend, 288
Sanibel Accommodations, 291
Sanibel Arms Condominium, 288
Sanibel Arms West Condominium, 288
Sanibel Art and Frame, 271
Sanibel Baptist Church, 60, 62
Sanibel Barber Shop, 293
Sanibel Beach Club I and II, 288
Sanibel Beauty Salon, 293
Sanibel Cafe, 267
Sanibel Candle Co., 279
Sanibel-Captiva Airport Shuttle, 37
Sanibel-Captiva Chamber of Commerce, 33, 204
Sanibel-Captiva Community Bank, 29
Sanibel-Captiva Conservation Foundation (SCCF), 25, 33, 69, 173, 176, 177, 189, **189,** 190, 196, 196, 203, 207
Sanibel-Captiva Conservation Foundation bookstore, 269, 273
Sanibel-Captiva First Church of Christ Scientist, 295
Sanibel-Captiva Islander, 69, 294
Sanibel Causeway, 15, 25, 27, 38, 40, 46, 68, 83, 162, 177, 195, 216, 245
Sanibel Cemetery, 25, 61, 75, 190, 204
Sanibel Chiropractic, 294
Sanibel City Hall, 141
Sanibel, city of, 255
Sanibel Civic Center, 242
Sanibel Coin and Jewelry, 280
Sanibel Community Association, 242
Sanibel Community Church, 61, 74, 295
Sanibel Community House, 65, 74, 241, 242
Sanibel Congregational Church, 242, 295
Sanibel Day Spa, 293

Sanibel drawbridge, 40, **40**, 41
Sanibel Fire Department, 293
Sanibel fishing pier, 245
Sanibel Fitness Center, 242
Sanibel Gallery, 272
Sanibel Goldsmith Gallery, 281
Sanibel Grill, 263, 269
Sanibel Harbour Resort & Spa, 46,
291
Sanibel Historical Village and
Museum, 17, 33, 74, 75, 235,
236, **236, 237,** 273
Sanibel Holiday, 291
Sanibel Inn, 28, 288
Sanibel Island Adventures, 209
Sanibel Island Bookshop, 84, 273
Sanibel Island Chowder Co. *See*
*Periwinkle Place Bistro*
Sanibel Island Cruise Line, 104, 209
Sanibel Island Goldsmith. *See Sanibel*
*Goldsmith Gallery*
Sanibel Island Taxi, 37
Sanibel lighthouse, **20,** 40, **48,** 49,
74, 76, 79, 203, 204, 236
Sanibel map, 8–9
Sanibel Marina, 40, **40,** 41, 62, 74,
209, 212, 216, 226
Sanibel Moorings Condominium, 288
Sanibel Music Festival, 242
Sanibel National Wildlife Refuge, 65,
188
Sanibel One, 291
Sanibel Packing Co., 60, **60,** 61, 70
Sanibel Plan, 71
Sanibel Police Department, 293
Sanibel Post Office, 255, 294
Sanibel Print and Graphics, 294
Sanibel Produce Co., 280
Sanibel Public Library, 178, **240,**
241, 242, 245
Sanibel Recreation Center. *See Sanibel*
*Recreational Complex*
Sanibel Recreational Complex, 204,
207, 242
Sanibel Rental Service, 91
Sanibel River, 177, 189, 190, 203,
207, 209, 287
Sanibel School, 61, **69,** 70, 189, 242,
255
Sanibel School for Colored Children,
62
Sanibel Seashell Industries, 281
Sanibel Shell, 293
Sanibel Siesta, 288, 289
Sanibel Spirits, 281
Sanibel Steakhouse, 259, 267
"Sanibel's Story," 47
Sanibel Surf Shop, 273, 282
Sanibel Vision Statement, 71
Sanibel Wellness, 293
Sanibel Wildlife Refuge. *See J.N.*
*"Ding" Darling National Wildlife*
*Refuge*
Santa Isybella, 44, 46
Santiva, 21
Santiva General Store, 277
Santiva Saltwater Fishing Team, 226
Sanybel, 46, 47
Sanybel's Finest, 279

Sargasso Sea, 130
Sargassum weed, 130, **130**
Satellites, 245
Saturn, 244
Saw grass, 196, **196**
Saw-toothed pen shell, 119, **119**
Sbarra's Captiva Day Spa, 293
SCA Periwinkle Playhouse, 238
Scallops, 119
Scarlett O'Hair's Beauty Salon, 293
Schein Performance Hall, 238
Schnapper's Hots, 33, 263, 267, 268
Schultz, George, 61
Scorched mussel, 117, **118**
Scorpion. *See brown scorpion*
Scotch bonnet, **126,** 127
Scott, Willard, 235
Sea bass. *See black sea bass*
Sea Bird, 45, 49
Sea foam, 93
Sea grape, 81, 196, **196,** 252
Sea grape jelly, 252
Sea horse, 130, **130**
Sea Horse Shops, 68
Sea oats, 196, **199**
Sea pork, 130, **130**
Sea Shells of Sanibel Condominium,
289
Sea star. *See starfish*
Sea turtles, 62
Sea urchin, 131, **131**
Sea whip, 131, **131**
Seafood Factory, The, 268
Seahorse Cottages, 289
Sealife Encounter tour, 177–178,
**178, 179**
Seashell shops, 281
Seaside Inn, 74, 289
Seatrout. *See spotted seatrout*
Seawave Boat Rental, 212
Seaweed Gallery, The, 272
Secondhand stores, 282
See, Terry, 241
Seminole Indians, 44
Shalimar Resort, 289
Shark, 163, 172, 180
Shark factory, 62
Shark's eye. *See Atlantic moon snail*
She Sells Sea Shells, 281, 282
Sheepshead, 231, **231**
Shell Harbor, 203
Shelling, 100–131
alphabet cone, 113, **114**
American star shell, **121,** 122
angel wing, 109, **109**
angulate periwinkle, 127, **127**
angulate wentletrap, **126,** 127
apple murex, **116,** 117
arks, 107
Atlantic baby's ear, **115,** 116
Atlantic false jingle, 123, **126**
Atlantic hair triton, 123, **123**
Atlantic kitten's paw, **126,** 127
Atlantic moon snail, **115,** 116,
128
Atlantic slipper shell, **126,** 127
Atlantic strawberry cockle, **111,**
112
Atlantic surf clam, **111,** 112

Atlantic winged oyster, 131
augers, 107
Australian trumpet, 106
banded tulip, 120, **121**
bay scallop, 119, **119**
bittersweets, 107, 109
broad-ribbed cardita, 123, **123**
brown spiny sea star, 131, **131**
buttercup lucine, 98, **114,** 116
calico clam, 109, **110**
calico scallop, 119, **119**
Caribbean milk moon, 116, **116**
ceriths, 107
chestnut mussel, 117, **117**
chestnut turban, **121,** 122
chione elevata, 109, **110**
clams, 109
cockles, 112
colorful Atlantic natica, **115,** 116
comb bittersweet, 107, **108**
common American auger, 107, **108**
common American sundial, 123,
**123**
common bubble shell, 117, **118**
common egg cockle, **111,** 112
common fig, 123, **123**
common nutmeg, **126,** 127
conchs, 114
cones, 114
coquina, 104, 109, **110**
cross-barred venus clam, 109, **110**
crown conch, **113,** 114
cut-ribbed ark, 107, **107**
dead man's fingers, 128, **128**
disk dosinia, 109, **110**
eastern oyster, **118,** 119
egg cases, 128, **128,** 129, **129**
elegant dosinia, 109, **110**
fallen angel wing, 109, **109**
false angel wing, 109, **109**
fargo's worm shell, 122, **122**
Florida cerith, 107, **108**
Florida cone, 113, **114**
Florida fighting conch, 97, **113,**
114
Florida horse conch, 106, 113, **115**
Florida lace murex, 117, **117**
Florida lucine, **114,** 116
Florida prickly cockle, 112, **112**
Florida spiny jewel box, 123, **126**
gafftopsail catfish, 128, **128,** 228
giant Atlantic cockle, 112, **112**
giant bittersweet, 107, **108**
giant clam, 106
golden olive, 117
hawk-wing conch, 113, **114**
hooked mussel, 117, **117**
horn shells, 107
imperial venus, 109, **110**
jingle shell, 123, **126**
junonia, 123, **124, 125**
ladder horn shell, 107, **108**
lady-in-waiting venus, 109, **111**
lemon pecten, 120
lettered olive, 117, **118**
lightning whelk, **100, 105, 121,**

122, 128
lion's paw, 120, **120**
lucines, 116
maculated ear moon, 116, **116**
mermaid's purse, 129
moon shells, 116
morton's egg cockle, 112, **112**
mossy ark, 107, **107**
murex, 117
mussels, 117
nine-pointed star, 131
olives, 117
oyster, 117, 119, 130
parchment tube worm, 129, **129**
pear whelk, 122, **122**
pen shells, 119
ponderous ark, 107, **107**
princess venus, 109, **111**
purple sea snail, 116, **116**
purplish semele, 109, **111**
rock oyster, **118,** 119
rose petal tellin, 98, **103,** 120, **120**
rough scallop, 120, **120**
sand dollar, 98, 102, 129, **129**
sargassum weed, 130, **130**
saw-toothed pen shell, 119, **119**
scallops, 119
scorched mussel, 117, **118**
Scotch bonnet, **126,** 127
sea horse, 130, **130**
sea pork, 130, **130**
sea urchin, 131, **131**
sea whip, 131, **131**
shiny dwarf tellin, 120, **121**
short-spined brittle star, 131
southern horse mussel, 117, **118**
southern quahog, **111,** 112
southern ribbed mussel, 117, **118**
spectral bittersweet, **108,** 109
spiny paper cockle, 112, **112**
starfish, 130, 131
stiff pen shell, 119, **119**
sunray venus clam, **111,** 112
sunrise tellin, 120, **121**
tellins, 120
thick lucine, **114,** 116
tiger lucine, **114,** 116
transverse ark, 107, **108**
true tulip, 120, **121**
tulip shells, 120, 128
turban shells, 122
turkey wing, 107, **108**
Van Hyning's cockle, 112, **113**
variable worm shell, 122, **122**
venuses, 109, 112
very small dwarf olive, **118,** 119
west Indian worm shell, 122, **122**
whelks, 122
worm shells, 122
yellow cockle, 112, **113**
zigzag scallop, 120, **120**
Shell Mound Trail. *See J.N. "Ding"*
*Darling National Wildlife Refuge*
Shell Museum. *See Bailey-Matthews*
*Shell Museum*
Shell Net, 282
Shiny dwarf tellin, 120, **121**
Shipping, 295
Shipwrecks, 45

Shoppe at Sundial, The, 268, 277
Shopping, 270–283
Short-spined brittle star, 131
Showcase Shells, 282
Signal Inn, 289
Silver Key, 82, 177, 190
Sirius, 245
Sisters, The, 53
Skate, 128, 129
Skinny-dipping, 70, 82
Skin-So-Soft, 28
A Slight Indulgence, 280
Slipper shell. *See Atlantic slipper shell*
Snake bird. *See anhinga*
Snakes, 161
Snapper. *See mangrove snapper*
Snook. *See common snook*
Snowy egret, **2,** 138, 146
Snyder School, 61
Soapfish. *See common snook*
Soft coral. *See sea whip*
Song of the Sea, 289
South Florida Museum, 170
South Seas Marina, 25
South Seas Plantation, 62
South Seas Resort, 21, 33, 35, 36, 62,
83, 170, 209, 218, 241, 290, **290,**
291
South Seas Resort Bayside Marina,
40, 41
South Seas Shoppe, 279
Southeastern snowy plover, 143
Southern black racer, 161
Southern Cross, 245
Southern horse mussel, 117, **118**
Southern quahog, **111,** 112
Southern ribbed mussel, 117, **118**
Southern stingray, 172, **173**
Southwest Florida International
Airport, 28, 35
Space Shuttle, 245
Spanish-American War, 61
Spanish mackerel, 230, **230**
Spectral bittersweet, **108,** 109
Spiny paper cockle, 112, **112**
Spirit Air, 36
"Splash," 169
Spoonbill. *See roseate spoonbill*
Sporty Seahorse, 274
Spotted-eagle ray, 172
Spotted seatrout, 231, **231,** 233
Spring training, 243
"Square grouper." *See marijuana*
Staircase Shell. *See angulate wentletrap*
Starfish, 130, 131
Stargazing, 244–245
Stars and Stripes, 216
Steamboats, 61
Steller sea cow, 166
Stevens Family Chiropractic, 294
Stiff pen shell, 119, **119**
Stingray, 172, 173
Stingray Shuffle, 172
Stokes, Marty, 272
Stork. *See wood stork*
Strangler fig, 196, 199, **199**
Striped bass. *See black sea bass*
Striped mullet. *See black mullet*
Submarine spotting tower, 74

Subway, 263, 268
Sulu Islands, 101
Sun Country, 36
Sundial Beach Resort, 28, 266, 268,
269, 289
Sunglasses Internationale, 283
Sun Harvest Citrus, 38, 243, **243,** 260
Sunray venus clam, **111,** 112
Sunrise tellin, 120, **121**
Sunscreen, 27, 28
Sunset Grill, 25, 33, 265, 268, **268,**
277
Sunset times, 87
Sunsets, 87, 89
Sunshine Cafe, 268
Sunshine Island Inn, 289
SunTrust Bank of Lee County, 29
Surf clam. *See Atlantic surf clam*
Surfrider Beach Club, 289, 290
"Sweet Home Alabama," 83, **83**
Sweetwater Boat Rentals, 212

**T**
T-Shirt Hut, 276, **276**
T-Shirt Place of Sanibel, 276
Tabu, 104
Tahitian Gardens Shopping Center,
204
Tahitian Surf Shop, 276
Tarpon, **50, 51,** 51, 223, 232, **232**
Tarpon Bay Explorers, 25, 33, 94,
177, 183, 187, 207, 212, 216,
226, 283
Tarpon Bay Road Beach, 81, 203,
204
Tarpon Tale Inn. *See Brennen's Tarpon*
*Tale Inn*
Taxis and limos, 36
Telegraph cable relay hut, 74
Television stations, 295
Tellins, 120
Temperatures, 30
Tennis, 241
Terry's Tennis Shop, 283
Thick lucine, **114,** 116
Thistle Lodge, 196, 268
Thomas Cook, 29
Three Crafty Ladies, 283
Three Islands. *See J.N. "Ding"*
*Darling National Wildlife Refuge*
Thrifty, 36, 37
Tide charts, 81, 141
Tides, 81, 93, 101
Tiger lucine, **114,** 116
Tiger shark, 172
Timbers, 263, 269
Times of the Islands magazine, 294
Tin Can Alley, 272
Tipping, 29
Torina, John, 92
Tortoise, gopher. *See gopher tortoise*
Touch of Sanibel Pottery, 272
Tourist tree. *See gumbo limbo*
Tower Gallery, 272
Toy stores, 282
Toys Ahoy, 282
Trader Rick's, 276
Trader's Store and Cafe, 28, 31, 263,
269, 279

Tram tour, 25, 176, 187
Transverse ark, 107, **108**
Travel Channel, 21, **21**
Traveler's checks, lost or stolen, 29
Travelex, 29
Treasures of the Atocha Exhibit and
   Gift Shop. *See Mel Fisher's Sanibel
   Treasure Company*
Tree House Gallery, 272
Trees and Plants, 192–201
Tricolored heron, 138, **138**
Tropical Rainfall Monitoring
   Mission, 245
Tropical Temptations, 269
Tropical Winds Motel, 290
True tulip, 120, **121**
Tube worm. *See parchment tube worm*
Tulip shells, 120, 128
Turban shells, 122
Turkey vulture, 151
Turkey wing, 107, **108**
Turner Beach, **14**, 25, 33, 81, 87, **87,
   90**, 204, 20/, 268
Turtle, loggerhead. *See loggerhead
   turtle*
Tuttle's Sea Horse Shell Shop, 279
'Tween Waters Inn, 41, 83, 266, **284,**
   291
'Tween Waters Marina, 33, 41, 104,
   209, 212, 226
Twilight Cafe, 269

**U**
Ultimate Charters, 226
Uneeda, 61, **61**
Unitarian-Universalist Society of the
   Islands, 295
United/United Express, 36
Unity of the Islands, 295
Univalve, 106
Upper Captiva. *See North Captiva*
Uranus, 244, 245
Ursa Major, 245
US Airways, 36

U.S. Army Corps of Engineers, 189
U.S. Coast Guard, 49, 65, 293
Useppa Island, 33, 44, 46, 213, 221,
   226
U.S. Fish and Wildlife Service, 65,
   188

**V**
Valhalla, 279
Van Hyning's cockle, 112, **113**
Variable worm shell, 122, **122**
Venus, 244, 245
Very small dwarf olive, **118,** 119
Veterinarians, 295
Victorian era, 54–59
Video rentals, 282
Video Scene, 282
Viking Voyages, 209
Village Cafe, 269
Vineyard Christian Fellowship of
   Sanibel, 295
VIP Realty Rental Division, 291
Virginia lady butterfly, 152, 153, **153**

**W**
Wachovia Bank, 29
Walking tree. *See red mangrove*
Walt Disney World, 37, 38
War of Indian Removal, 47
Ward, Barbara, 72
Waterside Inn On The Beach, 290
Watersports, 216, 218
Waverunner Safari, 25, 33, 216, 218,
   **218**
Weddings, 295
Weeds and Things, 293
Wentletrap. *See angulate wentletrap*
Westall, Mark "Bird," 73, 177, 180–
   181, 209
Westend Paradise of Sanibel, 290
Western sandpiper, **142,** 143, 146
West Gulf beaches, 81
West Indian manatee, 166
West Indian worm shell, 122, **122**

West Wind Inn Beach Resort, 207,
   290
West Wind Surf Shop, 276
Whelks, 122
White ibis, **140,** 141
White pelican, 150, **150, 184**
White stopper, 199
Why Knot, 276
Wildlife, 132–181
"Wildlife Emergency," Animal Planet,
   178
Wildlife refuge. *See J.N. "Ding"
   Darling National Wildlife Refuge*
Wilford & Lee, 279
Willet, **143,** 146
William & Frederick shipwreck, 45
William E. Wilson Fine Jewelry
   Design & Diamond Broker, 281
Wilson, Robby, 241
Windows on the Water, 269
Winds, 207, 273
Windsurfing, 83, 216, **217**
Wood stork, 141, **141,** 150
Wood Theatre. *See J. Howard Wood
   Theatre*
Wood, W.H., 49, 51
Woodring Road, 75
World War I, 61
World War II, 65
Worm shells, 122
Write Stuff, The, 283

**Y**
Ybel, 46
Yellow cockle, 112, **113**
Yellow-crowned night-heron, 135,
   **136, 137,** 138, 146
Yellow ray, 172
Yellowstone National Park, 180
YOLO Watersports, 33, 216, 218

**Z**
Zebra longwing butterfly, 153, **153**
Zigzag scallop, 120, **120**

*About the authors*

Julie and Mike Neal live on Sanibel's Clam Bayou with their daughter,
Micaela, and dog, Bear. Julie has had a passion for writing since she was a
young girl in Missouri. Julie first visited Florida on her high school senior
trip. After seeing the ocean, she swore to her friends that she would someday live in the Sunshine State. Mike grew up just a few miles from Julie,
on a lake. He spent nearly every summer afternoon on a water ski, and
developed a lifelong love of the water. Together they attended the Univer-
sity of Missouri; Julie as a biology major, Mike studying journalism. Ful-
filling Julie's dream, the couple moved to Florida in 1980, where Julie
finished her education at Florida State. After moving to Sanibel, Julie
became a volunteer docent for the J.N. "Ding" Darling National Wildlife
Refuge, and Mike served as president of the Children's Education Center
preschool. Today both enjoy coaching Micaela's soccer team.

MICAELA NEAL

**Julie and Mike Neal**

*Additional copies*

Additional copies of this book are available at coconutpress.com or by writing to Coconut Press,
5429 Shearwater Dr., Sanibel, FL 33957. Telephone: (239) 472-7784.